Real Math™

Dear Student:

We hope that this Real Math book will help you learn about mathematics in an interesting way.

You'll find stories about important people in the history of mathematics. Discussions and examples will show you how mathematics can help you solve problems and save you work. Seminars will show you ways that you can use mathematics to explore things and ideas in the world around you.

Games will give you practice with many of the skills that you will be learning and will help you understand what probability is about. Activities will introduce you to puzzles and other ways that you can enjoy mathematics in your free time.

You'll be discussing the ideas behind all this mathematics in class with your classmates and your teacher. We put most of this information in the book too so that you can go back over it and can take the book home to discuss these ideas with your family and friends. Mathematics is not something to do alone. To do a good job of learning and doing mathematics, you need other people.

You can see that Real Math is not all fun and games. You will need to think, to calculate, to estimate, and to measure, but doing these well can be very satisfying.

We hope that you enjoy this book and that you learn about many new things. But most of all we hope that you become very good at thinking and problem solving.

The Authors of Real Math

Dear Parent:

Recent international studies have shown that precollege students in the United States are behind those in other industrialized countries. An unchallenging, pedestrian mathematics curriculum receives much of the blame. Beyond that, many government commissions and professional societies have called for more emphasis on problem solving, estimation, data analysis, intelligent use of technology, and other higher-order thinking skills to prepare people for life in the twenty-first century.

Real Math™ is a challenging mathematics program, based on the learner's reality, that emphasizes those higher-order thinking skills. In Real Math the various strands of mathematics (arithmetic, algebra, geometry, statistics, probability, and so on) are integrated with each other and are constantly related to the real world.

We hope you will take the opportunity to join your student in studying the material in this book and learning more about mathematics and how it relates to the world around us. Perhaps you will even enjoy playing some of the mathematical games that provide not only practice in essential basic skills but opportunities to solve problems and work out strategies as well.

The Authors of Real Math

Real Math™

Stephen S. Willoughby
Carl Bereiter
Peter Hilton
Joseph H. Rubinstein

Jean J. Pedersen
Curriculum Consultant for Geometry

 Open Court   Chicago and Peru, Illinois

Design
James Buddenbaum/Design

Acknowledgments

Illustration
Bill and Judie Anderson: 238, 421. Lois Axeman: 256. Gwen Connelly: 411. David Cunningham: 17, 58, 100, 110, 269, 292-293, 294-295, 303, 329, 346, 349, 351, 370, 386. Mike Eagle: 36, 50 (middle illustration), 83. Larry Frederick: 28, 103, 114, 121, 127, 131, 166, 252, 308-309, 368-369, 388, 400. Diana Magnuson: 306. Dan Siculan: 31, 101, 155, 278. Joel Snyder: 107, 223. Justin Wager: 30, 104, 111, 125, 161, 181, 205, 233, 241, 245, 254, 283, 301, 379. John Walter, Jr.: 50 (top illustration).

Photography
The Bettmann Archive: 15, 78, 363. The Darwin D. Bearley Collection of Ohio Amish Quilts: 168. Government of Canada: Peter Martin, 12. Culver Pictures, Inc.: 79 (bottom), 277, 360. Da Capo Press: 52. E. F. Davenport: 172. Focus on Sports, Inc.: 234. The Marilyn Gartman Agency: 180; Lee Balterman, 235, 387; Gerard Fritz, 82; Michael Habicht, 271; Photri, 341, 367, 417; Rene Sheret, 137; Frank Siteman, 165. The Granger Collection: 290. Lew Harding: 24, 151, 164, 240, 253, 262, 285, 362, 364. Milt and Joan Mann, Cameramann, International, Ltd.: 79 (top). Mathematical Association of America: 39. Piet Mondrian, *Broadway Boogie Woogie,* 1942–43, oil on canvas, 50″ × 50″, Collection, The Museum of Modern Art, New York: 62. NASA: 383. National Portrait Gallery, Smithsonian Institution, Washington, D.C.: 18 (top). Photo Researchers, Inc.: 260. James P. Rowan: 208, 265. *The World of Mathematics*, copyright © 1956 by James R. Newman, reprinted by permission of Simon & Schuster, Inc.: 276. Courtesy of Sperry Corporation: 80. Stock, Boston, Inc.: Jeff Albertson, front x; W. K. Almond, 349 (top); Jerry Berndt, 215; Fred Bodin, 61; Michael Collier, 214; Donald Dietz, 23 (second from bottom), 296 (far right); Owen Franken, 237; Mike Mazzaschi, front vii; Peter Menzel, 184 (left), 296 (middle left); Richard Pasley, 184 (right); Donald Patterson, 60; Frank Siteman, 16; Cary Wolinsky, 23 (bottom). Taurus Photos: Czeslaw Czaplinski, 95; Pam Hasegawa, 296 (far left); Vance Henry, front vi; Terry McKoy, front ix; L.L.T. Rhodes, 376; Lenore Weber, 23 (top 3 photos), 296 (middle right). United Press International: 18 (bottom). U.S. Air Force Photo: 193.

CONTENTS

CHAPTER 1

**REVIEW
COUNTING AND
OPERATIONS WITH
WHOLE NUMBERS**

Counting in Base Ten / **2**
The Hand System: Counting in Base Five / **4**
Converting Between Base Five and Base Ten / **6**
Adding in Base Five / **8**
Roll a Problem Game (Base-Five Addition) / **11**
Multidigit Addition (Base Ten) / **12**
Multidigit Subtraction (Base Ten) / **13**
Stop at 1000 Game / **14**
Keeping Sharp: Addition and Subtraction / **15**
Keeping Sharp: More Addition and Subtraction / **16**
Presidential Puzzlers / **18**
All in a Row (Addition and Subtraction Facts) / **19**
Keeping Sharp: Multiplication and Division Facts / **20**
Cubomat / **21**
Mental Multiplication: Powers and Multiples of 10 / **22**
Seminar: Estimating Time in School / **23**
Multiplying Multidigit Numbers / **24**
Make 25,000 Game / **27**
Dividing Multidigit Numbers / **28**
Interpreting Remainders / **30**
Using Arithmetic: Applications / **31**
Subtracting in Base Five / **32**
Multiplying and Dividing in Base Five / **34**
Chapter Review / **36**
Enrichment: Word-Number Puzzles / **37**
Chapter Test / **38**
Enrichment: Babylonian Numbers / **39**

CHAPTER 2

**EFFICIENT WAYS
TO DO ARITHMETIC**

Karl Friedrich Gauss and a Shortcut / **42**
Commutative and Associative Laws / **44**
The Distributive Law / **46**
Order of Operations / **48**
Solving Problems Without Paper or Pencil / **50**
Mental Multiplication Game / **51**
Seminar: Robert Recorde's Method for Subtraction / **52**
Some Algorithms for Multiplication / **55**
Review of the Commutative, Associative, and Distributive Laws / **58**

Squares and Squaring / **59**
Patterns in Squares / **60**
Keeping Sharp: Operations / **63**
Square Scores / **64**
Keeping Sharp: Basic Facts / **65**
Casting Out Nines / **66**
Approximation and Rounding / **68**
Approximating by Rounding / **70**
More on Casting Out Nines / **71**
Chapter Review / **72**
Enrichment: Taking Multiple-Choice Tests / **73**
Chapter Test / **74**
Nimble 100 / **75**

CHAPTER 3

**CALCULATOR USE
FUNCTIONS
DECIMALS AND PERCENTS**

Calculators and Computers / **78**
Using a Calculator / **81**
Calculator Races / **83**
Constants and Exponents on Calculators / **84**
Key Keys Game / **85**
Exponents / **86**
Using Approximation / **88**
Approximation Game / **89**
Using the Constant Feature / **90**
Function Machines and Function Rules / **91**
Finding Function Rules / **92**
Function Charts / **93**
Composite Functions / **94**
Decimals and Place Value / **96**
Roll and Regroup a Decimal Game / **98**
Addition and Subtraction of Decimals / **99**
Multiplication and Division of Decimals / **102**
Make a Problem Game / **105**
Approximating Answers / **106**
Using Decimals: Applications / **107**
Keeping Sharp: Computation / **108**
Make 25 Game / **109**
Applications / **110**
Percents / **112**
Percents, Fractions, and Decimals / **113**
Using Percents: Applications / **114**
Doing Percents in Your Head / **116**

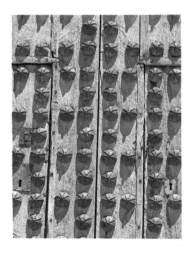

Using Percents: Applications / **117**
Tips Game / **119**
Keeping Sharp: Decimals, Fractions, and Percents / **120**
Seminar: Seed Germination / **121**
Chapter Review / **124**
Enrichment: Percent Error / **125**
Chapter Test / **126**
Enrichment: A Variation of the Approximation Game / **127**

CHAPTER 4

GEOMETRY

Describing Direction / **130**
Angles and Their Measure / **132**
Measuring Angles / **134**
Parallel Lines, Transversals, and Corresponding Angles / **138**
Sum of Angles of a Triangle / **140**
Triangles and Quadrilaterals / **142**
Keeping Sharp: Powers and Multiples of 10; Exponents / **144**
Notation and Terminology / **145**
Quadrilaterals / **146**
Parallelograms / **147**
3 Questions Game / **148**
Keeping Sharp: Percents / **149**
Bisecting Angles / **150**
Constructions / **151**
Congruent Figures / **152**
Copying Figures / **154**
Seminar: Constructing Figures / **155**
Similar Triangles / **156**
Constructing Triangles / **158**
Triangle Game / **159**
Keeping Sharp: Percents / **160**
Enrichment: Doing Puzzles for Fun / **161**
Paper Folding: Triangles / **162**
Paper Folding: Equilateral Triangles / **164**
Paper Folding: A Tetrahedron / **165**
Chapter Review / **166**
Enrichment: The Möbius Strip / **169**
Chapter Test / **170**
Enrichment: Paper Folding / **173**

CHAPTER 5

FRACTIONS

Factors and Factoring / **178**
Factors and Divisibility Rules / **180**
Equivalent Fractions / **182**
Reducing Fractions / **184**
Multiplying Fractions / **186**
Rolling Cubes / **189**
Improper Fractions and Mixed Numbers / **190**
Using Fractions: Applications / **192**
Probability / **194**
Practice with Probability / **196**
Adding Fractions / **198**
Adding and Subtracting Fractions / **200**
Make $\frac{1}{2}$ Game / **201**
A Sure Way to Add and Subtract Fractions / **202**
Practice with Fractions / **203**
More Practice with Fractions / **204**
Dividing Fractions / **206**
Roll a Fraction Game / **209**
Fractions: Applications / **210**
Keeping Sharp: Multiplying and Dividing Decimals / **212**
Exponent Game / **213**
Seminar: Conserving Electricity / **214**
Fractions and Decimals / **216**
Fraction-Decimal Equivalents / **218**
Up to 1 Game / **219**
Ratios and Rates / **220**
Interest Rates / **222**
Chapter Review / **224**
Constant Comparison / **225**
Chapter Test / **226**
Enrichment: Driving a Car / **227**

CHAPTER 6

**MEASUREMENT
MIXED NUMBERS
SIGNED NUMBERS**

Measurement of Time / **230**
Measuring Length in the Metric System / **234**
Metric Units of Area, Volume, Weight, and Temperature / **236**
Working with Different Units of Measurement / **238**
Converting Within the Metric System / **240**
The Traditional System of Measure / **242**
Keeping Sharp: Arithmetic with Fractions / **246**

Seminar: The Traditional System 120 Years Ago / **247**
Using Traditional Measures / **248**
Match the Measure / **249**
Adding and Subtracting Mixed Numbers / **250**
Practice with Mixed Numbers and Improper Fractions / **254**
Using Mixed Numbers and Improper Fractions: Applications / **255**
Multiplying and Dividing Mixed Numbers / **256**
Arithmetic with Mixed Numbers / **258**
Roll a Problem Fraction Game / **259**
Signed Numbers / **260**
Absolute Value of a Number / **262**
Adding and Subtracting Signed Numbers / **263**
Multiplication with Signed Numbers / **266**
Signed Mathness / **268**
Practice with Signed Numbers / **269**
Chapter Review / **270**
Enrichment / **271**
Chapter Test / **272**
Enrichment / **273**

CHAPTER 7

STATISTICS
RATIOS

Graunt and the Beginning of the Science of Statistics / **276**
Organizing Data / **278**
Cube Averaging Game / **280**
Computing the Mean / **281**
Averages: Applications / **282**
Mean, Median, and Mode / **284**
Statistics: Applications / **286**
Letter Arithmetic Activity / **288**
Keeping Sharp: Computation with Fractions / **289**
Halley and the First Life Insurance Tables / **290**
Using a Mortality Table / **292**
Ratios / **296**
Ratios and Gears / **297**
Ratios in Geometry / **298**
Ratios in Maps and Blueprints / **299**
Ratios and Statistics / **300**
Keeping Sharp: Signed Numbers / **302**
Seminar: Saltwater Fish / **303**
Chapter Review / **304**
Chapter Test / **306**
Enrichment: A Different Kind of "Addition" / **308**
Enrichment: Problems to Solve / **309**

CHAPTER 8

2- AND 3-DIMENSIONAL GEOMETRY

Area / **312**
Calculating Area / **314**
Area of a Parallelogram / **316**
Area of a Triangle / **318**
Calculating Areas / **319**
Finding Areas / **320**
Finding Areas of Unusually Shaped Figures / **322**
Area of Trapezoids / **324**
Finding Areas of Figures / **326**
Volume of Rectangular Boxes / **328**
Seminar: The Great Ice-Melting Contest / **330**
Volume of Prisms / **332**
Finding Volumes of Prisms / **334**
Area Game / **336**
Square and Cube Roots / **338**
The Tetrahedron and the Cube / **340**
Regular Polyhedra / **342**
The Octahedron, the Dodecahedron, and the Icosahedron / **344**
Seminar: Body Temperatures of Living Things / **346**
Chapter Review / **352**
Chapter Test / **354**
Enrichment: Polyhedra and Probability / **356**
Triangle Tangle / **357**

CHAPTER 9

ROOTS
ERROR ANALYSIS
π

Sir Isaac Newton / **360**
Calculator Errors / **361**
A Method for Finding Square Roots / **362**
Comparing Methods for Finding Square Roots / **364**
Cube Roots and Other Roots / **366**
Square Roots: Applications / **368**
Square and Cube Roots: Applications / **370**
Keeping Sharp: Function Charts / **371**
Right Triangles / **372**
The Pythagorean Theorem / **374**
Errors in Measurement / **376**
Upper and Lower Bounds / **378**
Measuring Circular Objects / **380**
The Value of π / **382**

Using π / **383**
Area of a Circle / **384**
Volume and Surface Area of a Cylinder / **386**
Seminar: Saving on Home Heating / **388**
Chapter Review / **390**
Chapter Test / **392**
Calculator Square Root Game / **394**
Enrichment: A Variation of Calculator Square Root Game / **395**

CHAPTER 10

FUNCTIONS
COMPUTER UNDERSTANDING

Function Rules and Function Charts / **398**
Standard Notation for Function Rules / **399**
Descartes and the Problem of the Fly / **400**
Locating Points on a Graph / **402**
Get the Point / **404**
Graphing Function Rules / **406**
Graphing Functions / **408**
Using Graphs / **410**
Cube Roots on a Graph / **412**
Roll a 15 Game / **413**
Computers and Programs / **414**
Cube 100 Game / **416**
Programming the Paper-Player Computer / **417**
Seminar: Graphing Results of Seed Germination Experiment / **418**
Chapter Review / **420**
Enrichment: Puzzling Problems / **421**
Chapter Test / **422**
Enrichment: Word-Number Puzzles / **423**

TABLES OF MEASURE / 424
GLOSSARY / 426
INDEX / 433

CHAPTER 1

REVIEW
COUNTING AND OPERATIONS WITH WHOLE NUMBERS

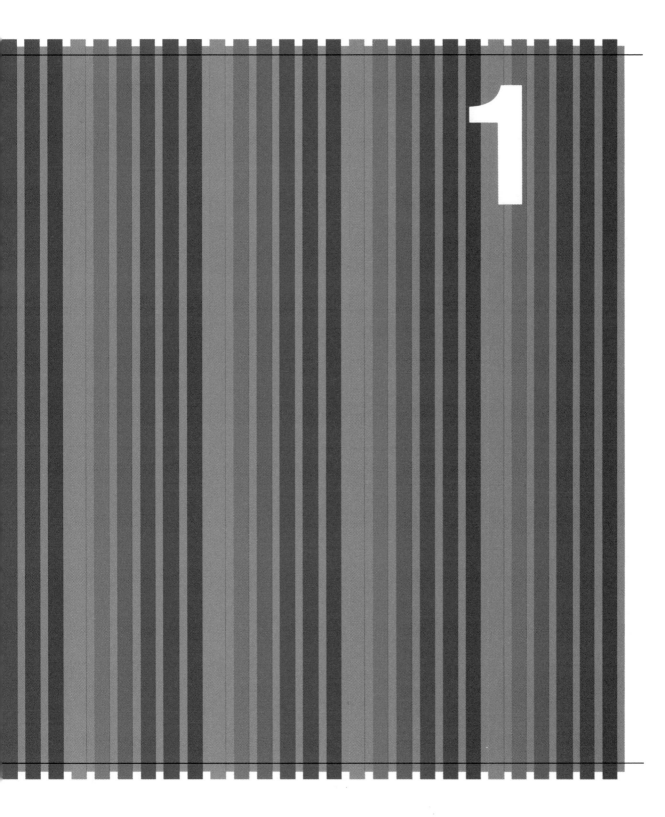

The system we use to say and to write names for numbers is the base-ten system. Because humans used their fingers to count, a base-ten system of arithmetic developed naturally.

Let's say you want to count the number of gold coins in a bag. You could count on your fingers as long as there are no more than 10 coins.

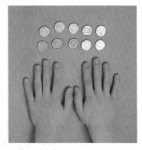

If there are 4 coins, you'd use 4 fingers.

If there are 8 coins, you'd use 8 fingers.

If there are 10 coins, you'd use 10 fingers.

But if there are more than 10 coins, you wouldn't have enough fingers. If another person helped you, you could just count up to 20.

But you could do better still. You could have that person keep track of how many times you use all your fingers. To show that you have counted all your fingers twice and still have 7 more coins, the two of you would show this:

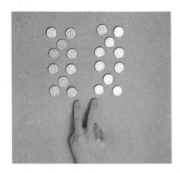

The other person shows 2 tens. There are 27 coins.

You show 7 ones.

How many coins are shown by the hands in each picture?

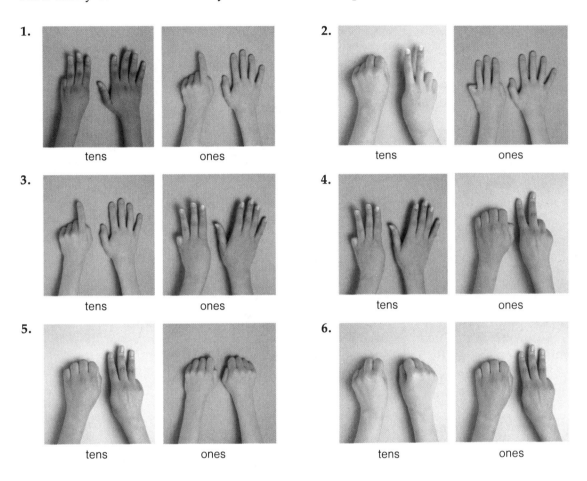

1.
tens   ones

2.
tens   ones

3.
tens   ones

4.
tens   ones

5.
tens   ones

6.
tens   ones

[1] Suppose there are 73 coins. If you were counting ones, how many fingers would the other person show? How many would you show?

[2] Suppose there are 5 coins. How many fingers would the other person show? How many would you show?

[3] Suppose there are 80 coins. How many fingers would the other person show? How many would you show?

[4] Suppose there are 99 coins. How many fingers would the other person show? How many would you show?

The Hand System: Counting in Base Five

Suppose people had only 5 fingers. Then you could count only to 5 using all your fingers. With another person helping, you could count to 6 fives.

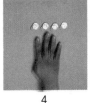  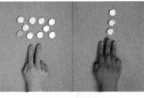 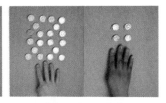

| 4 | 1 hand and 2 | 2 hands and 3 | 4 hands and 4 |

1. Draw the number of coins indicated by the hands in the pictures below.

a. 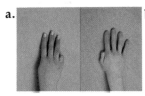 **b.** 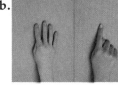 **c.** 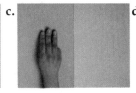 **d.**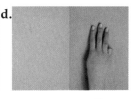

    3 hands and 4   4 hands and 1   3 hands   3

This system is known as base five, because it is based on the number 5. The digits 5, 6, 7, 8, and 9 are not used in base five.

If you count in base five, 32_f ("three-two, base five") stands for 3 hands and 2.

[1] Is that an even number?

[2] Can you put that many coins into 2 equal piles?

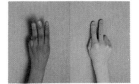

2. Each of the following numbers is a base-five number. Tell whether each number is odd or even.

    a. 4_f (four)
    b. 12_f (one hand and two)
    c. 13_f (one hand and three)
    d. 20_f (two hands)
    e. 21_f (two hands and one)
    f. 22_f (two hands and two)

    g. 30_f (three hands)
    h. 31_f (three hands and one)
    i. 34_f (three hands and four)
    j. 42_f (four hands and two)
    k. 43_f (four hands and three)
    l. 44_f (four hands and four)

[3] Can you give a rule for telling whether a number is odd or even in base five?

Notice that we write a small **f** below and to the right of all base-five numbers. This should help you remember which numbers are base five and which are base ten. Sometimes people use other ways to show which base is being used.

You cannot use the digit 5 when writing base-five numerals. Here are some examples that show what number (written in base five) comes next when you are counting in base five. The next number is 1 more than the given number.

32_f The next number is 33_f.
34_f The next number is 40_f.
44_f The next number is 100_f.

In the last example, if you were counting in base five using your fingers and hands, you would need a third hand to keep track of how many times the second hand had used up all its fingers.

3. For each of the following base-five numbers, write in base five the number that is 1 more.

a. 4_f	**e.** 41_f	**i.** 110_f	**m.** 200_f	**q.** 240_f	**u.** 404_f
b. 22_f	**f.** 44_f	**j.** 114_f	**n.** 203_f	**r.** 244_f	**v.** 432_f
c. 24_f	**g.** 101_f	**k.** 140_f	**o.** 204_f	**s.** 304_f	**w.** 440_f
d. 34_f	**h.** 104_f	**l.** 144_f	**p.** 231_f	**t.** 344_f	**x.** 444_f

4. Do you need 4 digits to show the number after 444_f?

5. Write the number that is 1 more.

a. 1000_f	**d.** 4040_f	**g.** 444_f
b. 4000_f	**e.** 4044_f	**h.** $44{,}444_f$
c. 4004_f	**f.** 4440_f	**i.** $444{,}444_f$

Instead of thinking of fingers and hands with base-five numerals, you could think of cents, nickels, and quarters. So you would think of 24_f as 2 nickels and 4 cents, or 14. 312_f would be 3 quarters, 1 nickel, and 2 cents, or 82.

1. What is the value in base ten of each of the following base-five numbers? Use whichever way of thinking you prefer.

   a. 4_f **e.** 44_f **i.** 333_f **m.** 440_f
   b. 10_f **f.** 100_f **j.** 400_f **n.** 444_f
   c. 22_f **g.** 200_f **k.** 420_f **o.** 1000_f
   d. 34_f **h.** 300_f **l.** 424_f **p.** $10,000_f$

[1] **Is there a coin worth 1000_f? If there were, how much would it be worth in base-ten money?**

[2] **Is there a coin worth $10,000_f$? If there were, how much would it be worth in base-ten money?**

You can also use a table to help convert base-five numbers to base ten. These 3 examples show how it works:

Base Five	625s	125s	25s	5s	1s	Base Ten
324_f			3	2	4	75 + 10 + 4 = 89
4013_f		4	0	1	3	500 + 0 + 5 + 3 = 508
$34,213_f$	3	4	2	1	3	1875 + 500 + 50 + 5 + 3 = 2433

2. Convert each of the following to base ten. Use any procedure you like.

   a. 234_f **c.** 2222_f **e.** $30,412_f$ **g.** $11,111_f$ **i.** $23,132_f$
   b. 1111_f **d.** 4321_f **f.** $44,444_f$ **h.** $34,021_f$ **j.** $40,000_f$

You can convert base-ten numbers to base-five numbers by reversing the procedures shown on page 6.

Example: What is 738 in base five?

To do this, find how many 625s, 125s, 25s, 5s, and 1s there are in 738.

$$
\begin{array}{rr}
 & 738 \\
1 \times 625 = 625 & -\ 625 \\ \hline
 & 113 \\
\end{array}
$$

$$
\begin{array}{rr}
0 \times 125 = 0 & -\quad 0 \\ \hline
 & 113 \\
\end{array}
$$

$$
\begin{array}{rr}
4 \times 25 = 100 & -\ 100 \\ \hline
 & 13 \\
\end{array}
$$

$$
\begin{array}{rr}
2 \times 5 = 10 & -\quad 10 \\ \hline
 & 3 \\
\end{array}
$$

$$
\begin{array}{rr}
3 \times 1 = 3 & -\quad 3 \\ \hline
 & 0 \\
\end{array}
$$

100s	10s	1s	=	625s	125s	25s	5s	1s
7	3	8		1	0	4	2	3

So 738 (base ten) = 10,423$_f$.

To convert numbers less than 125 (base ten), you may prefer to think about quarters, nickels, and cents. To convert 119 to base five, think of making $1.19 with 4 quarters, 3 nickels, and 4 cents. So 119 = 434$_f$. Remember, in base five you cannot use digits greater than 4.

Convert each of the following base-ten numbers to base five.

3. 4	**10.** 60	**17.** 118	**24.** 250	**31.** 1890
4. 9	**11.** 75	**18.** 124	**25.** 500	**32.** 2000
5. 19	**12.** 78	**19.** 125	**26.** 620	**33.** 2250
6. 25	**13.** 90	**20.** 126	**27.** 624	**34.** 2275
7. 50	**14.** 93	**21.** 200	**28.** 625	**35.** 2280
8. 53	**15.** 100	**22.** 225	**29.** 1250	**36.** 3333
9. 58	**16.** 115	**23.** 230	**30.** 1875	**37.** 3124

How would you add numbers in the hand (or base-five) system?

Example: How much is 1 hand and 3 plus 2 hands and 4?

$13_f + 24_f = ?$

$$\begin{array}{r} 1\,3_f \\ +\,2\,4_f \end{array}$$

  Line up corresponding digits.

$$\begin{array}{r} 1 \\ 1\,3_f \\ +\,2\,4_f \\ \hline 2 \end{array}$$

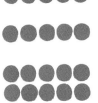 Start at the right. Add the fingers column.

$3_f + 4_f = 12_f$ (1 hand and 2)

Write 2 below the fingers column. Write 1 at the top of the hands column.

$$\begin{array}{r} 1 \\ 1\,3_f \\ +\,2\,4_f \\ \hline 4\,2_f \end{array}$$

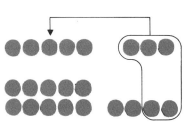 Add the hands column.

$1_f + 1_f + 2_f = 4_f$

There are 4 hands.
Write 4 below the hands column.
Write **f** to show the answer is in base five.

The answer is 4 hands and 2. We write 42_f.

We are talking about base five to help you understand how different base systems work. You don't have to master these ideas. Just have fun with them. Play with the numbers. Learn more about them.

Here is another example of adding in base five:

How much is 1 hand of hands of hands, 1 hand of hands, 2 hands, and 3 plus 2 hands of hands of hands, 4 hands of hands, 1 hand, and 4? $1123_f + 2414_f = ?$

$$\begin{array}{r} 1\,1\,2\,3_f \\ +\ 2\,4\,1\,4_f \\ \hline \end{array}$$ Start at the right.

$3_f + 4_f = 12_f$

$$\begin{array}{r} 1 \\ 1\,1\,2\,3_f \\ +\ 2\,4\,1\,4_f \\ \hline 2 \end{array}$$ Write 2 below the fingers column and 1 at the top of the hand column.

$1_f + 2_f + 1_f = 4_f$

$$\begin{array}{r} 1 \\ 1\,1\,2\,3_f \\ +\ 2\,4\,1\,4_f \\ \hline 4\ 2 \end{array}$$ There are 4 hands. Write 4.

$1_f + 4_f = 10_f$

$$\begin{array}{r} 1\ \ 1 \\ 1\,1\,2\,3_f \\ +\ 2\,4\,1\,4_f \\ \hline 0\ 4\ 2 \end{array}$$ There are 10 hands of hands. Write 0. Carry 1.

$1_f + 1_f + 2_f = 4_f$

$$\begin{array}{r} 1\ \ 1 \\ 1\,1\,2\,3_f \\ +\ 2\,4\,1\,4_f \\ \hline 4\ 0\ 4\ 2_f \end{array}$$ There are 4 hands of hands of hands. Write 4.

How is adding in base five similar to adding in base ten?

1. Try these problems in base five. Remember, the only digits you may use are 0, 1, 2, 3, and 4. Write answers in base five.

a. $\begin{array}{r} 2\ 1_f \\ +\ 1\ 3_f \\ \hline \end{array}$
b. $\begin{array}{r} 2\ 1_f \\ +\ 1\ 4_f \\ \hline \end{array}$
c. $\begin{array}{r} 2\ 4_f \\ +\ 3\ 2_f \\ \hline \end{array}$
d. $\begin{array}{r} 2\ 4\ 3_f \\ +\ 4\ 0\ 3_f \\ \hline \end{array}$
e. $\begin{array}{r} 3\ 2\ 0\ 4_f \\ +\ 2\ 1\ 3\ 3_f \\ \hline \end{array}$

Is it hard to remember addition facts for base five? An addition table might help. Copy and complete this addition table for base five.

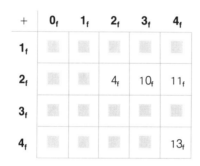

+	0_f	1_f	2_f	3_f	4_f
1_f					
2_f			4_f	10_f	11_f
3_f					
4_f					13_f

Now use your table to check your work on problems 1a–1e.

2. Use your base-five addition table to help solve for n in these problems. Write answers in base five.

a. $3_f + 4_f = n$ c. $4_f + 2_f = n$ e. $4_f + 3_f = n$
b. $2_f + 3_f = n$ d. $4_f + 1_f = n$ f. $3_f + 2_f = n$

3. Do these base-five problems.

a. $\begin{array}{r} 3\ 4\ 2_f \\ +\ \ \ 2\ 3_f \\ \hline \end{array}$
b. $\begin{array}{r} 1\ 0\ 2\ 3_f \\ +\ \ \ 3\ 4\ 2_f \\ \hline \end{array}$
c. $\begin{array}{r} 3\ 1\ 0\ 4_f \\ +\ 2\ 2\ 1\ 3_f \\ \hline \end{array}$
d. $\begin{array}{r} 2\ 2\ 2\ 2_f \\ +\ 2\ 3\ 2\ 3_f \\ \hline \end{array}$

4. Solve for n.

a. $2_f + n = 10_f$ c. $1_f + n = 3_f$ e. $2_f + n = 11_f$
b. $4_f + n = 11_f$ d. $3_f + n = 10_f$ f. $4_f + n = 13_f$

5. Use your base-five addition table to figure out the base-five subtraction facts ($13_f - 4_f$, $11_f - 3_f$, $10_f - 1_f$, and so on).

Players: 2 or more
Materials: One 0–5 cube
Object: To get the greatest sum

Rules

1. Use blanks to outline an addition problem on your paper like this.

$$\begin{array}{r} \underline{\ }\ \underline{\ }\ \underline{\ }\ \underline{\ }_f \\ +\ \underline{\ }\ \underline{\ }\ \underline{\ }\ \underline{\ }_f \end{array}$$

2. The first player rolls the cube 8 times. If a **5** is rolled, roll the cube again.

3. Each time the cube is rolled, write that number in one of the blanks in your outline.

4. When all the blanks have been filled in, find the sum of the 2 numbers in base five.

5. The player with the greatest sum wins the round.

Sample Game

	Rosa's problem	Willy's problem
The first roll was: **3**	$\begin{array}{r}\underline{\ }\ \underline{\ }\ \underline{3}\ \underline{\ }_f \\ +\ \underline{\ }\ \underline{\ }\ \underline{\ }\ \underline{\ }_f\end{array}$	$\begin{array}{r}\underline{\ }\ \underline{\ }\ \underline{\ }\ \underline{\ }_f \\ +\ \underline{\ }\ \underline{3}\ \underline{\ }\ \underline{\ }_f\end{array}$
The next 6 rolls were: **0** **4** **2** **1** **2** **3**	$\begin{array}{r}\underline{4}\ \underline{3}\ \underline{3}\ \underline{0}_f \\ +\ \underline{\ }\ \underline{2}\ \underline{2}\ \underline{1}_f\end{array}$	$\begin{array}{r}\underline{3}\ \underline{2}\ \underline{1}\ \underline{2}_f \\ +\ \underline{4}\ \underline{3}\ \underline{\ }\ \underline{0}_f\end{array}$
The last roll was: **4**	$\begin{array}{r}\underline{4}\ \underline{3}\ \underline{3}\ \underline{0}_f \\ +\ \underline{4}\ \underline{2}\ \underline{2}\ \underline{1}_f\end{array}$	$\begin{array}{r}\underline{3}\ \underline{2}\ \underline{1}\ \underline{2}_f \\ +\ \underline{4}\ \underline{3}\ \underline{4}\ \underline{0}_f\end{array}$
Rosa won.	$1\ 4\ 1\ 0\ 1_f$	$1\ 3\ 1\ 0\ 2_f$

Multidigit Addition (Base Ten)

The Canadian National Tower in Toronto is the world's tallest self-supporting tower. It is 553 meters high. Toronto is 109 meters above sea level. How far above sea level is the top of the Canadian National Tower?

$553 + 109 = ?$

```
  5 5 3
+ 1 0 9    Line up corresponding digits.
-------
```

```
    1
  5 5 3    Start at the right.
+ 1 0 9    3 + 9 = 12   (twelve, or 1 ten and 2).
-------
      2
```

Write 2 at the bottom of the ones column and 1 at the top of the tens column.

```
    1
  5 5 3    1 + 5 + 0 = 6
+ 1 0 9
-------    There are 6 tens. Write 6.
  6 2
```

```
    1
  5 5 3    5 + 1 = 6
+ 1 0 9
-------    There are 6 hundreds. Write 6.
  6 6 2
```

So the top of the tower is 662 meters above sea level.

Notice that when you add, you use the same procedure in each column.

Ms. Antonini has $6564. She is going to buy a used car that costs
$3358. How much money will she have after she buys it?

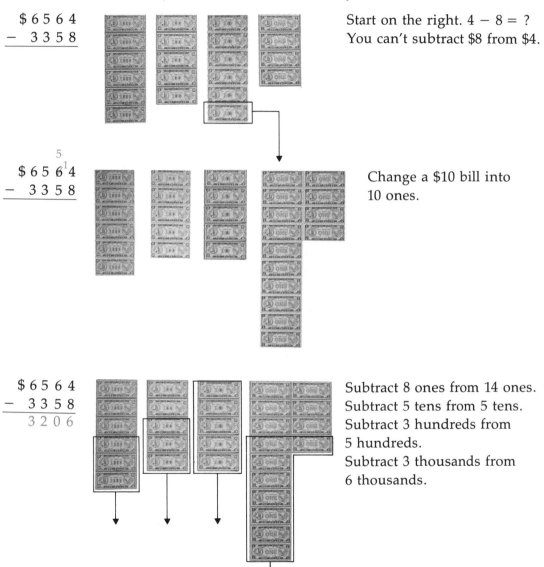

$$\begin{array}{r} \$6564 \\ -3358 \\ \end{array}$$

Start on the right. $4 - 8 = ?$
You can't subtract $8 from $4.

$$\begin{array}{r} ^{5}\\ \$65\,6^{1}4 \\ -3358 \\ \end{array}$$

Change a $10 bill into
10 ones.

$$\begin{array}{r} \$6564 \\ -3358 \\ \hline 3206 \\ \end{array}$$

Subtract 8 ones from 14 ones.
Subtract 5 tens from 5 tens.
Subtract 3 hundreds from
5 hundreds.
Subtract 3 thousands from
6 thousands.

So Ms. Antonini will have $3206 left after she buys the car.

Notice that to subtract you use the same procedure in each
column, just as you did to add.

STOP AT 1000 GAME

Players: 2 or more
Materials: Two 0–5 cubes, two 5–10 cubes, pencil, paper
Object: To be the person to reach 1000 exactly

Rules

1. Take turns rolling all 4 cubes.

2. On your turn, use 1, 2, or 3 of the numbers you roll to make a 1-, 2-, or 3-digit number. You can use a **10** if you regroup. For example, you might use **9** and **10** to get 100 (by making 9 tens and 10 ones) or to get 109 (by making 10 tens and 9 ones).

3. Start with 0. Keep 1 running total for all players. Just add your number to the total each time.

4. Each time you roll, you must make a number and add it to the total unless doing so will make the total more than 1000. In that case, the group score remains what it was before you rolled.

5. The player who reaches 1000 exactly is the winner.

Sample Game

Alfredo and Ruth started a game.   0

Alfredo rolled: **2** **2** **7** **9** He made 279:   + 279
                                                             279
Ruth rolled: **9** **2** **7** **0** She added 90:   + 90
                                                             369
Alfredo rolled: **0** **3** **5** **6** He added 630:   + 630
                                                             999
Ruth rolled: **2** **3** **6** **9** She couldn't add anything.

Alfredo rolled: **3** **5** **9** **8** He couldn't add anything.

Ruth rolled: **1** **4** **7** **9** She added 1:   +   1
                                                            1000

Ruth won this round.

Solve these problems in base ten. Use shortcuts when you can.

1. 3239 + 121		**2.** 7500 + 2500		**3.** 2135 − 838		**4.** 1297 + 838	
5. 7753 − 5506		**6.** 6364 + 5187		**7.** 9700 − 1		**8.** 9700 − 11	
9. 1296 + 6921		**10.** 8317 − 7021		**11.** 606 + 404		**12.** 682 − 459	
13. 15,000 + 54,000		**14.** 345 + 351		**15.** 15,345 + 54,351		**16.** 7216 − 4781	
17. 2806 − 7		**18.** 7000 − 3952		**19.** 4547 − 680		**20.** 4547 + 680	
21. 1198 + 1334		**22.** 2332 − 89		**23.** 1135 + 95		**24.** 2489 + 95	

25. John Fitzgerald Kennedy, the 35th president of the United States, was born in 1917. Lyndon Baines Johnson, the 36th U.S. president, was born in 1908.

  a. Which of the 2 was younger when he became president?

  b. Why can you answer this question with just the information given in the problem?

To add and subtract easily, you should be quick with the addition and subtraction facts. Try this speed test to see how well you know the facts.

1. 7 + 3	11. 3 + 7	21. 10 − 9	31. 17 − 7
2. 6 + 8	12. 4 + 9	22. 12 − 7	32. 17 − 8
3. 18 − 9	13. 14 − 5	23. 5 + 6	33. 17 − 9
4. 9 − 3	14. 11 − 3	24. 7 − 4	34. 9 + 6
5. 5 + 2	15. 5 − 2	25. 11 − 4	35. 4 + 5
6. 16 − 7	16. 5 + 4	26. 7 + 1	36. 8 − 3
7. 6 − 2	17. 2 + 6	27. 6 + 6	37. 10 − 2
8. 2 + 9	18. 9 − 2	28. 13 − 8	38. 3 + 9
9. 8 + 7	19. 12 − 3	29. 6 + 9	39. 4 + 8
10. 16 − 9	20. 5 + 7	30. 10 + 6	40. 7 + 6

If some addition facts are hard for you to remember, these suggestions may help:

A. The tens facts—10 + 7 = 17, 10 + 5 = 15, and so on—are easy. For example, 17 is just 1 ten and 7 more.

B. Get the nines facts by counting back 1 from the tens facts. For example, 9 + 7 is 1 less than 10 + 7 = 17, or 16. In the same way, 9 + 5 = 14, 9 + 2 = 11, and so on.

C. Learn the doubles. Then you can remember some facts as 1 more or 1 less than a double. For example, if you know 7 + 7 = 14, then 7 + 8 must be 15, and 7 + 6 must be 13.

D. The order in which you add 2 numbers makes no difference. (This is sometimes called the commutative law for addition.) So if you know that 8 + 3 = 11, you also know that 3 + 8 = 11.

E. Learn the combinations that sum to 10: 1 + 9, 2 + 8, 3 + 7, 4 + 6, and 5 + 5.

What are some helpful rules for remembering certain groups of subtraction facts?

Here's another speed test for more practice with addition and subtraction facts.

41. 10 + 4	**51.** 8 + 4	**61.** 2 + 7	**71.** 6 + 8
42. 9 + 4	**52.** 14 − 9	**62.** 9 + 3	**72.** 3 + 8
43. 10 + 7	**53.** 19 − 9	**63.** 9 − 6	**73.** 13 − 9
44. 9 + 7	**54.** 8 + 4	**64.** 17 − 8	**74.** 4 + 7
45. 7 + 9	**55.** 3 + 9	**65.** 4 + 7	**75.** 4 + 9
46. 8 + 6	**56.** 16 − 8	**66.** 8 + 8	**76.** 9 + 9
47. 14 − 7	**57.** 14 − 5	**67.** 15 − 9	**77.** 10 − 7
48. 15 − 7	**58.** 6 + 6	**68.** 13 − 8	**78.** 4 + 6
49. 16 − 7	**59.** 19 − 10	**69.** 13 − 7	**79.** 10 − 8
50. 5 + 3	**60.** 18 − 9	**70.** 11 − 7	**80.** 5 + 5

Do these problems.

1. John Quincy Adams was the sixth president of the United States, and Andrew Jackson was the seventh. Both men were born in the same year (Adams in July and Jackson in March). Which man was older when he became president?

2. Abraham Lincoln was born in 1809. Andrew Johnson, vice president for Lincoln's second term, was born in 1808. Johnson succeeded to the presidency when Lincoln was shot. Which man was older when he became president?

3. Theodore Roosevelt, William Howard Taft, and Woodrow Wilson were the 26th, 27th, and 28th presidents respectively. Roosevelt was born on October 27, 1858. Taft was born on September 15, 1857. Wilson was born on December 28, 1856.

   a. Of the 3, who was oldest when he became president?
   b. Who was youngest?

4. Franklin Delano Roosevelt served as president longer than any other person—12 years, 1 month, and 8 days. He was born on January 30, 1882, and died in office on April 12, 1945. He was succeeded by his vice president, Harry Truman. Truman was born on May 8, 1884.

   a. Which man was younger when he became president?
   b. How old was Roosevelt when he died?
   c. On what day did Roosevelt first become president?

5. Theodore Roosevelt was born on October 27, 1858, and became president upon the death of President William McKinley on September 14, 1901. John F. Kennedy was born on May 29, 1917, and became president on January 20, 1961. One of the two was the youngest person ever to be president. Which one?

6. Elections for president of the United States are held in years divisible by 4. One of the two presidents mentioned in problem 5 was the youngest person ever elected president. Which one?

Players: 2
Materials: Two 0–5 cubes, two 5–10 cubes, paper, pencils
Object: To fill in 3 squares in a row so that they sum to 20

Rules

1. Make a game board like this one:

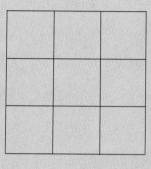

2. Take turns rolling any 2 cubes.

3. On each turn, write the sum or difference of the 2 numbers rolled in any empty space on your game board.

4. The first player to complete 3 squares in a row (horizontally, vertically, or diagonally) that sum to 20 wins the round.

Sample Game

1. Curtis rolled: 5 5
He made: 10

2. Tanya rolled: 8 10
She made: 2

3. Curtis rolled: 4 2
He made: 6

4. Tanya rolled: 7 1
She made: 8

5. Curtis rolled: 0 0
He made: 0

6. Tanya rolled: 6 2
She made: 4

7. Curtis rolled: 10 10
He made: 0

8. Tanya rolled: 6 4
She made: 10

Tanya won, because 10 + 10 + 0 = 20.

To multiply and divide easily, you should be quick with the multiplication and division facts. Try this speed test to see how well you know the facts.

1. 9 × 8	**11.** 18 ÷ 6	**21.** 7 × 8	**31.** 8 × 0
2. 6 × 7	**12.** 24 ÷ 3	**22.** 6 × 6	**32.** 7 × 10
3. 48 ÷ 8	**13.** 9 × 7	**23.** 54 ÷ 9	**33.** 6 × 2
4. 5 × 7	**14.** 81 ÷ 9	**24.** 63 ÷ 9	**34.** 24 ÷ 8
5. 15 ÷ 5	**15.** 36 ÷ 9	**25.** 5 × 8	**35.** 42 ÷ 7
6. 32 ÷ 8	**16.** 12 ÷ 3	**26.** 7 × 7	**36.** 4 × 2
7. 8 × 8	**17.** 5 × 5	**27.** 72 ÷ 8	**37.** 5 ÷ 5
8. 8 × 5	**18.** 18 ÷ 3	**28.** 7 × 2	**38.** 6 ÷ 2
9. 16 ÷ 4	**19.** 56 ÷ 7	**29.** 9 × 3	**39.** 5 × 3
10. 5 × 9	**20.** 9 × 6	**30.** 28 ÷ 7	**40.** 20 ÷ 5

These suggestions may help you remember some multiplication facts:

A. Multiplying by 10 is easy. Just write a zero to the right of the number. For example: $10 \times 7 = 70$ (7 tens).

B. To multiply a number n by 9, subtract n from $10 \times n$. For example: 9×7 is $70 - 7$, or 63.

Also notice that the sum of the digits of a multiple of 9 is 9 (or a multiple of 9). This will help you check when you multiply by 9. For example: $9 \times 8 = 72$, and $7 + 2 = 9$.

C. To multiply a number by 5, multiply the number by 10 and divide the result by 2. For example: 6×5 is $60 \div 2$, or 30; 7×5 is $70 \div 2$, or 35.

D. The order in which you multiply 2 numbers makes no difference. (This is sometimes called the commutative law for multiplication.) So if you know that $5 \times 9 = 45$, you also know that $9 \times 5 = 45$.

CUBOMAT

Players: 2
Materials: Two 0–5 cubes, two 5–10 cubes, paper, pencil
Object: To be the first player to have 3 squares in a row

Rules

1. Make a copy of the game card you will use for this game. (Both players use the same card.)

2. Take turns rolling all 4 cubes. Try to make 1 of the numbers on the card by using any combination of the 4 operations (addition, subtraction, multiplication, and division) on the numbers rolled. Use the number on each cube only once. (If 2 cubes have the same number, you must use both.) If you cannot make 1 of the numbers on the card, you lose your turn.

3. Put your initials on the square containing the number you make.

4. The first player to have 3 squares in a row (horizontally, vertically, or diagonally) is the winner.

Game Cards

1	13	16
23	20	10
8	4	25

3	15	7
11	21	19
17	6	26

2	5	18
12	22	24
9	14	27

Sample Game

JK 3	15	JK 7
SF 11	JK 21	JK 19
SF 17	SF 6	SF 26

1. Jeff rolled: `1` `1` `9` `10`
   He made: 10 + 9 + 1 + 1 = 21

2. Sally rolled: `1` `4` `6` `7`
   She made: (6 + 7 + 4) × 1 = 17

3. Jeff rolled: `1` `2` `8` `10`
   He made: 8 − (10 ÷ 2) × 1 = 3

4. Sally rolled: `2` `2` `7` `10`
   She made: (7 × 2) + 10 + 2 = 26

5. Jeff rolled: `1` `2` `8` `10`
   He made: 10 + 8 + 2 − 1 = 19

6. Sally rolled: `3` `3` `6` `10`
   She made: (6 × 3) + 3 − 10 = 11

7. Jeff rolled: `0` `3` `9` `10`
   He made: (10 − 3) + (9 × 0) = 7

8. Sally rolled: `3` `5` `7` `8`
   She made: (8 + 7) ÷ 5 + 3 = 6   Sally won.

Remember: Numbers like 10, 100, 1000, and 10,000 are called powers of 10.

[1] What is 23 × 10,000?

[2] What is the rule for multiplying a number by a power of 10?

Multiply.

1. 3 × 100	**4.** 23 × 1000	**7.** 63 × 10,000
2. 3 × 10,000	**5.** 36 × 1000	**8.** 123 × 1000
3. 23 × 100	**6.** 39 × 100	**9.** 247 × 10,000

[3] What is 8 × 900?

[4] What is a rule for multiplying a number by a multiple of a power of 10?

Multiply.

10. 8 × 300	**13.** 7 × 700	**16.** 400 × 8
11. 30 × 9	**14.** 60 × 7	**17.** 8000 × 7
12. 6 × 500	**15.** 40 × 8	**18.** 9000 × 6

[5] What is 70× 800?

[6] What is a rule for multiplying 2 multiples of powers of 10?

Multiply.

19. 80 × 90	**22.** 400 × 600	**25.** 200 × 90
20. 300 × 80	**23.** 70 × 300	**26.** 30 × 500
21. 60 × 600	**24.** 30 × 30	**27.** 40 × 50

[7] What might cause a problem when you multiply 40 × 50?

Multiply.

28. 60 × 50	**34.** 6 × 400	**40.** 7 × 70
29. 12 × 1000	**35.** 29 × 1000	**41.** 7 × 100
30. 9 × 700	**36.** 80 × 500	**42.** 7 × 1000
31. 90 × 700	**37.** 400 × 50	**43.** 70 × 1000
32. 24 × 100	**38.** 90 × 90	**44.** 800 × 400
33. 12 × 200	**39.** 900 × 900	**45.** 400 × 800

Work on these problems in groups. Discuss. Then make your best estimates. Remember, real problems often have different answers, depending on your assumptions. So your group and the other groups may have different answers that are all reasonable.

1. During your lifetime, about how many hours will you spend in school?

2. During your lifetime, about how many hours will you spend sleeping?

3. During your lifetime, about how many hours will you spend eating?

There are about 180 school days each year. About how many hours will be spent this school year?

Will including sick days make a big difference?

Should we include the 2 days we missed last year because of the snowstorm?

What about college? Should we include nursery school? Should we include music school?

We spend about 5–6 hours a day in school.

When we finish high school, we'll have spent 13 years in school, including kindergarten.

In Beverly Red Horse's office, 27 people have decided to contribute $43 each to Channel 43, their local educational TV station. Pretend you don't know how to multiply. How might you figure out how much money they paid altogether?

Suppose each person gave four $10 bills and three $1 bills. You could imagine the bills laid out as they are below. Then you could count all the $10 bills, multiply that number by 10, and add the number of $1 bills to get the total.

A quicker way would be to notice that each group of ten $10 bills makes $100.

Step A In the red box are 2 × 4, or 8, groups of ten $10 bills. That's 800.

Step B In the blue box are 2 × 3, or 6, groups of ten $1 bills. That's $60.

Step C In the green box are 7 × 4, or 28, $10 bills. That's $280.

Step D In the black box are 7 × 3, or 21, $1 bills. That's $21.

Then add to find the total amount of money:

$$\$800 + \$60 + \$280 + \$21, \text{ or } \$1161.$$

To check this answer, think: The answer should be more than 20 × 40 (800) and less than 30 × 50 (1500). And it is. You could also estimate the answer as about 30 × 40 (1200) or as about 25 × 40 (1000).

In the procedure you usually use to multiply, steps A–D are taken in reverse order.

Step D   4 3 $7 \times 3 = 21$

             × 2 7   Write 1 directly below 7. Remember 2.

                1

Step C   43 $7 \times 4 = 28$

             × 27   Add 2 from step 1, getting 30. Write 0 to

            301   the left of 1. Since there are no more digits

                      to the left of 4, write 3 to the left of 0.

Step B   43 $2 \times 3 = 6$

             × 27   Write 6 under the 2 in the multiplier.

            301

              6

Step A   43 $2 \times 4 = 8$

             × 27   Write 8 to the left of 6.

            301

            8 6

Final step   43   Finally, as before, add. You'll get 1161.

             × 27

            301

             86

          1161

Do these problems.

1. 27 people each contributed \$143 to be used for their vacation. How much did they contribute altogether?
   Can you use the answer to an earlier problem to find this answer quickly?

2. 27 people each contributed \$243 to a vacation fund. How much is that?

3. 27 people each contributed \$1243 to a vacation fund. How much is that?

4. 127 people each contributed \$1243 to a vacation fund. How much is that?

5. 27 people each listed 43 cities they would like to visit on a vacation.

    a. How many cities is that altogether?

    b. What is the smallest possible answer?

    c. What is the largest possible answer?

Using this procedure you do not have to worry about place value. Because of the base notation, each digit will fall naturally in the right place, even if there are zeros in the multiplier.

Example

```
     137
  × 5008
    1096
 685
 686096
```
Notice that the 5 in the partial product is written directly below the 5 in the multiplier.

Multiply. Use shortcuts when you can. Check your answers to be sure they make sense.

6.   326
  × 50
	7. 606
	  × 333
		8. 712
		  × 455
			9. 404
			  × 25

10.   629
  × 34
	11. 1324
	  × 81
		12. 229
		  × 101
			13. 187
			  × 82

14.   825
  × 52
	15. 903
	  × 270
		16. 54
		  × 56
			17. 540
			  × 560

18.   702
  × 99
	19. 1415
	  × 633
		20. 983
		  × 7
			21. 983
			  × 700

22.   983
  × 707
	23. 1807
	  × 22
		24. 326
		  × 55
			25. 1489
			  × 44

MAKE 25,000 GAME

Players: 2 or more
Materials: Two 0–5 cubes, two 5–10 cubes
Object: To get closest to 25,000 without going over

Rules

1. Each player chooses and writes down a number between 300 and 800. This number will be a factor for a multiplication problem.

2. The first player rolls all 4 cubes. Use 2 of the cubes to make a 2-digit number, which will be your other factor. If a **10** is rolled, you may regroup. Try to make the product as close to 25,000 as you can without going over.

3. Write your second factor under the first one. Don't calculate the product yet.

4. The player whose product is closest to, but not over, 25,000 is the winner. You don't need to calculate precise answers unless you can't tell by looking or by making approximations which product is greater than, but not over, 25,000.

Sample Games

Margo chose 525 as her first factor.

Sara chose 302 as her first factor.

Sara rolled: **3** **5** **7** **9**

Margo made this problem:
$$\begin{array}{r} 525 \\ \times\ 39 \\ \hline \end{array}$$

Sara made this problem:
$$\begin{array}{r} 302 \\ \times\ 79 \\ \hline \end{array}$$

They decided without calculating that Sara's product was closer to, but not greater than, 25,000. If they hadn't agreed, they would have had to calculate the precise products.

In another game, Sara's problem was 302 × 86 and Margo's problem was 457 × 19. They calculated that Sara's product was 25,972. Since Margo's product was well under 25,000, she was the winner.

Mrs. Ramos gave her 11 nieces $7968 to share equally. 7 of the nieces volunteered to take one $1000 bill each and to leave the rest of the money for the other 4. The other 4 objected to this idea. So they all decided to go to the bank and trade the seven $1000 bills for $100 bills.

[1] How many $100 bills would they get?

[2] How many $100 bills would they have altogether, including the 9 with which they started?

[3] Then how many $100 bills could each of the 11 nieces take?

If each of them took seven $100 bills, that would use up seventy-seven $100 bills.

The nieces kept a record of what was done, as shown here:

$$
\begin{array}{r}
\text{\$100 bills} \\
7 \quad\text{money each niece gets} \\
\text{Number of nieces: 11} \quad 7968 \quad\text{money to be divided} \\
77 \quad\text{number of \$100 bills shared} \\
\hline
2 \quad\text{number of \$100 bills left}
\end{array}
$$

[4] What could the nieces do with the two $100 bills?

[5] How many $10 bills would they get for the two $100 bills?

[6] How many $10 bills would that be in all?

[7] How many $10 bills should each person get? (Think: There are about 10 people and about twenty $10 bills. Guess 2. If this guess were wrong, you would cross it off and try again.)

[8] How many $10 bills does that use up?

[9] How many are left?

This is what their record looks like now:

```
                        ┌──────── $100 bills
                     ┌──│─────── $10 bills
                     ▼  ▼
                     72 ──────── money each niece gets
Number of nieces: 11  7968 ───── money to be divided
                     77 ──────── number of $100 bills shared
                     26 ──────── number of $10 bills
                     22 ──────── number of $10 bills shared
                      4 ──────── number of $10 bills left
```

The four $10 bills can be changed to forty $1 bills, giving a total of forty-eight $1 bills. Each niece can take four $1 bills, using up forty-four and leaving four.

[10] What could they do with the remaining $4?

We usually put in some extra lines as shown to separate the number of persons (divisor, 11) from the number of dollars to be divided (dividend, 7968) and the dividend from the answer (quotient, 724). We'll just leave the remaining money (remainder, 4), because we don't know what will be done with it.

Sometimes we write the answer 724 R4, showing that the quotient is 724 and the remainder is 4.

If you do have to cross off digits in the quotient because of unlucky estimates, it is a good practice to rewrite the answer elsewhere so it is easy to read.

$$
\begin{array}{r}
724 \\
11\overline{)7968} \\
77 \\
\hline
26 \\
22 \\
\hline
48 \\
44 \\
\hline
4
\end{array}
$$

Each of the following problems has a remainder of zero. Find the quotient in each problem.

1. $5166 \div 14$
2. $22{,}112 \div 691$
3. $13{,}932 \div 43$
4. $139{,}320 \div 430$
5. $5074 \div 86$
6. $15{,}535 \div 239$
7. $19{,}092 \div 258$
8. $34{,}496 \div 98$
9. $51{,}993 \div 53$

Often you may need to think about what the remainder means in order to solve a problem. For example, all the questions below involve the same numbers, but the answers are not the same.

300 members of a senior citizens group in Bloomington are going to a baseball game in Chicago. The buses they are chartering can carry 48 persons.

[1] How many buses should the group charter?

Ms. Pelka is making curtains. She needs to cut pieces of fabric that are 48 centimeters long.

[2] How many pieces can she cut from a 300-centimeter-long piece of fabric?

A $300 refund was sent to the Hollow Hill Ski Club after the club's last ski trip. The members voted to share the refund equally among the 48 members who went on the trip.

[3] How much did each person get?

The Fifth National Bank sent Mr. Suarez 300 pencils to distribute to the 48 seventh graders at Sixth Street School.

[4] How can he do this fairly?

The answers to these questions show how important it is to think about the meaning of the remainder before deciding on the answer to a problem.

[5] What division problem was used to answer each of these questions?

Using Arithmetic: Applications

1. Yolanda has $24.00. Does she have enough money to buy 5 softballs that cost $4.10 each?

2. How many cents are in a billion dollars?

3. How many dimes are in a billion dollars?

4. How old will you be in the year 2000?

5. Assume that there are 365 days in a year. How many times a year does the hour hand on a clock point to 6?

6. This ad appeared in the Star News on July 9:

> TEMPORARY SUMMER JOB
>
> 35 students wanted to detassel corn. $4.00 per hour. No experience necessary. Apply at Colonel Corn Company.

85 students applied for these jobs.
   a. Would more than half of the students get jobs?
   b. How many students would not get jobs?

7. Tony got one of the jobs detasseling corn. He worked 7 hours a day for 10 days. How much money did he earn?

8. Elaine didn't get one of the jobs detasseling corn. But she got a job as a carpenter's helper. She worked 20 hours a week for 8 weeks and earned $600.
   a. Did Tony or Elaine earn more per hour?
   b. How much more?

9. Gregorio bought 5 books at the library sale. 3 cost $2.49 each, 1 cost 99¢ , and the other cost $1.49. Which book was the best buy?

10. Abbie, Olga, and Peter have 523 campaign buttons altogether. Abbie is going to give Peter 37 buttons, and Olga is going to give Peter 13 buttons.
   a. How many buttons will Peter have then?
   b. What will the total number of buttons in the 3 collections be after this?

Subtracting in Base Five

When you learned about the hand system, you were learning about base-five arithmetic. You learned to count and to add in base five. All the other operations can also be done in base five. This example will show you how to subtract in base five.

$$
\begin{array}{r}
\overset{3}{} \\
4\ 0\ \overset{3}{4}\,\overset{1}{2}_f \\
-\ 1\ 3\ 2\ 4_f \\
\hline
3_f
\end{array}
\qquad
\begin{array}{l}
\text{Start at the right.} \\
\text{Change one of the } 4_f \text{ hand to fingers.} \\
12_f - 4_f = 3_f
\end{array}
$$

$$
\begin{array}{r}
\overset{3}{} \\
4\ 0\ \overset{1}{4}\,2_f \\
-\ 1\ 3\ 2\ 4_f \\
\hline
1\ 3_f
\end{array}
\qquad
3_f - 2_f = 1_f
$$

$$
\begin{array}{r}
\overset{3}{}\quad\overset{3}{} \\
\overset{1}{4}\,0\ \overset{1}{4}\,2_f \\
-\ 1\ 3\ 2\ 4_f \\
\hline
2\ 1\ 3_f
\end{array}
\qquad
\begin{array}{l}
\text{You can't take 3 from 0.} \\
\text{Change } 4_f \text{ hands of hands of hands to } 3_f \text{ hands} \\
\text{of hands of hands and } 10_f \text{ hands of hands.} \\
10_f - 3_f = 2_f
\end{array}
$$

$$
\begin{array}{r}
\overset{3}{}\quad\overset{3}{} \\
\overset{1}{4}\,0\ \overset{1}{4}\,2_f \\
-\ 1\ 3\ 2\ 4_f \\
\hline
2\ 2\ 1\ 3_f
\end{array}
\qquad
3_f - 1_f = 2_f
$$

Notice that the same procedure is used in each column.

This is an addition table for base five:

How can you use the base-five addition table to help you subtract?

+	0_f	1_f	2_f	3_f	4_f	10_f
0_f	0_f	1_f	2_f	3_f	4_f	10_f
1_f	1_f	2_f	3_f	4_f	10_f	11_f
2_f	2_f	3_f	4_f	10_f	11_f	12_f
3_f	3_f	4_f	10_f	11_f	12_f	13_f
4_f	4_f	10_f	11_f	12_f	13_f	14_f
10_f	10_f	11_f	12_f	13_f	14_f	20_f

All the problems on this page are in base five. Write answers in base five.

1. Try these subtraction problems. Remember, the only digits you can use are 0, 1, 2, 3, and 4.

   a. 4321_f **b.** 3421_f **c.** 3421_f
       $-\ \ 210_f$ $-\ \ 101_f$ $-\ \ 102_f$

   d. 2120_f **e.** 2324_f **f.** 2324_f
       $-\ 1101_f$ $-\ \ 123_f$ $-\ \ 223_f$

   g. 2240_f **h.** 132_f **i.** 331_f
       $-\ \ 113_f$ $-\ \ 23_f$ $-\ 121_f$

   j. 1000_f **k.** 3000_f **l.** 2444_f
       $-\ \ 444_f$ $-\ 2444_f$ $-\ 1333_f$

   m. 2044_f **n.** 403_f **o.** 100_f
       $-\ 1431_f$ $-\ 204_f$ $-\ \ 24_f$

2. Try these addition and subtraction problems. Use the base-five addition table. Watch the signs.

   a. 421_f **b.** 421_f **c.** 2112_f
       $+\ 124_f$ $-\ 124_f$ $-\ 1021_f$

   d. 3231_f **e.** 2311_f **f.** 3322_f
       $+\ 1041_f$ $+\ \ 104_f$ $-\ \ 102_f$

   g. 4444_f **h.** 4444_f **i.** 1441_f
       $-\ 3232_f$ $+\ 3232_f$ $+\ 4004_f$

   j. 3210_f **k.** 2301_f **l.** 2431_f
       $+\ \ 123_f$ $+\ 1032_f$ $-\ 1324_f$

You can multiply and divide in base five. Remember, in base-five arithmetic, the digits 5, 6, 7, 8, and 9 are not used.

1. Think about what multiplication and division mean, and try these problems in base five. (Hint: The answers to the division problems are whole numbers.)

a. 342_f
     $\times\ \ 31_f$

b. 403_f
     $\times\ \ 24_f$

c. $4_f\overline{)233_f}$

d. $13_f\overline{)11231_f}$

Did you get $22{,}202_f$ for exercise 1a? The procedure for multiplying in base five is the same as in base ten.

342_f First multiply by the 1s digit.
$\times\ \ 31_f$ The 1s digit is 1, so this is easy.
$\overline{342}$

342_f Now multiply by the hands (or 5s) digit.
$\times\ \ 31_f$ A. $3_f \times 2_f = 11_f$. Write 1, remember 1.
$\overline{342}$ B. $3_f \times 4_f = 22_f$. Add 1 from step A to get 23_f.
2131 Write 3, remember 2.
             C. $3_f \times 3_f = 14_f$. Add 2 from step B to get 21_f.
                Write 21.

342_f Add.
$\times\ \ 31_f$
$\overline{342}$
2131
$\overline{22202_f}$ The answer is $22{,}202_f$.

Did you get 32_f for exercise 1c? Division in base five uses the same procedure as in base ten.

$\begin{array}{r}3\\4_f\overline{)233_f}\\22\\\hline1\end{array}$ There are three 4s in 23_f.
          $4_f \times 3_f = 22_f$; $23_f - 22_f = 1_f$.

$\begin{array}{r}32_f\\4_f\overline{)233_f}\\22\\\hline13\\13\\\hline0\end{array}$ There are two 4s in 13_f.
          $4_f \times 2_f = 13_f$; $13_f - 13_f = 0_f$.

Having a multiplication table for base five would make problems like these easier, since you could read both multiplication and division facts from it.

2. Copy and complete the following multiplication table for base five.

$\times$	0_f	1_f	2_f	3_f	4_f
0_f					
1_f			2_f		
2_f				11_f	
3_f					
4_f				22_f	

3. Use your table to help you do these problems in base five. Write answers in base five.

a. 34_f
   $\times\ 43_f$

b. $4_f\overline{)2303_f}$

c. 22_f
   $\times\ 11_f$

d. 21_f
   $\times\ 14_f$

e. $31_f\overline{)4022_f}$

f. 33_f
   $\times 11_f$

g. 314_f
   $\times\ 402_f$

h. $34_f\overline{)13441_f}$

i. $12_f\overline{)3413_f}$

j. 204_f
   $\times\ 12_f$

k. $43_f\overline{)3222_f}$

l. $21_f\overline{)4334_f}$

Do these problems. Watch the signs. Use shortcuts when you can.

1.   665
  + 667

2.   1665
  + 677

3.   1034
  × 100

4.   1034
  ×   50

5.   925
  + 868

6.   925
  − 868

7.   925
  × 868

8. 25) 925

9.   456
  × 16

10.   4560
  ×   16

11.   498
  + 87

12.   498
  × 87

13. 56) 4704

14.   84
  × 56

15.   64,225
  + 14,547

16.   5953
  − 893

17.   1365
  × 706

18.   1365
  + 706

19.   1365
  − 706

20. 76) 1365

21. Ismail needs 30 cans of cat food. He can get 5 cans of Fancy Feline cat food for $1.59 or 15 cans of the same cat food for $4.68.

 a. What is the most he would pay for the 30 cans?
 b. What is the least he would pay for the 30 cans?

22. William Henry Harrison was born on February 9, 1773, and became president of the United States in 1841. Ronald Reagan was born on February 6, 1911, and became president in 1981. One was the oldest person ever to become president. Which one?

23. The first presidential election took place in 1788. There is a presidential election every 4 years. How many presidential elections occurred before Theodore Roosevelt became president in 1901?

24. Do these problems in base-five arithmetic.

 a. 432_f
   + 321_f

 b. 221_f
   + 123_f

 c. 434_f
   + 243_f

 d. 1332_f
   + 132_f

You know that *TWO + TWO = FOUR*. A good puzzle is to replace each letter—*T, W, O, F, U,* and *R*—by a different digit from 0 to 9 and still have the equation be true.

$$\begin{array}{r} TWO \\ + \ TWO \\ \hline FOUR \end{array} \qquad \begin{array}{r} TWO \\ + \ TWO \\ \hline 1OUR \end{array}$$

First, we see that *F* must be 1, since the total from the hundreds column cannot be as great as 20. We also see that for *F* to be 1, *T* must be 5 or more ($T \geq 5$).

Try *T* = 5.

$$\begin{array}{r} 5WO \\ + \ 5WO \\ \hline 10UR \end{array}$$

If *T* = 5, *O* = 0 or 1.
But *F* = 1. So *O* cannot be 1.

If *O* = 0, then 0 + 0 = *R*.
Since *R* cannot also be 0, *O* cannot be 0.

So *T* does not equal 5 ($T \neq 5$).

Try *T* = 6.

If *T* = 6, *O* = 2 or 3.

If *O* = 3, then *R* must equal 6.
Since *T* = 6, *R* cannot equal 6, and so *O* ≠ 3.

If *O* = 2, then *R* = 4. Also *W* cannot be greater than 4, so *W* = 0 or 3.

If *W* = 0, then 0 + 0 = *U*.
Since *U* cannot also be 0, *W* ≠ 0.

If *W* = 3, then *U* = 6.
But *T* = 6, so *U* ≠ 6.

So *T* ≠ 6.

Now continue working on the puzzle. Try *T* = 7, 8, and 9. You'll find at least 1 solution for each.

If you enjoyed this puzzle, try these two.

1. How many ways can you show that *ONE + ONE = TWO*?
2. Find out how much money Agnes wanted when she sent this message. (Assume that *M* is not 0.)

$$\begin{array}{r} SEND \\ + \ MORE \\ \hline MONEY \end{array}$$

Do these problems. Watch the signs. Use shortcuts when you can.

1. 894
    + 487

2. 894
    + 1487

3. 788
    − 89

4. 788
    × 89

5. 2932
    × 80

6. 2932
    × 40

7. 2932
    − 40

8. 42) 9121

9. 86,700
    + 14,998

10. 8670
    − 4998

11. 52,386
    + 31,906

12. 7452
    × 81

13. 92) 7452

14. 390
    × 535

15. 3900
    − 535

16. 128,942
    + 301,078

17. 2109
    + 828

18. 2109
    × 828

19. 99) 868230

20. 868,230
    − 18,770

21. Miss Rantoul is a buyer for a bakery. Each week she purchases 720 kilograms of flour. She can get the flour in 10-kilogram bags or in 18-kilogram bags. The 10-kilogram bags cost $1.10, and the 18-kilogram bags cost $2.00.

    a. What is the most she could pay for 720 kilograms of flour?
    b. What is the least she could pay for 720 kilograms of flour?

22. Martin Van Buren, the eighth U.S. president, was born in 1782. William Henry Harrison, the ninth U.S. president, was born in 1773. Which man was older when he became president?

23. George Washington was born on February 22, 1732, and became president at the age of 57, in 1789. Ronald Reagan was born on February 6, 1911, and became president at the age of 69, in 1981. What does this tell you about the inauguration date in 1789 and in 1981?

24. Do these problems in base-five arithmetic.

    a. 3240_f
        + 1334_f

    b. 4222_f
        + 2403_f

    c. 2113_f
        + 2004_f

    d. 3131_f
        + 1231_f

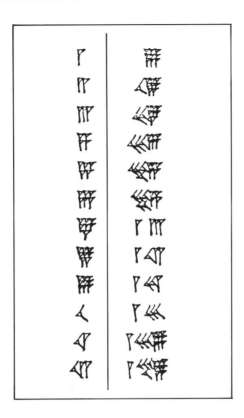

The figure above was copied from part of a cuneiform tablet found in Babylonia. The tablet measures about 8 centimeters by 13 centimeters and apparently was made about 3700 years ago.

Look at the symbols to the left of the line. What do you think they might represent? What might the symbol ∢ represent?

Now look at the symbols to the right of the line. How do they relate to those on the left of the line? Check your guess for the first 6 lines. Could this be part of a multiplication table written by a student?

What seems to have happened in the seventh row? What is 9 × 7? Could the student have made a mistake? What is 9 × 8? Do you think the student made another mistake? Assume the student did not make a mistake. What could the 1 followed by a 3 stand for?

Discuss the questions on this page with friends. Check to see if your answers make sense.

CHAPTER 2

EFFICIENT WAYS TO DO ARITHMETIC

Many years ago, a teacher gave his students an arithmetic problem: to calculate the sum of the numbers from 1 through 100. The teacher probably thought he could keep the students busy this way while he did other work.

After a minute or two, the youngest student in the class said that he had the answer. His answer was correct.

That student was Karl Friedrich Gauss (1777–1855), who became one of the world's greatest mathematicians. His photographic memory, ability to do incredible mental calculations, and unsurpassed understanding of number and function led him to many discoveries in both pure and applied mathematics.

[1] **How do you think young Gauss found the answer to the problem so quickly?**

[2] **See if you can figure out how to add the numbers from 1 through 100 without a lot of work.**

[3] **Can you use the same method to add the numbers from 1 to 10? From 1 to 1000?**

Here are some hints you can use to solve the problem of calculating the sum of the numbers from 1 through 100:

A. Can you think of arranging the numbers in a different order that would make the problem easier?
B. Is there a way to pair the numbers so that the sum of every pair is the same?
C. Can you pair the numbers so that each pair has a sum of 100? How many such pairs are there? Did you pair the last number (100) with another number? Is there another number that wasn't paired? What is it? What's the total?
D. Think about other ways to use this pairing idea to determine sums of successive integers.

If a calculator is available, you may want to have a race. Let one person use a method like the Gauss shortcut while another uses a calculator to do the following problems.

1. Find the sum of the numbers from
   a. 1 through 20.
   b. 1 through 99.
   c. 1 through 500.
   d. 1 through 999.
   e. 25 through 75.
   f. 5 through 37.
   g. 26 through 134.

2. Find the sum of
   a. the even numbers from 2 through 98 (that is, $2 + 4 + 6 + 8 + 10 + 12 + 14 + \ldots + 86 + 88 + 90 + 92 + 94 + 96 + 98 = ?$).
   b. the even numbers less than 1000 (2 through 998).
   c. the odd numbers less than 100 (1 through 99).

There are many ways you can make calculations easier. You already use some of these. For example, you know that the order in which you add 2 numbers makes no difference.

$$4 + 8 = 8 + 4$$
$$173 + 389 = 389 + 173$$

In general, for all numbers x and y,

$$x + y = y + x$$

This is sometimes called the commutative law for addition. You probably use the commutative law for addition so often that you hardly think about it anymore. But when you were young, you used it to avoid having to learn so many addition facts. If you knew $7 + 4 = 11$, you also knew $4 + 7 = 11$.

[1] State the commutative law for multiplication.

Parentheses are used to show the order in which operations are carried out. $(7 + 6) + 4$ means that you add 7 and 6 together first and then add 4 to the sum.

The parentheses are often not used for a problem like $(7+ 6) + 4$ because of another principle, which says they aren't really needed in a multiple addition problem. For example:

$$(7 + 6) + 4 = 7 + (6 + 4)$$
$$(38 + 49) + 51 = 38 + (49 + 51)$$

In general, for all numbers x, y, and z,

$$(x + y) + z = x + (y + z).$$

This rule is sometimes called the associative law for addition.

[2] What is the associative law for multiplication?

To help you remember which is the commutative law and which is the associative law, remember that a commuter goes from home to the office and from the office to home. The x and the y commute in the commutative law. In the associative law, y first associates with x and then associates with z.

Because the commutative and associative laws are true, you can rearrange the terms of an addition problem or the factors of a multiplication problem without changing the result.

Examples: $73 + 39 + 27 = ?$ By adding the 73 and 27 first, you can make the easier problem $100 + 39$.

$5 \times 37 \times 2 = ?$ By multiplying the 5 and 2 first, you can make the easier problem 10×37.

There are ways to do problems 1–12 easily. Try to find them.

1. $84 + 73 + 16$	**7.** $17 \times 5 \times 20$
2. $35 + 65 + 399$	**8.** $7 \times 17 \times 0 \times 46$
3. $41 + 73 + 27$	**9.** $20 \times 73 \times 5$
4. $38 + 27 + 73$	**10.** $69 \times 25 \times 4$
5. $298 + 11 + 89$	**11.** $30 \times 13 \times 5 \times 2$
6. $399 + 399$	**12.** $27 \times 2 \times 5 \times 0$

For problems 13–16, it will help you to know that $284 \times 95 = 26{,}980$.

13. 950×284	**15.** $284 \times 19 \times 5$
14. $4 \times 95 \times 284 \times 25$	**16.** $71 \times 95 \times 4 \times 10$

If there were a commutative law for subtraction, it would say: For all numbers x and y, $x - y = y - x$.

[3] Is this true?

[4] Can you find a pair of numbers for which it is true?

[5] Can you find any pair of numbers in which $x \neq y$ for which it is not true?

If you can find 1 pair of numbers for which the law is not true, then the law itself is not true, because the law says it is true for *all* pairs of numbers.

[6] State a commutative law for division. Is it true? Why?

[7] State an associative law for subtraction. Is it true? Why?

[8] State an associative law for multiplication. Is it true? Why?

The distributive law is very useful. It says that for all numbers a, b, and c,

$$a \times (b + c) = (a \times b) + (a \times c).$$

Example: $7 \times (5 + 3) = (7 \times 5) + (7 \times 3)$

Check: Is 7×8 the same as $35 + 21$?

Try several other numbers for a, b, and c. Can you find 3 numbers for which the distributive law is not true?

Even though you have not been able to find a set of 3 numbers for which the distributive law fails, you might still suspect that such a set exists.

The following picture should help you believe that the distributive law must in fact be true for all sets of 3 numbers a, b, and c.

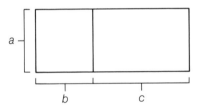

[1] What is the area of the rectangle on the left?

[2] What is the area of the rectangle on the right?

[3] What is the area of the big rectangle (with base *b* + *c*)?

Since a, b, and c could be any numbers, does it seem reasonable to say that for all numbers a, b, and c, $(a \times b) + (a \times c) = a \times (b + c)$? Is that the same as $a \times (b + c) = (a \times b) + (a \times c)$?

Two ways the distributive law can be helpful are shown here:

A. $(23 \times 7) + (23 \times 3) = ?$
   Using the distributive law, $(23 \times 7) + (23 \times 3) = 23 \times (7 + 3) = 23 \times 10 = 230.$

B. $8 \times 74 = ?$
   Think: $8 \times 70 = 560$ and $8 \times 4 = 32$. So $8 \times 74 = 560 + 32 = 592.$

When subtraction is involved, the distributive law works like this:

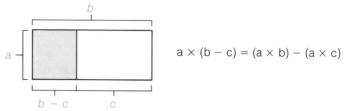

$$a \times (b - c) = (a \times b) - (a \times c)$$

The area of the shaded rectangle equals the area of the big rectangle minus the area of the unshaded rectangle.

In this form, the distributive law can be used to take shortcuts like these:

C. $9 \times 25 = ?$

Think: $(10 - 1) \times 25$ is $250 - 25 = 225$.

D. $18 \times 65 = ?$

Think: $(20 - 2) \times 65$ is $1300 - 130 = 1170$.

Try to use shortcuts to do the following problems.

1. $(4 \times 7) + (6 \times 7)$
2. $(5 \times 8) + (5 \times 12)$
3. $(9 \times 8) + (9 \times 12)$
4. $(37 \times 83) + (37 \times 17)$
5. $(136 \times 75) + (64 \times 75)$
6. 7×203
7. 5×1007
8. 4×2025
9. 307×9
10. 410×8

11. $(12 \times 7) - (2 \times 7)$
12. $(184 \times 13) - (84 \times 13)$
13. $(67 \times 43) - (17 \times 43)$
14. $(67 \times 43) - (67 \times 33)$
15. 9×45
16. 99×45
17. 11×45
18. 101×45
19. 18×75
20. 18×35

Marva and Kirsten were arguing about what $7 + 3 \times 4$ was. Marva said, "If I have \$7 and sell 3 books for \$4 each, then I'll have \$19." Kirsten said, "If I sell 7 books and then 3 more books, and the price of each book is \$4, then I'll have \$40."

Who is right, Marva or Kirsten? Does $7 + 3 \times 4$ equal 19 or 40?

They're both right. Marva is right for the example she suggested, and Kirsten is right for her example. But without a specific example, it's hard to tell what $7 + 3 \times 4$ means.

Usually we use parentheses to make our meaning clear.

Marva would write: $7 + (3 \times 4) = 7 + 12 = 19$
Kirsten would write: $(7 + 3) \times 4 = 10 \times 4 = 40$

In algebra, we usually omit times signs and write divisions with a fraction bar.

Examples: $7 + (3 \times x)$ is written $7 + 3x$.

$9 + (x \div y)$ is written $9 + \dfrac{x}{y}$.

Notice that the 3 and the x seem very close together, as do the x and y in the second line. This will help you remember that we always do multiplications and divisions before additions and subtractions when there are no parentheses.

Ordinarily, parentheses are used to make the meaning of an arithmetic statement perfectly clear. Occasionally you will find arithmetic problems where needed parentheses are missing— especially on tricky questions in tests.

In cases where there are no parentheses and in algebraic problems involving letters, follow these rules:

A. First do all calculations within parentheses. If 1 set of parentheses is inside another, start inside the innermost parentheses.

B. Next do all multiplications and divisions. (If exponents are involved, do those computations before the multiplications and divisions.)

C. Finally do the additions and subtractions.

Examples: Compute: $3 + 4 \times 7 - 6$

Solution: $3 + 4 \times 7 - 6 = 3 + 28 - 6 = 31 - 6 = 25$

Compute: $(3 + 4) \times (7 - 6)$

Solution: $(3 + 4) \times (7 - 6) = 7 \times 1 = 7$

Evaluate: $3x - 8$ when $x = 5$

Solution: $3 \times 5 - 8 = 15 - 8 = 7$

Evaluate: $12 - 2x + 4(2x - 7)$ when $x = 5$

Solution: $12 - 2 \times 5 + 4(2 \times 5 - 7) =$
$12 - 2 \times 5 + 4(10 - 7) =$
$12 - 2 \times 5 + 4 \times 3 =$
$12 - 10 + 12 = 2 + 12 = 14$

Evaluate the following expressions for the given values of x.

1. $3x + 5$, when $x = 2$
2. $8 - 2x$, when $x = 4$
3. $7(x - 4)$, when $x = 10$
4. $7x - 28$, when $x = 10$
5. $8x - 6$, when $x = 10$
6. $8(x - 6)$, when $x = 10$
7. $8x - 48$, when $x = 10$
8. $6 + 5(3x + 8)$, when $x = 4$
9. $6 + 15x + 40$, when $x = 4$
10. $6 + 15x + 8$, when $x = 4$

11. $2x^2$, when $x = 5$*
12. $5x^2$, when $x = 2$
13. $2x^3$, when $x = 5$
14. $3x^2$, when $x = 5$
15. $15 - 4x + 5(3x - 3)$, when $x = 2$
16. $15 - 4x + 15x - 15$, when $x = 2$
17. $15 - 4x + 15x - 3$, when $x = 2$
18. $7(2x + 5)$, when $x = 3$
19. $14x + 5$, when $x = 3$
20. $14x + 35$, when $x = 3$

Compute the following.

21. $100 - 4 \times 7$
22. $(100 - 4) \times 7$
23. $(7 + 3) \times (8 - 3)$
24. $(7 + 3) \times 8 - (7 + 3) \times 3$
25. $7 \times (8 - 3) + 3 \times (8 - 3)$
26. $7 \times 8 - 7 \times 3 + 3 \times 8 - 3 \times 3$
27. $7 + 3 \times 8 - 3$
28. $7 + 3 \times 8 - 7 + 3 \times 3$
29. $7 \times 8 - 3 + 3 \times 8 - 3$
30. $24 \div 6 - 3$

31. $24 \div (6 - 3)$
32. $8 - 2 \times 4$
33. $(8 - 2) \times 4$
34. $8 - (2 \times 4)$
35. $6 + 5(3 \times 4 + 8)$
36. $6 + 15 \times 4 + 40$
37. $6 + 15 \times 4 + 8$
38. $15 - 4 \times 2 + 5(3 \times 2 - 3)$
39. $15 - 4 \times 2 + 15 \times 2 - 15$
40. $15 - 4 \times 2 + 15 \times 2 - 3$

*Remember: exponents before multiplication.

Try to find ways to solve these problems in your head. It's all right to use paper and pencil if you need to. Be ready to discuss the way you did each problem.

1. What will be the cost of
   a. 4 pears and 4 apples?
   b. 8 pears and 8 apples?

2. Whenever it snows, Marlene clears the snow from Dr. Luk's driveway and Claire clears Mr. Bugbee's driveway. Marlene earns $2.50 each time, and Claire earns $2.75. Last year it snowed 10 times.
   a. Who made more money?
   b. How much more?

3. Marcus wants to buy a hamburger and a glass of milk for himself and the 19 other people in his group. Hamburgers cost $1.45 each, and a glass of milk costs 55¢, tax included. How much will all of this cost Marcus?

4. What will be the cost of
   a. 5 pens?
   b. 5 pencils?
   c. 5 pens and 5 pencils?
   d. 5 note pads?
   e. 5 pens, 5 pencils, and 5 note pads?

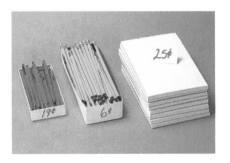

MENTAL MULTIPLICATION GAME

Players: 2 or 3
Materials: Two 0–5 cubes, two 5–10 cubes
(A calculator is helpful for checking but is not essential.)
Object: To multiply 2 numbers without using paper or pencil

Rules

1. Take turns rolling all 4 cubes.

2. Use numbers rolled to make a 2-digit-by-2-digit or 3-digit-by-1-digit multiplication problem. (If you roll a `10` , you can make larger numbers.)

3. Solve the problem you make mentally, without using paper or pencil. Explain your method aloud.

4. If 1 factor is a number from 0 through 10 and your answer is correct, you win 1 point. If both factors are greater than 10 and your answer is correct, you win 2 points.

5. After 2 rounds, the player with the most points wins. There will probably be some tie games.

Sample Game

Wendy rolled:

`2` `5` `9` `8` She made the problem 98 × 25.
She explained that 100 × 25 = 2500 and that 98 × 25 is 2 × 25, or 50, less than 2500. So the answer is 2450.

Since the answer was correct and both factors were more than 10, Wendy won 2 points.

Tito rolled:

`10` `5` `3` `7` He made the problem 10 × 537.
He said that the answer is 5370 because you can multiply by 10 by adding a zero to the right of a number.

Since Tito's answer was correct and the multiplier was not more than 10, Tito won 1 point. He could have made 103 × 75, which is 7500 + 225, or 7725. Then he would have won 2 points.

This block of print shows a part of Robert Recorde's book, *The Grounde of Artes.* The book was published in London in 1542. In this part, Recorde explains how to subtract when a digit to be subtracted is greater than the digit from which it is to be subtracted.

$$825003456$$
$$53984722$$
$$34$$

S   . . . then take 17 out of fower, but that I can not, what shall I nowe doe? M. Marke well what I shall tell you now, how you shall do in this case and in all other like. If any fygure of the nether summe be greater thē the fygure of the summe that is ouer hym, so that it can not be taken out of the figure ouer him, then muste you put 10 to the ouer fygure, and thē consydre how muche it is: and oute of that whole summe withdrawe the nether figure, and wryte the reste vnder them.   . . . but nowe muste you marke an other thinge also: that when so euer you do so put 10 to any figure of the ouer numbre, you must adde one still to the figure or place that foloweth nexte in the nether lyne, as in this example there foloweth 4, to whiche you muste putte 1 and make hym 5, & then go on, as I haue taughte you.

Since this is hard to read, we have rewritten it for you twice on the next page. The first time we simply used the letters of our alphabet for the old script letters. The spellings and grammar are the same as those Robert Recorde used. The second rewriting is in more modern language and should be easier to understand.

$$
\begin{array}{r}
825003456 \\
- 53984722 \\
\hline
34
\end{array}
$$

Scholar: . . . then take I 7 out of fower, but that I can not, what shall I nowe doe?

Master: Marke well what I shall tell you now, how you shall do in this case and in all other like. If any fygure of the nether summe be greater tha the fygure of the summe that is over hym, so that it can not be taken out of the fygure over him, then muste you put 10 to the overfigure, and tha consydre how muche it is: and oute of that whole summe withdrawe the nether figure, and wryte the reste under them. . . . but nowe muste you marke an other thinge also: that when so ever you do so put 10 to any figure of the over numbre, you must adde one still to the figure or place that foloweth nexte in the nether lyne, as in this example there foloweth 4, to whiche you muste putte 1 and make hym 5, and then go on, as I have taught you.

Student: Then I take 7 from 4, but I can't. What shall I do now?

Teacher: The rule for this case and all others like it is the following: If any digit of the subtrahend (lower number) is greater than the corresponding digit in the minuend (upper number), then add 10 to the digit in the minuend, subtract the subtrahend digit from the sum, and write the difference under those digits. . . . You must also remember that whenever you add 10 to any digit of the minuend, you must add 1 to the next digit (to the left) of the subtrahend. In this example, there is a 4 to the left of the 7. Add 1 to 4, making it 5, and proceed as I have taught you.

Robert Recorde wrote *The Grounde of Artes* at a time when Europeans were still using Roman numerals and an abacus to do calculations. You just saw part of his method of subtracting on pages 52 and 53. Notice that his procedure, or *algorithm*, is different from the one used in this book.

The following problem is done using the procedure in this book and using Robert Recorde's procedure:

Real Math Procedure   Robert Recorde's Procedure

$$
\begin{array}{r}
3\ 1\ \overset{9}{\cancel{0}}\ 5 \\
-\ 1\ 2\ 4\ 7 \\
\hline
8
\end{array}
\qquad
\begin{array}{r}
3\ 1\ 0\ \overset{1}{5} \\
-\ 1\ 2\ \overset{5}{\cancel{4}}\ 7 \\
\hline
8
\end{array}
$$

$$
\begin{array}{r}
\overset{0\ \ 9}{3\ \cancel{1}\cancel{0}}\,\overset{1}{5} \\
-\ 1\ 2\ 4\ 7 \\
\hline
5\ 8
\end{array}
\qquad
\begin{array}{r}
3\ 1\ \overset{1}{0}\overset{1}{5} \\
-\ 1\ 2\ \overset{3}{\underset{}{}}\overset{5}{\cancel{4}}\ 7 \\
\hline
5\ 8
\end{array}
$$

$$
\begin{array}{r}
\overset{2\ 10\ 9}{3\ \cancel{1}\cancel{0}}\,\overset{1}{5} \\
-\ 1\ 2\ 4\ 7 \\
\hline
1\ 8\ 5\ 8
\end{array}
\qquad
\begin{array}{r}
3\ \overset{1}{1}\,\overset{1}{0}\overset{1}{5} \\
-\ 1\overset{2}{\cancel{2}}\overset{3}{}\overset{5}{\cancel{4}}\ 7 \\
\hline
1\ 8\ 5\ 8
\end{array}
$$

The answers, of course, are the same, but the procedures are different. Recorde's procedure can be justified by thinking of subtraction as the inverse, or opposite, of addition. The goal is to find a number that can be added to 1247 to get 3105.

What can you add to 7 to get 5? This is not possible, but you can get 15 by adding 8.

$$
\begin{array}{r}
3\ 1\ 0\ 5 \\
-\ 1\ 2\ 4\ 7 \\
\hline
8
\end{array}
$$

This leaves an extra 10; so add 1 to the 4 in the tens column, making it 5. Then to get 0, add 5 to 5, getting 10. Write 5 and add 1 to the 2.

$$
\begin{array}{r}
3\ 1\ 0\ 5 \\
-\ 1\ 2\ \overset{3}{}\overset{5}{4}\ 7 \\
\hline
5\ 8
\end{array}
$$

$3 + 8 = 11$; so 8 goes at the bottom of the column, and 1 is added to the 1 in the thousands column. Since $1 + 2 = 3$, the last digit to be written is 1.

$$
\begin{array}{r}
3\ 1\ 0\ 5 \\
-\ 1\overset{2}{}\overset{3}{2}\overset{5}{4}\ 7 \\
\hline
1\ 8\ 5\ 8
\end{array}
$$

Try this subtraction algorithm and see if you like it. Many people use it today.

There are many algorithms for doing each of the arithmetic operations. Here are several ways to multiply 278 × 134. Study these and use the methods to do other problems.

A. "European Peasant" method (often identified by other names, since it apparently developed independently in several countries)

278 × 134	
556	67
1112	33
2224	16
4448	8
8896	4
17792	2
35584	1
37252	

Double the larger and halve the smaller factor on each step. Drop fractions. Stop when the smaller factor is 1.

Add the numbers in the first column that correspond to odd numbers in the second column.

556 + 1112 + 35,584 = 37,252

B. The diagonal method

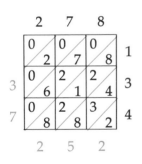

Answer: 37,252

Write the factors along 2 sides of squared paper with diagonals as shown. Fill in each square with the product of its row and column digits. (The tens digit goes above the diagonal; you may omit zeros if you prefer.)

Add down the diagonals from bottom right to top left to get the answer. The sum on the first diagonal is simply 2. The sum on the second is 4 + 3 + 8 = 15. Write 5, carry 1 to the next diagonal, and so on. Read the answer, 37,252, starting at the top left.

C. Partial products method

$$
\begin{array}{r}
278 \\
\times\ 134 \\
\hline
32 \\
280 \\
800 \\
240 \\
2100 \\
6000 \\
800 \\
7000 \\
20000 \\
\hline
37252
\end{array}
$$

Multiply each digit in the multiplicand by each digit in the multiplier (8 by 4, 7 by 4, 2 by 4; 8 by 3, 7 by 3, 2 by 3; 8 by 1, 7 by 1, 2 by 1).

Place as many zeros after each of these products as there are digits to the right of the 2 digits in the factors. (Here the 3 × 2 multiplication requires 3 zeros, for example.)

Add the partial products. The answer is 37,252.

D. Shorter partial products method

$$
\begin{array}{r}
278 \\
\times\ 134 \\
\hline
1112 \\
834 \\
278 \\
\hline
37252
\end{array}
$$

Follow the method above, but write only the units digits of each product and carry the excess digit to the next place. (For example, for 4 × 8 = 32, write the 2 and carry the 3 to the next place.) This requires that you follow a special order.

This is probably the algorithm that you are familiar with.

E. The shortest method—all in your head

$$\begin{array}{r} 278 \\ \times\ 134 \\ \hline 37{,}252 \end{array}$$

Follow method D, but use all products that contribute to each digit of the answer together and add them in your mind, writing only the answer.

$$\begin{array}{r} 278 \\ \times\ 134 \\ \hline 2 \end{array}$$

In this case, $4 \times 8 = 32$. Write 2; carry 3.

$$\begin{array}{r} 278 \\ \times\ 134 \\ \hline 52 \end{array}$$

$(4 \times 7 = 28) + (3 \times 8 = 24) + 3$ carried $= 55$. Write 5; carry 5.

$$\begin{array}{r} 278 \\ \times\ 134 \\ \hline 252 \end{array}$$

$(4 \times 2 = 8) + (3 \times 7 = 21) + (1 \times 8 = 8) + 5$ carried $= 42$. Write 2; carry 4.

$$\begin{array}{r} 278 \\ \times\ 134 \\ \hline 7252 \end{array}$$

$(3 \times 2 = 6) + (1 \times 7 = 7) + 4$ carried $= 17$. Write 7; carry 1.

$$\begin{array}{r} 278 \\ \times\ 134 \\ \hline 37{,}252 \end{array}$$

$(1 \times 2 = 2) + 1$ carried $= 3$. Write 3. The answer is 37,252.

Use each of the 5 algorithms to do the following problems. That is, do each problem 5 ways.

1.	234	2.	807	3.	786	4.	3407
	× 179		× 596		× 958		× 598

Have a race. Each racer is assigned 1 of the 5 algorithms for multiplication you've just learned about. Everyone does the same problem. Keep track of the time needed to finish and the number of mistakes with each algorithm.

Solve. Use shortcuts when you can.

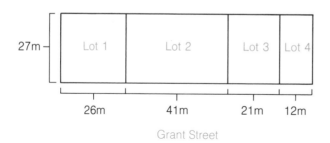

1. Mrs. Collins bought 4 lots of land all in a row on Grant Street. Each lot was 27 meters from front to back, and the widths of the lots were 26, 41, 21, and 12 meters. What is the total area of the 4 lots?

2. Melvin bought 100 pencils for 8¢ each, 100 pads of paper for 32¢ each, and 102 erasers for 10¢ each. How much did all of this cost? Assume there was no sales tax or other charges.

3. Marylee bought 200 apples for 7¢ each, 200 oranges for 17¢ each, and 199 pears for 16¢ each. How much did the fruit cost?

4. What is the sum of the numbers from 1 to 30?

5. What is the sum of the even numbers from 1 to 30?

6. What is the sum of the odd numbers from 1 to 30?

7. What is the sum of the numbers from 101 to 130?

Solve for n. It may help you to know that $378 \times 596 = 225{,}288$.

8. $596 \times 378 = n$

9. $379 \times 596 = n$

10. $4 \times (378 \times 149) = n$

Find the areas of these figures.

1. Rectangle **2.** Square **3.** Square

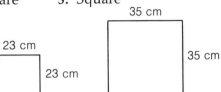

[1] A square is a special kind of rectangle in which all 4 sides are the same length. To find the area of a square, is it necessary to know both the height and the width, or would just 1 of the sides be enough?

What are the areas of squares that have sides of the following lengths?

4. 10 cm	**7.** 1 cm	**10.** 2 cm	**13.** 7 cm	**16.** 90 cm
5. 8 cm	**8.** 9 cm	**11.** 3 cm	**14.** 20 cm	**17.** 100 cm
6. 4 cm	**9.** 5 cm	**12.** 6 cm	**15.** 40 cm	**18.** 50 cm

[2] When we multiply a number by itself, we say we have "squared the number." Why do you think multiplying a number by itself is called squaring the number?

[3] What do you think it means to *cube* a number? What do you think 5 cubed is?

Sometimes we write a small number above and to the right of another number to tell how many times the number is to be used as a factor. For example:

$$5^3 = 5 \times 5 \times 5 = 125$$
$$2^8 = 2 \times 2 \times 2 \times 2 \times 2 \times 2 \times 2 \times 2 = 256$$
$$2^3 = 2 \times 2 \times 2 = 8$$
$$5^2 = 5 \times 5 = 25$$
$$7^2 = 7 \times 7 = 49$$

Find the value of each of the following.

19. 2^3 **20.** 3^2 **21.** 5^2 **22.** 10^2 **23.** 8^2 **24.** 12^2

Patterns in Squares

To square a number is to multiply it by itself (or to find the area of a square when the number is the length of a side). A small 2 written above and to the right of a number means that the number is squared.

$$So\ 15^2 = 15 \times 15 = 225,$$
$$25^2 = 25 \times 25 = 625,$$

and so on.

Look at this list of squares. Are there any interesting patterns?

$$15^2 = 225$$
$$25^2 = 625$$
$$35^2 = 1225$$
$$45^2 = 2025$$
$$55^2 = 3025$$
$$65^2 = 4225$$
$$75^2 = 5625$$
$$85^2 = 7225$$
$$95^2 = 9025$$
$$105^2 = 11025$$

[1] Do you think the last 2 digits are always the same?

[2] Can you find a way to determine the other digits using the number to be squared?

The rule you found for squaring a number that ends in 5 can be shown to be true by using the distributive law.

Another rule for squaring numbers involves the squares of 2 successive integers. Look at this table of squares.

$20^2 = 400$ ← If you know $20^2 = 400$, how could you determine
$21^2 = 441$ $21^2 = 441$ without multiplying?

$22^2 = 484$ ← Can you see a way to use 22, 484, and 23 to get 529?
$23^2 = 529$ Can you see a way to use 529, 23, and 22 to get 484?

$24^2 = 576$ Is there a pattern that always seems to work to find
$25^2 = 625$ $(x + 1)^2$ or $(x - 1)^2$ when you know x^2? What is it?

$26^2 = 676$ Try your pattern for several numbers to see if it works.

Using the distributive law, we can show that for any number x, $(x + 1)^2 = x^2 + x + (x + 1)$.

$$(x + 1)^2 = (x + 1) \times (x + 1) = [(x + 1) \times x] + [(x + 1) \times 1]$$
$$= (x \times x) + (1 \times x) + (x \times 1) + (1 \times 1) = x^2 + x + x + 1$$

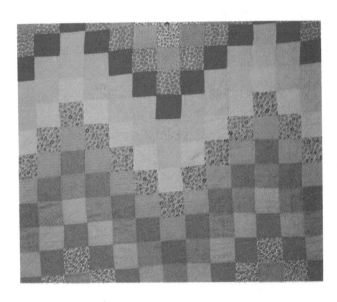

Here are 3 rules about squaring numbers:

A. If the number ends in 5 (for example, 45), drop the 5, multiply the remaining number (4) by 1 more than itself (5), and write 25 after the product (2025). Another way to explain this rule is to drop the 5 (let's use 45 again), add the remaining number (4) to its square (16), and write 25 after the sum (2025).

B. If you know the square of an integer (for example, $25^2 = 625$), the square of the next larger integer (26) can be found by adding the square, the integer, and the next larger integer ($625 + 25 + 26 = 676 = 26^2$).

C. If you know the square of an integer (for example, $25^2 = 625$), the square of the next smaller integer (24) can be found by subtracting the integer and the next smaller integer from the square (that is, $625 - (25 + 24) = 576 = 24^2$).

Use the 3 rules to do these problems without actually multiplying.

1. 20^2	6. 35^2	11. 30^2	16. 95^2
2. 21^2	7. 36^2	12. 29^2	17. 96^2
3. 25^2	8. 50^2	13. 60^2	18. 100^2
4. 41^2	9. 51^2	14. 59^2	19. 101^2
5. 45^2	10. 61^2	15. 19^2	20. 115^2

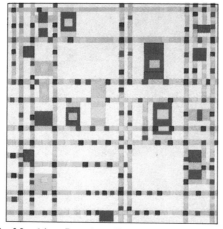

Piet Mondrian, *Broadway Boogie Woogie*, 1942-43.

Add.

1.   378
     + 592

2.   1005
      + 195

3.   592
     + 378

4.   6321
     + 1236

Subtract.

5.   707
     − 555

6.   1555
      − 707

7.   6321
     − 1236

8.   1005
      − 195

Multiply.

9.   1005
      × 195

10.   236
       × 74

11.   543
       × 15

12.   543
       × 55

Divide.

13. 95$)\overline{9975}$

14. 15$)\overline{4995}$

15. 45$)\overline{5535}$

16. 80$)\overline{19688}$

Do these problems.

17.   1776
      − 1492

18. 79$)\overline{10672}$

19. 11$)\overline{1221}$

20.   2020
       × 303

21.   123
       × 45

22.   8644
        138
      + 473

23. 13$)\overline{160654}$

24.   1987
       − 1066

25.   183
        17
      + 223

26.   212
       × 33

27. 33$)\overline{6996}$

28.   313
       × 22

SQUARE SCORES

Players: 2 or more
Materials: One 0–5 cube or one 5–10 cube
Object: To get the highest total score

Rules

1. Draw a 3-by-3 square on your paper, to make a score sheet like this:

2. The lead player rolls the cube 9 times. After each roll, each player writes the number in a blank box.

3. When all the boxes are filled in, add the numbers in each row and in each column. You'll get 6 sums.

4. Multiply each sum by itself (square the sum). Then add the 6 squared sums. That total is your score.

5. The player with the highest score wins.

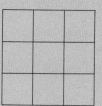

Sample Game

Using a 0–5 cube, Cassandra rolled these numbers, one at a time:

3 1 0 4 2 5 1 4 1

Cassandra's score sheet: Christy's score sheet:

			Sums	Squared Sums					Sums	Squared Sums
5	4	4	13	169	4	1	1	6	36
1	3	1	5	25	4	5	2	11	121
1	2	0	3	9	0	1	3	4	16
7	9	5		203	8	7	6		173
49	81	25	155	358	64	49	36	149	322

Cassandra won because her score (358) was higher.

Try this speed test to see how well you know the addition and subtraction facts.

1. 3 + 2	**11.** 9 − 5	**21.** 14 − 7	**31.** 3 + 6
2. 9 − 7	**12.** 19 − 9	**22.** 8 + 6	**32.** 5 + 5
3. 4 + 3	**13.** 3 + 9	**23.** 12 − 8	**33.** 16 − 8
4. 6 − 1	**14.** 8 − 6	**24.** 3 + 8	**34.** 7 + 4
5. 6 + 5	**15.** 10 − 5	**25.** 7 − 5	**35.** 5 + 9
6. 7 − 3	**16.** 9 + 2	**26.** 7 + 1	**36.** 12 − 6
7. 7 + 5	**17.** 8 + 5	**27.** 8 − 5	**37.** 15 − 7
8. 9 + 6	**18.** 13 − 7	**28.** 6 − 4	**38.** 9 + 4
9. 20 − 10	**19.** 11 − 6	**29.** 6 + 7	**39.** 5 + 4
10. 9 + 7	**20.** 9 + 9	**30.** 10 − 7	**40.** 17 − 8

Try this speed test to see how well you know the multiplication and division facts.

41. 4 × 3	**51.** 30 ÷ 6	**61.** 21 ÷ 3	**71.** 6 × 8
42. 54 ÷ 6	**52.** 16 ÷ 4	**62.** 9 × 3	**72.** 9 × 9
43. 6 × 5	**53.** 2 × 7	**63.** 42 ÷ 6	**73.** 9 ÷ 3
44. 35 ÷ 7	**54.** 72 ÷ 8	**64.** 8 × 7	**74.** 9 × 8
45. 18 ÷ 3	**55.** 4 × 5	**65.** 6 × 4	**75.** 45 ÷ 9
46. 9 × 7	**56.** 48 ÷ 6	**66.** 63 ÷ 7	**76.** 8 × 4
47. 5 × 9	**57.** 7 × 6	**67.** 27 ÷ 9	**77.** 56 ÷ 7
48. 7 × 3	**58.** 28 ÷ 7	**68.** 20 ÷ 4	**78.** 9 × 6
49. 12 ÷ 3	**59.** 36 ÷ 4	**69.** 8 × 8	**79.** 7 × 7
50. 7 × 0	**60.** 4 × 7	**70.** 25 ÷ 5	**80.** 32 ÷ 8

A method known as casting out nines is a quick check for multiplication. To use this process, you need to know how to find the digit sum of a number. To get the digit sum of a number, add the digits in the number. If the sum has more than 1 digit, keep adding the digits until the sum is 9 or less. If it is 9, the digit sum is 0. If it is less than 9, that sum is the digit sum.

To find the digit sum of 17,995, simply add $1 + 7 + 9 + 9 + 5$, getting 31. Then add $3 + 1$, getting 4, which is the digit sum. Here are a few more examples: $276 \rightarrow 15 \rightarrow 6$; $63,108 \rightarrow 18 \rightarrow 9 \rightarrow 0$; $5,482,030 \rightarrow 22 \rightarrow 4$; $88,996,999,989,998 \rightarrow 119 \rightarrow 11 \rightarrow 2$.

To check a multiplication problem by casting out nines, just find the digit sums of the factors and the product. If the multiplication is correct, the product of the digit sums of the factors will equal the digit sum of the product. Here's an example:

$$
\begin{array}{ll}
3758 & 23 \rightarrow 5 \qquad\qquad 5 \times 2 = 10 \rightarrow 1 \\
\underline{\times\ 4898} & 29 \rightarrow 11 \rightarrow 2 \\
18406684 & 37 \rightarrow 10 \rightarrow 1
\end{array}
$$

In this case, $5 \times 2 = 10$ has the same digit sum (1) as the product of the multiplication problem.

It is important to remember that this check will catch many errors, but not all errors. For instance, if the product had been 17,506,684, the sum of the digits would have been the same.

There are 3 errors in the following multiplications, all of which can be found by casting out nines. Find them.

1. $\quad$ 387 $\\ \underline{\times\ 496} \\ 191{,}952$	**2.** $\quad$ 318 $\\ \underline{\times\ 876} \\ 278{,}568$	**3.** $\quad$ 506 $\\ \underline{\times\ 624} \\ 315{,}844$	**4.** $\quad$ 873 $\\ \underline{\times\ 203} \\ 177{,}219$	**5.** $\quad$ 853 $\\ \underline{\times\ 132} \\ 112{,}596$
6. $\quad$ 299 $\\ \underline{\times\ 259} \\ 77{,}441$	**7.** $\quad$ 611 $\\ \underline{\times\ 455} \\ 278{,}005$	**8.** $\quad$ 985 $\\ \underline{\times\ 860} \\ 847{,}100$	**9.** $\quad$ 559 $\\ \underline{\times\ 474} \\ 264{,}966$	**10.** $\quad$ 772 $\\ \underline{\times\ 165} \\ 129{,}380$
11. $\quad$ 881 $\\ \underline{\times\ 204} \\ 179{,}724$	**12.** $\quad$ 939 $\\ \underline{\times\ 183} \\ 171{,}837$	**13.** $\quad$ 526 $\\ \underline{\times\ 144} \\ 75{,}794$	**14.** $\quad$ 547 $\\ \underline{\times\ 619} \\ 338{,}593$	**15.** $\quad$ 635 $\\ \underline{\times\ 782} \\ 496{,}570$

Multiples of 9 are

	1	2	3	4	5	6	7	8	9	10	11	12
	9	18	27	36	45	54	63	72	81	90	99	108

[1] What is interesting about the digit sums of multiples of 9?

[2] Will this be true for all multiples of 9?

If it is true for 1 multiple of 9 (for example, 72) and the next multiple of 9 is found by adding 9 (81), then the digit sum for the next multiple must also be 0. So it seems to be true for all multiples of 9.

There are 6 multiples of 9 listed below. What are they?

16. 73	**26.** 235	**36.** 4321	**46.** 202,434	**56.** 15,978,321
17. 80	**27.** 247	**37.** 5447	**47.** 321,076	**57.** 20,134,777
18. 95	**28.** 358	**38.** 6318	**48.** 540,298	**58.** 21,112,368
19. 106	**29.** 381	**39.** 7912	**49.** 616,089	**59.** 30,671,840
20. 123	**30.** 399	**40.** 9908	**50.** 727,821	**60.** 52,974,302
21. 126	**31.** 401	**41.** 36,231	**51.** 2,100,237	**61.** 63,782,015
22. 136	**32.** 441	**42.** 42,437	**52.** 5,112,231	**62.** 444,320,012
23. 161	**33.** 452	**43.** 54,921	**53.** 6,093,215	**63.** 659,300,621
24. 163	**34.** 463	**44.** 61,376	**54.** 7,295,110	**64.** 875,632,212
25. 187	**35.** 501	**45.** 70,892	**55.** 8,362,195	**65.** 9,877,653,210

A number trick:

Pick any number. Add 4. Multiply by 6. Add 18. Divide by 2. Multiply by 3. Subtract 7. Find the digit sum (cast out nines until you have an answer from 0 through 8). Your answer is 2.

---

[3] Figure out why this trick works. Try to make up another one like it.

In real life, we often do not need a precise numerical answer. Usually a good approximation will do.

If you have $20 and are buying groceries, you probably do not care what the precise total bill will be. But you do need to know whether it will be more than $20 or not.

If you are going to buy paint for a room, you don't have to know the area of the wall space to the nearest square centimeter. An estimate to the nearest square meter will tell you how much paint to buy.

When doing approximate calculations, we usually first round each number to the nearest number that has only 1 nonzero digit.

Examples

You have $20. You have put items in your grocery cart that cost the following amounts: $2.73, $5.84, $1.49, $1.49, 73¢, 73¢, 73¢, $4.83. Do you have enough money to pay for all this? You might round each number to the nearest dollar, getting the following numbers of dollars: 3, 6, 1, 1, 1, 1, 1, 5. You can add these easily, getting 19. That is close enough to 20 to worry you. You could try again, rounding all numbers up this time—3, 6, 2, 2, 1, 1, 1, 5—and getting 21. Since rounding $1.49 up to $2 twice added at least $1 to the total, you are certainly still under $20.

Your family has just finished a meal at a restaurant. Here is the bill that the waiter left at the table. Your parents ask you to check it. You think: $10 + $4 + $3 + $1 + $1 + $5 = $24. So something is probably wrong. When the waiter rechecks, he discovers that he wrote 3 and carried 9 in the second column instead of writing 9 and carrying 3.

If you round 34,561 to the nearest thousand, you get 35,000, because 34,561 is closer to 35,000 than to 34,000.

If you round 34,492 to the nearest thousand, you get 34,000, because 34,492 is closer to 34,000 than to 35,000.

In general, to round a number to any place, change all digits to the right of that place to 0. Add 1 to the digit in that place if the digit to its right was 5 or more.

For example, to round a number to the nearest hundred, change all the digits to the right of the hundreds place to 0, and if the digit in the tens place was 5 or more, add 1 to the hundreds digit (otherwise leave it alone).

Examples: 87,543   203,500   3489   456

Round each of the numbers above to the nearest thousand.

88,000   204,000   3000   0

Round each of the numbers above so that all the digits are zero except the first one.

90,000   200,000   3000   500

Round each of the following to the nearest hundred.

1. 387	**5.** 596	**9.** 32,549	**13.** 57	**17.** 1000
2. 67,792	**6.** 485	**10.** 107	**14.** 7406	**18.** 4447
3. 23	**7.** 3485	**11.** 2732	**15.** 1146	**19.** 1459
4. 192	**8.** 731	**12.** 42,462	**16.** 87,724	**20.** 94,521

Now round each number in problems 1–20 so that all the digits are zero except the first one.

Approximating by Rounding

You should be able to determine the correct answer for each of the following problems by approximating. Round the given numbers so that all the digits are zero except the first one. Then calculate. Only 1 of the given answers should be close to your approximation. Choose the correct answer.

1. $387 \times 412 =$
   a. 1,549,444   b. 1594   c. 159,444   d. 15,944

2. $86{,}203 \times 37 =$
   a. 389,511   b. 3,189,511   c. 38,951   d. 3951

3. $4219 \times 2394 =$
   a. 10,100,286   b. 1,100,286   c. 11,286   d. 101,286

4. $4219 + 2394 =$
   a. 613   b. 6113   c. 66,113   d. 6613

5. $4219 - 2394 =$
   a. 125   b. 825   c. 18,125   d. 1825

6. $39 \times 52{,}684 =$
   a. 2546   b. 254,676   c. 25,476   d. 2,054,676

7. $83{,}839 \div 413 =$
   a. 23   b. 203   c. 2013   d. 3

8. $11{,}244{,}275 \div 4795 =$
   a. 2345   b. 12,345   c. 345   d. 215

9. $83 \times 5796 =$
   a. 4168   b. 41,068   c. 481,068   d. 4,881,068

10. $773 \times 8952 =$
    a. 619,896   b. 61,896   c. 6,919,896   d. 69,919,896

You can use casting out nines to check addition and subtraction problems as well as multiplication problems. For each of the following, you can eliminate all the wrong answers by casting out nines. Choose the correct answer in each case.

1. $3692 \times 814 =$
   a. 3,003,288   **b.** 3,004,288   **c.** 3,005,288   **d.** 3,006,288

2. $5729 \times 493 =$
   a. 2,824,397   **b.** 2,823,397   **c.** 2,822,397   **d.** 2,821,397

3. $694 \times 5725 =$
   a. 3,953,150   **b.** 3,963,150   **c.** 3,973,150   **d.** 3,983,150

4. $(995)^2 =$
   a. 990,325   **b.** 990,225   **c.** 990,125   **d.** 990,025

5. $(1836)^2 =$
   a. 3,370,896   **b.** 3,380,896   **c.** 3,390,896   **d.** 3,400,896

6. $43,921 + 68,341 + 18,902 =$ *
   a. 101,164   **b.** 111,164   **c.** 121,164   **d.** 131,164

7. $873,901 + 64,846 + 24,345,919 =$
   a. 25,184,666   **b.** 25,284,666   **c.** 25,384,666   **d.** 25,484,666

8. $22,846,741 + 31,509,422 + 28,703,541 =$
   a. 83,079,704   **b.** 83,069,704   **c.** 83,059,704   **d.** 83,049,704

9. $28,703,541 - 22,846,741 =$ †
   a. 5,854,800   **b.** 5,855,800   **c.** 5,856,800   **d.** 5,857,800

10. $31,509,422 - 22,846,741 =$
   a. 8,661,681   **b.** 8,662,681   **c.** 8,663,681   **d.** 8,664,681

*Remember, *add* the digit sums here.
†Subtract the digit sums. You may add 9 to the first digit sum if necessary.

Try to find easy ways to do these problems.

1. 51 + 73 + 49
2. 630 + 478 + 370
3. 545 + 455 + 379

4. 73 + 27 + 11 + 0
5. 73 × 27 × 11 × 0
6. 1 × 2 × 3 × 4 × 5

7. 1 × 2 × 4 × 5 × 25
8. 50 × 47 × 2
9. 125 × 70 × 40

Try to find these squares without multiplying each number by itself.

10. 35^2
11. 85^2

12. 41^2
13. 39^2

14. 99^2
15. 81^2

In each problem, 1 of the answers is wrong and 1 is correct. Choose the correct answer.

16. 378 × 923 =
    a. 348,794
    b. 348,894

17. 8561 × 733 =
    a. 6,235,213
    b. 6,275,213

18. 6783 × 1542 =
    a. 10,459,386
    b. 10,459,486

Round each number 2 ways: first to the nearest hundred, then to a number with only 1 nonzero digit.

19. 121
20. 763
21. 2468
22. 1891
23. 5071
24. 33,403
25. 56,489
26. 75,555
27. 90,749

28. What is the sum of all the numbers from 1 through 200? (This means 1 + 2 + all the numbers up to and including 200.)

29. What is the sum of all the even numbers from 1 through 200?

30. What is the sum of all the odd numbers from 1 through 200?

When taking a multiple-choice test, you can often use some of the methods described in this chapter to decide which of the given possible answers is correct. Approximating, checking answers by casting out nines, using the distributive, commutative, or associative laws, or using patterns may help you. But beware: you might waste more time trying to decide which of these methods to use than it would take you to do the problem the long way.

Every problem in the following test lends itself to solution by 1 or more of the methods described in this chapter. Try to use what you've learned in this chapter to do these problems.

1. What is the sum of 11, 12, 13, 14, 15, 16, 17, 18, and 19?
   a. 90   b. 105   c. 130   d. 135   e. 170

2. What is the sum of 150, 152, 154, 156, 158, 160, 162, 164, 166, 168, and 170?
   a. 780   b. 960   c. 1100   d. 1440   e. 1760

3. What is the sum of 41, 43, 45, 47, 49, 51, 53, 55, 57, and 59?
   a. 450   b. 500   c. 550   d. 600   e. 651

4. $7 \times 8 \times 3 \times 5 \times 0 \times 4 = ?$
   a. 0   b. 4   c. 840   d. 1680   e. 3360

5. $18 + 27 + 82 + 73 + 39 + 61 = ?$
   a. 271   b. 286   c. 300   d. 310   e. 350

6. $99 \times 425 = ?$
   a. 21,250   b. 32,450   c. 39,845   d. 42,075   e. 42,500

7. $8357 \times 4185 = ?$
   a. 34,974,045   b. 25,392,405   c. 45,381,625   d. 35,815   e. 43,585

8. $389 \times 586 = ?$
   a. 248,754   b. 146,284   c. 22,594   d. 82,594   e. 227,954

9. $9 \times 8 \times 7 \times 6 \times 5 \times 4 \times 3 \times 2 \times 1 = ?$
   a. 362,870   b. 362,875   c. 362,880   d. 362,885   e. 362,890

Try to find easy ways to do these problems.

1. 21 + 87 + 79
2. 67 + 23 + 37 + 10
3. 389 + 476 + 111

4. 32 + 68 + 95
5. 45 + 99 + 0 + 55
6. 45 × 99 × 0 × 55

7. 25 × 33 × 40
8. 250 × 11 × 20
9. 125 × 77 × 8

Try to find these squares without multiplying each number by itself.

10. 65^2 **12.** 31^2 **14.** 39^2
11. 95^2 **13.** 29^2 **15.** 61^2

In each problem, 1 of the answers is wrong and 1 is correct. Choose the correct answer.

16. 859 × 323 =

   a. 275,457
   b. 277,457

17. 4519 × 321 =

   a. 1,650,599
   b. 1,450,599

18. 9753 × 8642 =

   a. 84,285,426
   b. 84,286,426

Round each number 2 ways: first to the nearest hundred, then to a number with only 1 nonzero digit.

19. 231
20. 864
21. 1357
22. 1894
23. 6073
24. 43,409
25. 67,479
26. 85,555
27. 90,698

28. What is the sum of all the numbers from 100 through 200? (This means 100 + 101 + 102 + all the numbers up to and including 200.)

29. What is the sum of all the even numbers from 100 through 200?

30. What is the sum of all the odd numbers from 100 through 200?

NIMBLE 100

Players: 2
Materials: Nothing is needed.
Object: To be the first to reach 100

Rules

1. The first player chooses a whole number between 1 and 10.

2. The second player chooses a whole number between 1 and 10 and adds it to the first player's number.

3. The first player adds a whole number between 1 and 10 to the second player's sum.

4. The second player adds a whole number between 1 and 10 to the first player's sum.

5. Repeat steps 4 and 5 until a player reaches 100.

6. The player who makes 100 exactly is the winner.

Sample Game

	José chooses:	The sum is:	Miriam chooses:	The sum is:
Turn 1	2		9	11
Turn 2	8	19	7	26
Turn 3	9	35	8	43
Turn 4	3	46	10	56
Turn 5	6	62	10	72
Turn 6	3	75	10	85
Turn 7	1	86	2	88
Turn 8	1	89	1	90
Turn 9	10	100		

José is the winner.

CHAPTER 3

CALCULATOR USE
FUNCTIONS
DECIMALS AND
PERCENTS

Every once in a while history has noted persons who were truly calculating wonders. They could do remarkable calculations in their heads without using anything at all—not even paper and pencil.

Two such wonders were Zerah Colburn and George Parker Bidder.

Zerah Colburn, the son of a Vermont farmer, was born in 1804. By the time he was 8 years old he could multiply two 4-digit numbers in his head instantly, although he usually hesitated a moment if both numbers were greater than 10,000. He could also instantly raise single-digit numbers to the 10th and higher powers. Two examples of these calculations are $2^{10} = 1024$ and $8^{16} = 281,474,976,710,656$. (Remember: $2^{10} = 2 \times 2 \times 2 \times 2 \times 2 \times 2 \times 2 \times 2 \times 2 \times 2$.) Raising 2-digit numbers, such as 48 and 69, to high powers took him more time.

George Parker Bidder

George Parker Bidder, another calculating wonder, was the son of a stonemason in Devonshire, England. In 1818, when Bidder was 12, he competed against Colburn, who was then 14 years old. According to reports of those present, Bidder appeared to be the better calculator, though each was better than the other at some kinds of calculations.

Here is a calculation Bidder did at the age of 9: If the moon is 123,256 miles from the earth and sound travels at 4 miles a minute, how long would it take for the inhabitants of the moon to hear the Battle of Waterloo (which was then going on)? He gave the answer—21 days, 9 hours, and 34 minutes—in less than 1 minute.

At the age of 10, Bidder was asked how many hogsheads of cider could be made from a million apples if 30 apples made one quart. (A hogshead is a barrel that holds 63 gallons.) In 35 seconds he gave the answer: 132 hogsheads, 17 gallons, and 1 quart of cider, with 10 apples left over.

There have been other persons with these exceptional calculating abilities. No special relationship between computing ability and general intelligence has ever been found. In fact, some of the calculating whizzes were remarkably dull in all other ways. A person who has one very special talent but is rather stupid about all other things is called an *idiot savant*. (This French phrase means "learned idiot.")

In some cases, people who were human calculators did scientific calculations and computed tables that would help others do scientific computations. Most scientists, however, did not have such persons available. So mathematicians have tried from time to time to create machines that would do laborious computations for them.

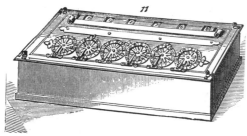

In 1642 Pascal, one of the world's great mathematicians, created a machine that would add. Using wheels and gears designed so that one wheel moved 1 step when another moved 10, he created a machine that would carry automatically.

Almost 30 years later Leibniz invented a machine that could add, subtract, multiply, and divide. Leibniz also recognized the advantage of using base two rather than base ten in computing machines. If numbers are written in base two, each place has only 2 possible digits, 0 and 1, which are equivalent to off and on for an electric switch or up and down for a mechanical switch.

From 1828 to 1839 Charles Babbage made the plans for a modern calculating machine that he called the Analytical Engine. But he ran out of money in 1842, before construction of the machine was complete. His plans and the part of the Analytical Engine that was built are now in a museum in England.

In 1939 Howard H. Aiken began to build a machine that would be the first programmed computer to operate successfully. This machine was called the Harvard Mark I Calculator.

Mark I did its computing by means of relays, or switching devices. In 1946 ENIAC, the first fully electronic digital computer, was completed. About 18,000 vacuum tubes controlled the computing operations of ENIAC. Since that time there has been steady progress in creating ever smaller, faster, and more efficient calculators and computers.

Although calculators and computers can do amazing computations in extremely short periods of time, they are in many respects like *idiots savants*. They are unable to think independently, and they must be told in the simplest terms precisely what to do. So an intelligent human being is needed both to tell the machines what to do and to interpret their results.

A calculator can calculate, but it can't think.

A calculator will do only what you tell it to do. You should learn its language. Then the calculator will add when you want it to add, subtract when you want it to subtract, and so on.

Example: Add 493 and 387 on the calculator.

What to Do: What the Display Shows:

A. Turn on the calculator. ·······································∴· [0.]

B. Push 4 , then 9 , then 3 . ·······················∴· [493.]

C. Push + . ···∴· [493.]

D. Push 3 , then 8 , then 7 . ·······················∴· [387.]

E. Push = . ···∴· [880.]

F. Use the answer and turn off the calculator. ····∴· [   ]

To do other operations with 493 and 387, follow similar steps, except for step C. On step C, push the button with the sign of operation you want to do.

Examples

To subtract 387 from 493, push − for step C.

To multiply 493 by 387, push ✕ for step C.

To divide 493 by 387, push ÷ for step C.

Different calculators work in slightly different ways. With some small changes, the instructions we give in this book will work for most calculators.

The key  is used to turn on the calculator and also acts as a clear key. On some calculators this key is labeled differently. Some even have separate keys for turning on and clearing the calculator. Clear keys are like erasers. To start over completely, push twice. That will erase almost everything in the calculator.

If you push once, you will erase only the last number you put into the calculator. (You will erase the entire number, though, not just the last digit.)

Here's how it works:

Example: Add 589, 793, and 864.

What to Do: What the Display Shows:

Push 5 , 8 , 9 . ·············· 589.

Push ✚ . ·············· 589.

Push 7 , 9 , 3 . ·············· 793.

Push ✚ . ·············· 1382.

Push 8 , 4 , 6 . ·············· 846.

But 846 is the wrong number.

Push ON/C . ·············· 0.

Push 8 , 6 , 4 . ·············· 864.

Push ═ . ·············· 2246.

Race the Calculator I

See how fast you can solve these problems for n. Some students should use calculators while the rest of the class works without calculators. If you are using a calculator, you *must* use it and you must enter every number in each problem. Do not start until you are told to. Write only the answers.

1. $100 + 57 = n$
2. $57 + 100 = n$
3. $100 \times 57 = n$
4. $57 \times 100 = n$
5. $100 - 57 = n$
6. $85 \times 10 = n$
7. $85 \times 100 = n$
8. $1000 \times 85 = n$
9. $5 \times 7 = n$
10. $7 + 7 + 7 + 7 + 7 = n$

11. $n = 837 \times 0$
12. $n = 20^2$
13. $n = 21^2$
14. $n = 25^2$
15. $n = 50 \times 70$
16. $n = 700 \times 500$
17. $6 \times 5 \times 4 \times 3 \times 2 \times 1 \times 0 = n$
18. $2000 \div 10 = n$
19. $n = 2000 \div 100$
20. $n = 1200 \div 40$

When you finish, *stop* and put your pencil down.

Race the Calculator II

Follow the game rules for the first race. You are allowed to think in this race, however, even if you have a calculator.

21. $5963 + 8749 = n$
22. $12,000 - 3756 = n$
23. $278 \times 5864 = n$
24. $10 \times 9 \times 8 \times 7 \times 6 \times 5 \times 4 \times 3 \times 2 \times 1 = n$
25. $n = 389,934 \div 498$
26. $111 \times 111 = n$
27. $n = 1111 \times 1111$
28. $n = 11,111 \times 11,111$
29. $111,111^2 = n$
30. $n = 5000 \times 40,000$

   Do you see why thinking is useful, even if you have a calculator?

Most calculators have a constant feature. This works differently on different calculators. On some you must push a special constant switch or key (usually ). On others you must push the operation key (▦, ▬, ✕, or ÷) twice. On most calculators the constant function will work if you just push the ▬ key repeatedly. Read the instructions or try some examples to see how your calculator works.

One kind of problem that is easier to do if you use the constant feature is to raise a number to a certain power.

Remember

In 2^{10} the small 10 is called an exponent.

2^{10} says to use 2 as a factor 10 times.

$2^{10} = 2 \times 2 \times 2 \times 2 \times 2 \times 2 \times 2 \times 2 \times 2 \times 2$

2^{10} is called the 10th power of 2.

To "raise" 2 to the 10th power means to calculate 2^{10}.

Example: Use the calculator to find 2^{10}.

Push: Display Shows:

Notice that you push ▬ only 9 times to raise 2 to the 10th power.

Calculate the following on a calculator.

1. 2^{10}	**5.** 2^{12}	**9.** 27^4	**13.** 2^{16}
2. 4^5	**6.** 4^6	**10.** 3^{12}	**14.** 4^8
3. 3^8	**7.** 8^4	**11.** 9^6	**15.** 16^4
4. 9^4	**8.** 5^{10}	**12.** 7^7	**16.** 3^6

KEY KEYS GAME

Players: 1 or more
Materials: 1 calculator
Object: To reach a given number using only permitted keys

Rules

1. Pick several keys ("permitted keys") and a number.
2. Try to get the display to show the number. See who can get to the number with the fewest steps. (You don't have to push ▣ after each operation.)

Sample Game

Marilyn and Enid chose these keys: ➕ , ➖ , ✖ , ➗ , ▣ , 7

They wanted to reach this number: 22
Marilyn reached 22 in 10 steps:

7 , ➗ , 7 , ➕ , 7 , ➕ , 7 , ➕ , 7 , ▣

Enid reached 22 in 8 steps:

7 , 7 , ➕ , 7 , 7 , ➗ , 7 , ▣

Enid won the round.

Can you do these? Count your steps.

1. Permitted keys: ➕ , ➖ , ✖ , ➗ , ▣ , 8
   Try to reach: **a.** 24   **b.** 11   **c.** 19   **d.** 640   **e.** 2   **f.** 56
2. Permitted keys: ➕ , ➖ , ✖ , ➗ , ▣ , 9
   Try to reach: **a.** 45   **b.** 81   **c.** 82   **d.** 360   **e.** 4   **f.** 98
3. Permitted keys: ➕ , ➖ , ✖ , ➗ , ▣ , 5
   Try to reach: **a.** 25   **b.** 550   **c.** 280   **d.** 165   **e.** 11   **f.** 13

Solutions may be different with different calculators. Now make up problems of your own. Share them.

Exponents

You know that exponents tell how many times another number (the *base*) is to be used as a factor.

In $2^3 = 8$, 2 is the base and 3 is the exponent. 8 is called the third *power* of 2. We say 2 is raised to the third power.

Use these definitions to do the following problems. You may discuss the problems with other people. When in doubt, write out the expression using multiplication. To save time, you can use a dot instead of a times sign ($\times$) to show multiplication. $2 \cdot 3$ is the same as 2×3. $n \cdot n = n \times n$.

Solve for x. For problems 20, 30, and 40, give your answer for x in terms of n and m.

1. $2^4 = x$ 5. $3^2 = x$ 9. $3^3 = x$
2. $4^2 = x$ 6. $2^3 = x$ 10. $2^2 = x$
3. $2^5 = x$ 7. $2^{10} = x$
4. $5^2 = x$ 8. $10^2 = x$

11. $2^3 \cdot 2^2 = 2^x$ 16. $10^2 \cdot 10^5 = 10^x$
12. $2^5 \cdot 2^5 = 2^x$ 17. $10^3 \cdot 10^7 = 10^x$
13. $2^7 \cdot 2^3 = 2^x$ 18. $10^x \cdot 10^2 = 10^5$
14. $3^5 \cdot 3^2 = 3^x$ 19. $10^4 \cdot 10^x = 10^6$
15. $3^4 \cdot 3^5 = 3^x$ 20. $b^n \cdot b^m = b^x$

21. $(3 \cdot 3 \cdot 3 \cdot 3 \cdot 3 \cdot 3) \div (3 \cdot 3) = 3^x$ 26. $10^{10} \div 10^7 = 10^x$
22. $3^6 \div 3^2 = 3^x$ 27. $10^{10} \div 10^3 = 10^x$
23. $3^{10} \div 3^4 = 3^x$ 28. $10^5 \div 10^2 = 10^x$
24. $3^{10} \div 3^5 = 3^x$ 29. $10^6 \div 10^4 = 10^x$
25. $2^{10} \div 2^5 = 2^x$ 30. $b^n \div b^m = b^x$

31. $(2^5)^2 = 2^x$ 36. $(10^4)^3 = 10^x$
32. $(2^2)^5 = 2^x$ 37. $(10^5)^4 = 10^x$
33. $(3^6)^2 = 3^x$ 38. $(10^4)^5 = 10^x$
34. $(10^3)^4 = 10^x$ 39. $(10^3)^3 = 10^x$
35. $(3^2)^6 = 3^x$ 40. $(b^n)^m = b^x$

As you worked on page 86, you may have discovered the following rules:

$$b^n \times b^m = \overbrace{(b \cdot b \cdot b \cdot b \cdot \ldots \cdot b)}^{n \text{ factors}}\overbrace{(b \cdot b \cdot b \cdot \ldots \cdot b)}^{m \text{ factors}} = b^{n+m}$$

$$b^n \div b^m = \dfrac{\overbrace{b \cdot b \cdot b \cdot b \cdot \ldots \cdot b}^{n \text{ factors}}}{\underbrace{b \cdot b \cdot b \cdot \ldots \cdot b}_{m \text{ factors}}} = \overbrace{b \cdot b \cdot \ldots \cdot b}^{n-m \text{ factors}} = b^{n-m} \text{ when } n > m$$

$$(b^n)^m = \underbrace{\overbrace{(b \cdot b \cdot b \cdot \ldots \cdot b)}^{n \text{ factors}}\overbrace{(b \cdot b \cdot b \cdot \ldots \cdot b)}^{n \text{ factors}} \ldots \overbrace{(b \cdot b \cdot b \cdot \ldots \cdot b)}^{n \text{ factors}}}_{m \text{ sets of parentheses}} = b^{n \cdot m}$$

Solve for x. Use the rules to help you.

41. $2^x = 4$	**48.** $3^6 = 9^x$	**55.** $243 \div 243 = 3^x$
42. $2^{10} = 4^x$	**49.** $27^x = 3^6$	**56.** $10^8 \div 10^8 = 10^x$
43. $16 = 4^x$	**50.** $27^4 = 3^x$	**57.** $100{,}000{,}000 \div 100{,}000{,}000 = 10^x$
44. $16 = 2^x$	**51.** $16^5 = 2^x$	**58.** $2^5 \div 2^5 = 2^x$
45. $16^x = 2^{12}$	**52.** $4^x = 64^{16}$	**59.** $2^0 = x$
46. $16^x = 4^6$	**53.** $16^x = 64^{16}$	**60.** $10^0 = x$
47. $32^x = 2^{10}$	**54.** $3^5 \div 3^5 = 3^x$	**61.** $3^0 = x$

[1] In problems 54–61 we asked you to use the division rule ($b^n \div b^m = b^{n-m}$) even though n was not greater than m. If the rule is to work, what must b^0 be defined as?

[2] See if you can find a way to define 2^{-1} so that the rules of exponents work for it. (Try $2^1 \times 2^{-1}$, for example.) Try to do this for any negative exponent.

62. $0^2 = x$ **63.** $0^{10} = x$ **64.** $0^{873} = x$ **65.** $0^{1000} = x$

[3] What is 0^n?

[4] In discussion question 1 you decided that $b^0 = 1$ (for positive values of b, $b > 0$). In discussion question 3 you decided that $0^n = 0$ (for $n > 0$). What do you think 0^0 should be?

Using Approximation

When you use a calculator or a computer, approximating the answer helps you catch mistakes such as not pushing a key you thought you pushed or pushing a key too often. Each of the following problems was done 3 times on a calculator or computer. But in each problem, only 1 of the 3 answers is correct. Use approximation (not a calculator) to decide which one is correct.

1. 73,589 + 3876 =   a. 107,465   b. 112,465   c. 77,465
2. 489 × 7564 =   a. 3,698,796   b. 373,596   c. 36,980,396
3. 8432 + 9514 =   a. 9386   b. 17,946   c. 97,946
4. 8432 × 9514 =   a. 8,010,788   b. 80,222,048   c. 841,342,048
5. 3942 ÷ 54 =   a. 730   b. 7   c. 73

6. 630,924 ÷ 777 =   a. 81   b. 812   c. 8194
7. 43,821 − 16,549 =   a. 27,272   b. 2727   c. 272,727
8. 100,000 − 73,589 =   a. 26,411   b. 2611   c. 264,411
9. 9^5 =   a. 4,782,969   b. 531,441   c. 59,049
10. 11^8 =   a. 1,771,561   b. 19,487,171   c. 214,358,881

11. 3862 × 5914 =   a. 9776   b. 22,839,868   c. 2052
12. 3862 + 5914 =   a. 9776   b. 22,839,868   c. 2052
13. 44,435,556 ÷ 6666 = a. 66,720   b. 6666   c. 667
14. 3456 ÷ 72 =   a. 494   b. 48   c. 5
15. 3456 − 72 =   a. 3384   b. 3528   c. 3456

16. 44,435 − 6666 =   a. 45,101   b. 43,769   c. 37,769
17. 93,857 + 4622 =   a. 140,479   b. 14,479   c. 98,479
18. 93,857 × 4622 =   a. 140,479   b. 43,361,934   c. 433,807,054
19. $(512)^3$ =   a. 134,217,728   b. 13,421,728   c. 1,342,178
20. $(512)^4$ =   a. 68,719,476,736   b. 34,359,738,368   c. 17,179,184

APPROXIMATION GAME

Players: 3 or more
Materials: 1 calculator for the lead player
Object: To get the most points by making close approximations

Rules

1. Make a game form like this:

Round	Approximation	Point for Correct First Digit	Points for Correct Number of Digits	Score for Round
1				
2				

2. Decide how many rounds will be played. List them on the game form and add a space at the bottom for the total.

3. The lead player writes a problem on the board (for example, 73 × 59) and uses the calculator to find the answer.

4. Each player writes an approximate answer on the game form. Do not make any calculations.

5. The lead player rounds the correct answer to a number with only 1 nonzero digit and writes it on the board, saying the first digit and the number of digits in the answer.

6. Look at your approximation and score yourself as follows: 1 point for the correct first digit and 2 points for the correct number of digits. Record your points on your game form.

If your approximation was:	and the correct answer is:	then you score:
4000	3652 → 4000	3 points
50,000	44,370 → 40,000	2 points
950	9231 → 9000	1 point

7. The player with the highest total score at the end of the game is the winner.

The constant feature on a calculator can also be used to do the same thing to each of several numbers.

Example: Suppose that you want to know how many seconds there are in a day, a week, a 28-day month, a 29-day month, a 30-day month, a 31-day month, a 365-day year, and a 366-day year.

You know there are 60 seconds in 1 minute, 60 minutes in 1 hour, and 24 hours in 1 day. So you use your calculator to find the number of seconds in 1 day.

Push: Display Shows:

6 , 0 , × , 6 , 0 , × , 2 , 4 , = ·········⫶· 86400.

[1] What does 86,400 represent?

Now enter this number as a constant in your calculator. Then just push the buttons for the number of days. The display will show the number of seconds in that many days.

Push: Display Shows:

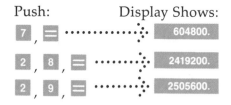

7 , = ··············⫶· 604800.

2 , 8 , = ········⫶· 2419200.

2 , 9 , = ········⫶· 2505600.

and so on.

[2] What does the 7 represent?

[3] What does the 28 represent?

[4] What does the 29 represent?

[5] Can you think of other times you might need to do the same thing to each number in a set of numbers?

Function Machines and Function Rules

If your calculator has a constant feature, you can use it as a function machine. That's a machine that does the same thing to every number that is put into it.

Example

Push: Display Shows:

5 , + , 5 , = ·········· 10.

0 , = ·················· 5.

1 , 7 , = ·············· 22.

The calculator is working as a plus-5 machine. It adds 5 to any number that is put into it.

We can show this with an arrow.

$$x \longrightarrow \boxed{+5} \longrightarrow y$$

x stands for the number you put into the machine and y stands for the number that comes out.

[1] If we know 7 goes into the machine, what will come out? (If x is 7, what is y?)

[2] If we know 13 came out of the machine, what went in? (If y is 13, what is x?)

The rule that tells what happens to a number is called a function rule.

You can use a chart to show how a function rule works.

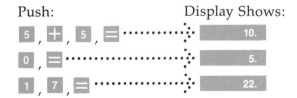

$$x \longrightarrow \boxed{\times 6} \longrightarrow y$$

In	Out
3	18
7	42
5	30

The function rule is ×6.

If we put 3 in, 18 comes out.

If we put 7 in, 42 comes out.

If we put 5 in, 30 comes out.

Finding Function Rules

In each case, find the function rule.

1. $x \rightarrow (?) \rightarrow y$

In	Out
2	22
5	25
7	27
13	33

2. $x \rightarrow (?) \rightarrow y$

In	Out
9	0
13	4
19	10
24	15

3. $x \rightarrow (?) \rightarrow y$

In	Out
3	1
12	4
18	6
24	8

4. $x \rightarrow (?) \rightarrow y$

In	Out
0	1001
2	1003
10	1011
20	1021

5. $x \rightarrow (?) \rightarrow y$

In	Out
0	0
3	18
5	30
8	48

6. $x \rightarrow (?) \rightarrow y$

In	Out
1	10
3	30
5	50
10	100

You can use x and y when you make a function chart.

$x \rightarrow (\div 7) \rightarrow y$

x	y
49	7
35	5
70	10

This chart tells you that
if x is 49, then y is 7;
if x is 35, then y is 5;
and if x is 70, then y is 10.

You can also think about doing these function problems in reverse. The chart above also tells you that if y is 7, then x is 49; if y is 5, then x is 35; and if y is 10, then x is 70.

Copy and complete these function charts.

1. $x \longrightarrow (+5) \longrightarrow y$

x	y
7	▨
10	▨
▨	10
▨	5

2. $x \longrightarrow (\times 5) \longrightarrow y$

x	y
1	▨
3	▨
▨	30
▨	0

3. $x \longrightarrow (-7) \longrightarrow y$

x	y
10	▨
7	▨
▨	1
▨	15

4. $x \longrightarrow (\div 3) \longrightarrow y$

x	y
12	▨
39	▨
▨	5
▨	7

5. $x \longrightarrow (\times 8) \longrightarrow y$

x	y
1	▨
0	▨
▨	40
▨	0

6. $x \longrightarrow (\times 2) \longrightarrow y$

x	y
2	▨
▨	2
3	▨
▨	8

7. $x \longrightarrow (\times 4) \longrightarrow y$

x	y
1	▨
3	▨
▨	0
▨	8

8. $y \longrightarrow (\div 4) \longrightarrow x$

y	x
▨	1
▨	3
0	▨
8	▨

9. $x \longrightarrow (\times 0) \longrightarrow y$

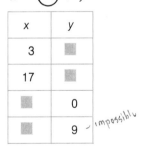

x	y
3	▨
17	▨
▨	0
▨	9

— impossible

To find y (the output) when you know x (the input), simply do what the rule tells you.

[1] What can you do to find x (the input) if you know y (the output)? Look at function charts 7 and 8. Do they help you answer this question?

[2] Look at function chart 9. Can you explain why we say division by zero is not possible?

Composite Functions

We often combine function rules. Copy and complete these function charts.

1. $x \longrightarrow \times 3 \longrightarrow n \longrightarrow +4 \longrightarrow y$

x	y
2	10
5	▨
1	▨

2. $x \longrightarrow \times 2 \longrightarrow n \longrightarrow -3 \longrightarrow y$

x	y
2	▨
5	▨
▨	5

3. $x \longrightarrow \div 5 \longrightarrow n \longrightarrow +2 \longrightarrow y$

x	y
10	▨
35	▨
▨	5

4. $x \longrightarrow \div 3 \longrightarrow n \longrightarrow -7 \longrightarrow y$

x	y
21	▨
35	▨
▨	1

5. $x \longrightarrow +4 \longrightarrow n \longrightarrow \times 3 \longrightarrow y$

x	y
2	▨
5	▨
1	▨

6. $x \longrightarrow -1 \longrightarrow n \longrightarrow \div 3 \longrightarrow y$

x	y
1	▨
4	▨
▨	3

7. $x \longrightarrow +3 \longrightarrow n \longrightarrow \div 2 \longrightarrow y$

x	y
1	▨
0	▨
2	▨

8. $x \longrightarrow -3 \longrightarrow n \longrightarrow \times 2 \longrightarrow y$

x	y
5	▨
▨	6
▨	0

9. $x \longrightarrow +13 \longrightarrow n \longrightarrow -4 \longrightarrow y$

x	y
3	▨
7	▨
▨	19

10. $x \longrightarrow -4 \longrightarrow n \longrightarrow +13 \longrightarrow y$

x	y
3	▨
7	▨
▨	19

11. $x \longrightarrow \div 5 \longrightarrow n \longrightarrow \times 10 \longrightarrow y$

x	y
5	▨
15	▨
▨	20

12. $x \longrightarrow \times 10 \longrightarrow n \longrightarrow \div 5 \longrightarrow y$

x	y
5	▨
15	▨
▨	20

In Long Bend, taxicab drivers charge according to this rule: 90¢ as they begin the first $\frac{1}{10}$ mile and 10¢ at the beginning of each additional $\frac{1}{10}$ mile. As a function rule, this could be written:

$$x \longrightarrow \boxed{\times 100} \longrightarrow n \longrightarrow \boxed{+90} \longrightarrow y,$$

where x is the number of miles traveled (rounded down to the nearest tenth of a mile) and y is the cost of the trip in cents.

13. Does a fraction of a mile less than $\frac{1}{10}$ mile count as $\frac{1}{10}$ mile?

14. Why is x multiplied by 100?

15. 4 values for x or y are given below. In each case, use both the word rule and the function rule to find the other value. See if you get the same results both ways.

  a. $x = \frac{1}{10}$ $y = ?$ **c.** $x = 2$ $y = ?$

  b. $x = 1$ $y = ?$ **d.** $x = 2\frac{1}{2}$ $y = ?$

16. Use the function rule to find the missing value of x or y in each case.

  a. $x = 3$ $y = ?$ **d.** $x = ?$ $y = 180$

  b. $x = \frac{3}{10}$ $y = ?$ **e.** $x = ?$ $y = 330$

  c. $x = ?$ $y = 200$ **f.** $x = ?$ $y = 1080$

17. If you were charged $10.90 for a cab trip, how long was the trip in miles?

18. How many miles could you go in a cab for $3.30?

19. Bus fare to ride anywhere in Long Bend is 75¢ a person.

  a. If you want to go to a museum that is 2 miles away, is it cheaper to go by bus or by taxi?

  b. Is it cheaper by bus or by taxi for 2 persons?

  c. 3 persons?

  d. 4 persons?

  e. 5 persons?

If you divide 1 by 4 on a calculator, it shows $\boxed{0.25}$. This number is twenty-five hundredths. Other ways to say it are "point two five" or "zero point two five."

The symbol .25 or 0.25 is a decimal fraction, usually called simply a decimal. We work with decimals in connection with money, measurement, and many other practical situations.

We can tell the place value of any digit in a number by the decimal point. The decimal point is always between the ones and the tenths place. On both sides of the decimal point, each place has a value 10 times that of the place to the right.

In 12.345:

The 5 stands for 5 thousandths.	0.005
The 4 stands for 4 hundredths.	0.04
The 3 stands for 3 tenths.	0.3
The 2 stands for 2 ones.	2.
The 1 stands for 1 ten.	10.

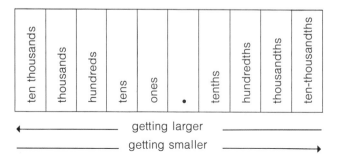

1. What does the 3 stand for in each of these numbers?
   a. 167.321 **c.** 123.025 **e.** 629.342 **g.** 160.893
   b. 237.109 **d.** 192.031 **f.** 326.041 **h.** 249.367

2. 0.571 is standard form for 5 tenths, 7 hundredths, 1 thousandth. Write these numbers in standard form.

   a. 3 tenths, 9 hundredths, 2 thousandths   **d.** 0.9 + 0.08 + 0.007
   b. 6 tenths, 0 hundredths, 3 thousandths   **e.** 0.1 + 0.003
   c. 0 tenths, 4 hundredths, 7 thousandths   **f.** 0.02 + 0.006

The symbol > means "is greater than" and the symbol < means "is less than." So it is true to say 5 > 3 and 7 < 10.

Copy each pair of numbers, but replace ⬤ by > or < to make a true statement. For example, 0.07 ⬤ 0.3 would be 0.07 < 0.3.

3. 10 ⬤ 4
4. 1.05 ⬤ 2.36
5. 73.4 ⬤ 8.47
6. 0.14 ⬤ 0.028
7. 0.20 ⬤ 0.34

8. 4.36 ⬤ 2.159
9. 0.024 ⬤ 0.023
10. 0.157 ⬤ 0.246
11. 0.079 ⬤ 0.12
12. 1.2 ⬤ 2.1

13. 83 ⬤ 79
14. 8.3 ⬤ 7.9
15. 0.83 ⬤ 0.79
16. 0.083 ⬤ 0.79
17. 0.0083 ⬤ 0.0079

To help make comparing and calculating with decimals easier, we sometimes put zeros in places to the right of the decimal point. This doesn't change the value of the decimal.

To tell whether 0.94 or 0.904 is greater, we can put a zero after 0.94, making it 0.940, so that both decimals have the same number of places after the decimal point. Now it is easier to see that 0.940 is greater than 0.904.

Copy each pair of numbers, but replace ⬤ with >, <, or =.

18. 0.8 ⬤ 0.008
19. 0.092 ⬤ 0.92

20. 0.63 ⬤ 0.603
21. 0.07 ⬤ 0.070

22. 10.01 ⬤ 1.1
23. 0.909 ⬤ 0.990

You may write extra zeros to the right of the point and the last digit if it makes the arithmetic easier for you. But never put zeros between 2 digits or between a digit and the decimal point. That would change the value of the number.

Someone has added zeros to each of the numbers below. Tell whether the number with the added zeros has the same value as the first number.

24. 2.376   2.3760
25. 23.76   23.076
26. 237.6   237.06
27. .2376   0.23760
28. 2376   23760

29. 59.565   59.5650
30. 5.9565   5.956500
31. 595.65   5950.650
32. 59,565   59,565.00
33. 5956.5   50956.50

ROLL AND REGROUP A DECIMAL GAME

Players: 2 or more
Materials: One 0–5 cube, one 5–10 cube
Object: To make the largest decimal number

Rules

1. Draw blanks on your paper like this:

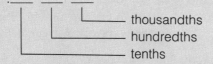

      thousandths
      hundredths
      tenths

2. The first player rolls both cubes. Every player writes the sum of the cubes in one of the blanks.

3. The cubes are rolled twice more, and each time every player writes the sum of the numbers in one of the remaining blanks.

4. After the 3 rolls, the players find the value of their decimal numbers, regrouping where necessary.

5. The player who makes the largest number is the winner of the round.

Sample Game

Numbers Rolled	David's Sums	Debbie's Sums	Janet's Sums
First roll: 5 3	.__ 8 __	.__ __ 8	.8 __ __
Second roll: 8 3	.11 8 __	.__ 11 8	.8 __ 11
Third roll: 10 4	.11 8 14	.14 11 8	.8 14 11

David regrouped 11 tenths, 8 hundredths, and 14 thousandths to get 1.194.
Debbie regrouped 14 tenths, 11 hundredths, and 8 thousandths to get 1.518.
Janet regrouped 8 tenths, 14 hundredths, and 11 thousandths to get 0.951.

Debbie won this round.

Decimals are added and subtracted much the same way as whole numbers. The main difference is in how place value is handled. With whole numbers the ones digit is always the digit farthest to the right. With decimals the ones digit is always the digit just to the left of the decimal point.

When adding or subtracting whole numbers, line up the rightmost digits:

$$
\begin{array}{r} 347 \\ +28 \\ \hline 375 \end{array}
\qquad
\begin{array}{r} 347 \\ -28 \\ \hline 319 \end{array}
$$

When adding or subtracting decimals, line up the decimal points:

$$
\begin{array}{r} 34.6 \\ +2.75 \\ \hline 37.35 \end{array}
\qquad
\begin{array}{r} 34.6 \\ -2.75 \\ \hline 31.85 \end{array}
$$

Measurements should be made at the same level of precision if the results are to be combined. In most real situations, then, the number of digits to the right of the point will be the same for numbers that you work with. But sometimes they won't be the same. So you do need to practice working with decimals that have different numbers of places.

If you do have to add or subtract decimals with different numbers of places to the right of the decimal point, you can make the arithmetic easier by writing extra zeros to the right of a decimal number. This may help, especially when you are subtracting. For example, 2.1 has the same value as 2.10 and as 2.100; so 2.1 − 1.476 may be written this way:

$$
\begin{array}{r} 2.100 \\ -\ 1.476 \\ \hline 0.624 \end{array}
$$

If there is no decimal point, it is assumed to be to the right of the ones digit. For example, 23 = 23., 147 = 147., and so on. The ones digit is always just to the left of the decimal point.

Remember that you may write extra zeros to the right of the point and the last digit if it helps to make the arithmetic easier for you. But remember also not to put zeros between 2 digits or between a digit and the decimal point.

Add or subtract. Watch the signs.

1. $23 + 168$
2. $2.3 + 1.68$
3. $2.3 + 16.8$
4. $2.3 - 1.68$
5. $0.23 - 0.168$

6. $0.23 - 0.0168$
7. $23 - 16.8$
8. $23 - 1.68$
9. $230 - 16.8$
10. $41.87 + 3.46$

11. $41.87 - 3.46$
12. $41.87 - 34.6$
13. $41.87 + 34.6$
14. $34 - 2.78$
15. $34 + 27.8$

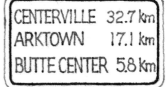

16. Which of the 3 towns mentioned on the road sign is farthest away?

17. How much farther away is Centerville than Arktown?

18. If all 3 towns are on the same straight road that the sign is on, how far is it from Butte Center to Arktown?

19. How far is it from Arktown to Butte Center?

20. If you are in a car at the sign now, and you plan to drive through Butte Center and Arktown to Centerville, how far do you plan to drive altogether?

21. Galina measured the distance from her house to school. It was 2.3 kilometers. The distance from school to Beth's house is 4.8 kilometers. If Galina rides from her house to school to Beth's house, how far will she ride?

22. 2 hoses are each 9.1 meters long. If they are joined together, how long a hose will they make?

23. A kite string is 102.7 meters long. If you cut off a piece 1.4 meters long to tie up a package, how long will the remaining kite string be?

24. You spend $1.12 for hamburger, $1.27 for bread, and $0.98 for milk.

   a. How much is that altogether?
   b. If you gave the cashier a $5 bill, how much change should you get?

25. Edgar lives 2.1 kilometers from the West Side fire station. Olivia lives 0.3 kilometers from the East Side fire station. How far does Edgar live from Olivia?

Add or subtract. Watch the signs.

26. $3.4 + 7.1$
27. $8.26 + 5.74$
28. $19.3 + 8.7$
29. $13.4 - 9.6$
30. $5.7 - 2.8$

31. $8.34 - 5.13$
32. $0.76 + 1.8$
33. $0.76 + 0.18$
34. $0.76 - 0.18$
35. $1.00 - 0.34$

36. $100 - 38$
37. $1 - 0.38$
38. $0.023 + 0.15$
39. $1.004 - 0.9$
40. $100.4 - 90$

41. Mary bought a book for $7.98 and a pencil for 13¢.

    a. How much did she have to pay?
    b. She paid with a $10 bill. What was her change?

42. Bill measured the space in his room between 2 walls to be 3.4 meters. His friend Michael offered to give him a bed and a desk. Michael said the bed was 1.97 meters long and the desk was 1.42 meters long.

    a. How long are the bed and desk together?
    b. Will they fit between the 2 walls in Bill's room?
    c. How much space will be left between the walls?
    d. Suppose Bill measured correctly to the nearest tenth of a meter, but to the nearest hundredth of a meter the walls are 3.42 meters apart. How does that change your answers to questions b and c?
    e. Suppose the walls are 3.38 meters apart when measured to the nearest hundredth of a meter. How does that change your answers to questions b and c?

43. The label on a package of kite string says it is exactly 100 meters long. Nell cut off a piece that was 5.42 meters long. Gwyn cut off a piece that was 7.84 meters long. Meg cut off a piece that was 20.00 meters long.

    a. How much string did the 3 people cut off?
    b. How long should the piece of string that is left be?
    c. They measured the remaining piece of string. It was 67.01 meters long. How much longer or shorter was it than it should have been?

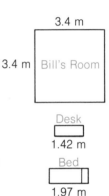

3.4 m

3.4 m | Bill's Room

Desk
1.42 m

Bed
1.97 m

Multiplication of decimals is just like multiplication of whole numbers except that you need to place the decimal point correctly. If you multiply 3.28 by 2.47, you get the digits 81016, but where do you put the point?

One way to decide is to approximate the answer. If you round both numbers down to the nearest whole number and multiply, you get 3 × 2 = 6, and if you round them up and multiply, you get 4 × 3 = 12. So the answer should be between 6 and 12. Put the point after the 8: 8.1016.

A good rule to remember when multiplying is that the number of decimal places to the right of the decimal point in the product is equal to the total number of places to the right of the points in the 2 factors.

$$\underbrace{3}_{} \qquad \underbrace{4}_{} \qquad \underbrace{3 + 4 = 7}_{}$$
$$52.387 \times 0.0346 = 1.8125902$$

Examples

24 × 1.57   There are 0 places to the right of the point in the first factor and 2 in the second factor. So there are 2 places to the right of the point in the product (37.68).

3.756 × 0.24   There are 3 places to the right of the point in the first factor and 2 in the second factor. So there are 5 places to the right of the point in the product (0.90144).

0.306 × 0.6   There are 3 places to the right of the point in the first factor and 1 in the second factor. So there are 4 places to the right of the point in the product (0.1836).

1.75 × 8.008   There are 2 places to the right of the point in the first factor and 3 in the second factor. So there are 5 places to the right in the product (14.01400).

Division with decimals is also much the same as with whole numbers except for placing the decimal point. Suppose you want to find out how many 1.23-meter lengths of string you can cut from a string that is 74.95 meters long.

One way to find the answer is to change the units to centimeters. The problem then becomes how many 123-centimeter lengths you can cut from a string that is 7495 centimeters long. The division problem 1.23$\overline{)74.95}$ has been changed to 123$\overline{)7495}$. The answer is 60 (with some left over) in either case.

A good rule to remember when dividing is that you may move the decimal points in the divisor and dividend the same number of places in the same direction without changing the answer to the problem.

$$82.34.\overline{)7.61.5} \quad \text{or} \quad 8.2.34\overline{).7.615}$$

$$\quad 2 \qquad 2 \qquad\quad 1 \qquad 1$$

Usually you'll move the decimal point in the divisor so that the divisor becomes a whole number. But sometimes, in order to make it easier to approximate the quotient, you'll move the decimal point so that the divisor is a number between 1 and 10.

Examples

364.544 ÷ 8.9   Approximate the answer first. This is about 360 ÷ 9. So the answer will be about 40. Now go back to the original example. Move the points 1 place to the right, getting 3645.44 ÷ 89, and the answer is 40.96.

0.523 ÷ 0.21   Approximate first. Move the points 1 place to the right. This is about 5.23 ÷ 2, or about 2.6. Go back to the original example. Move the points 2 places to the right, getting 52.3 ÷ 21, and the answer is 2.49 (rounded to the nearest hundredth).

3768.32 ÷ 102.4   Approximate first. Move the points 2 places to the left, getting 37.6832 ÷ 1.024. Think: This is about 37.6 ÷ 1. So the answer will be about 37.6. Do the division, 37683.2 ÷ 1024, getting 36.8.

First approximate the answers to these problems. Then multiply.

1. 4.31 × 7.04
2. 43.1 × 0.704
3. 6.12 × 3.74
4. 0.2 × 0.05
5. 4 × 3.2

6. 0.021 × 0.005
7. 34.3 × 0.7
8. 0.4 × 0.8
9. 0.612 × 37.4
10. 3.43 × 0.007

First approximate the answers to these problems. Then divide.

11. 0.2 ÷ 0.05
12. 0.4 ÷ 0.8
13. 3.2 ÷ 4
14. 4 ÷ 3.2
15. 18.4318 ÷ 3.14

16. 80 ÷ 0.4
17. 0.8 ÷ 0.4
18. 0.02 ÷ 0.005
19. 34.3 ÷ 0.7
20. 3.430 ÷ 0.07

21. One box of Wonder Wheat cereal costs $1.37. How much do 3 boxes cost?

22. Kyoko paid $3.62 for 9.3 liters of gasoline. What was the price per liter?

23. Arnold paid $9.35 for 20.2 liters of gasoline. Helga paid $8.45 for 21.7 liters of gasoline. Who paid less per liter, Arnold or Helga?

24. As Ms. Mersenne passed milepost 73 on the Prime Highway, she noticed that her odometer read 034876.4. She drove 100 miles until she passed milepost 173, where her odometer read 034974.3.

    a. How far did her odometer say she had gone?
    b. How much less than 100 miles is that?

MAKE A PROBLEM GAME

Players: 2 or more
Materials: One 5–10 cube, paper, pencil, calculator
Object: To score as close to a goal number as possible

Rules

1. Each player uses blanks to outline the same computation problem and goal. For example:

$$\_\_\_ + \_\_ = 100$$

Any operation and any number of blanks may be used.

2. Take turns rolling the cube. Each time the cube is rolled, write that number in one of the blanks in your outline. Try to fill in the blanks to get as close to the goal as possible.

3. When all the blanks are filled in, you may place decimal points where you like.

4. The player who is closest to the goal wins the game. Calculate exact answers only if necessary.

Sample Game

Vine and Lois chose this problem: $\_\_\_ \times \_\_ = 64$.

Number Rolled	Vine's Outline	Lois's Outline
8	$\_\_\_ \times \underline{8}\,\_$	$\underline{8}\,\_\_ \times \_\_$
6	$\_\_\_ \times \underline{8}\ \underline{6}$	$\underline{8}\ \underline{6}\,\_ \times \_\_$
6	$\underline{6}\,\_\_ \times \underline{8}\ \underline{6}$	$\underline{8}\ \underline{6}\,\_ \times \_\ \underline{6}$
9	$\underline{6}\,\_\ \underline{9} \times \underline{8}\ \underline{6}$	$\underline{8}\ \underline{6}\ \underline{9} \times \_\ \underline{6}$
7	$\underline{6}\ \underline{7}\ \underline{9} \times \underline{8}\ \underline{6}$	$\underline{8}\ \underline{6}\ \underline{9} \times \underline{7}\ \underline{6}$

Vine placed decimal points this way: 6.79×8.6
Lois placed 1 decimal point: $.869 \times 76$

Because they couldn't decide who was closer to 64, they used a calculator. Vine had 58.394 and Lois had 66.044. Lois was the winner.

Approximating Answers

Often in practical situations an approximation is all that's needed for an answer. Even when you take a multiple-choice test, you can often eliminate some alternatives by using approximation.

Decide which answer is correct for each problem by using approximation. Even though some ink has spilled on the page, you can still choose the right answers.

1. $65.4 \times 3.708 =$
   a. 2.425032   b. 24.25032   c. 242.5032   d. 2425.032

2. $5.13 \times 61.04 =$
   a. 313.1352   b. 31.31352   c. 3.131352   d. 0.131352

3. $7.85 \div 62.8 =$
   a. 12.5   b. 1.25   c. 0.125   d. 0.0125

4. $0.01411 \div 0.0017 =$
   a. 83   b. 8.3   c. 0.83   d. 0.083

5. $3.41 \times 61.$
   a. 0.2   b. 2.109767   c. 21.09767   d. 210.9767

6. $58.12 \times 3.$
   a. 21.73   b. 217.3688   c. 2173.688   d. 21736.88

7. $43.78 \div 0.022 =$
   a. 1.99   b. 19.9   c. 199   d. 1990

8. $56.088 \div 0.1$
   a. 4.56   b. 45.6   c. 456   d. 4560

9. $1000 \div 0.001 =$
   a. 1,000,000   b. 100,000   c. 10,000   d. 0.000001

10. $0.003 \times 0.0005 =$
   a. 0.015   b. 0.00015   c. 0.000015   d. 0.0000015

Solve. Remember to round answers appropriately.

1. Pat picked up a package of hamburger that weighed 0.68 kilograms. The label showed that hamburger cost $4.73 per kilogram, but it didn't give a price for the package. How much should the package of hamburger cost?

2. Mike bought 1.46 kilograms of hamburger for $7.27. The package didn't show the cost per kilogram, but Mike wanted to know what it was.

   a. How much was Mike's hamburger per kilogram?
   b. How much more or less per kilogram of hamburger did Mike pay than Pat?

3. Mrs. Saheed bought a 0.296-liter bottle of orange juice for $0.25. How much does the orange juice cost per liter?

4. Leann got 136 hits in 452 times at bat. What was her batting average? (Hint: To find a batting average, divide the number of hits by the number of times at bat and round the answer to the nearest thousandth.)

5. If Leann goes on hitting at the same rate, about how many hits would you expect her to get in the next 100 times at bat?

6. In Brightsville, electricity costs $1.03 per unit. If the meter shows you used 47.6 units this month, what should your electricity bill be?

7. In Dullsville, electricity costs $2.47 per unit. How much would you pay there for 47.6 units of electricity?

8. Someone in Grayville paid $93.77 for 47.6 units of electricity one month. How much does electricity cost per unit in Grayville?

Add.

1.	37	**2.**	137	**3.**	58	**4.**	258
	63		263		58		258
	+ 49		+ 349		+ 58		+ 258

Subtract.

5.	3000	**6.**	6001	**7.**	6893	**8.**	8001
	− 1753		− 607		− 233		− 998

Multiply.

9.	654	**10.**	349	**11.**	349	**12.**	1063
	× 32		× 11		× 22		× 55

Divide.

13. $73\overline{)16863}$ **14.** $52\overline{)6968}$ **15.** $31\overline{)20646}$ **16.** $21\overline{)13734}$

Do these problems. Watch the signs. Use shortcuts when you can.

17.	5466	**18.**	5466	**19.**	5466	**20.** $64\overline{)9280}$
	+ 1017		− 1017		× 1017	

21. $128\overline{)18560}$

22.	908	**23.**	908	**24.**	908
	× 202		+ 202		× 202

Solve for n. Don't forget the point.

25. $8.3 + 0.74 + 28.14 = n$
26. $43.07 − 1.4 = n$
27. $54.66 × 1.017 = n$
28. $9.280 ÷ 64 = n$
29. $n = 3.2 ÷ 0.08$
30. $n = 0.32 ÷ 0.8$

MAKE 25 GAME

Players: 2 or more
Materials: Two 0–5 cubes, two 5–10 cubes, a calculator
Object: To get the product closest to 25

Rules

1. Take turns rolling all 4 cubes. If you roll a **10** , roll that cube again.

2. Use each number once to make two 2-digit numbers whose product is close to 25. You may make decimals. Do not make calculations with a calculator or with pencil and paper in making these numbers.

3. The player with the product closest to 25 wins the round. Use a calculator or pencil and paper to check the products only if necessary.

Sample Game

Alicia rolled: **0** **1** **5** **7**
She made: 5.1 × 7.0

Jorge rolled: **1** **5** **5** **2**
He made: 5.1 × 5.2

Alicia and Jorge knew that 5.1 × 7.0 is about 35 and that 5.1 × 5.2 is only a little more than 25. So they knew that Jorge was the winner of the round. If the products had been closer, Alicia and Jorge would have checked them on a calculator.

Applications

For the following problems, approximate the answers first. Sometimes that removes the need for actually doing the calculation.

1. You have $20. You plan to buy the following groceries:

   2 containers of milk at $1.05 each
   1 box of cereal at $1.53
   1 loaf of bread at $1.49
   1 jar of popcorn at $1.99
   $5 worth of hamburger
   1 box of oatmeal at $1.55
   1 box of crackers at $1.39
   3 cans of soup at 89¢ each

   About how much change can you expect from your $20 bill?

2. At another time you go to the store with a $20 bill to buy the following items:

   5 containers of milk at $1.05 each
   1 can of grapefruit juice at 79¢
   1 package of cheese at $1.43
   $7.50 worth of meat
   1 jar of peanut butter at $4.69
   2 bags of apples at $1.19 each

   How much change should you receive?

3. Which items listed in problem 2 would you have to put back before you could pay for everything else with your $20 bill?

4. A can of Back Bay Clam Chowder costs 89¢. How many cans could you buy for $20?

5. A jar of Munchy-Crunchy peanut butter costs $4.69. How many jars could you buy for $20?

Ms. Soong wants to paint her bedroom walls and ceiling. The ceiling is about 2.40 meters high, the north and south walls are about 3.25 meters long, and the east and west walls are about 4.15 meters long. A 4-liter can of paint will cover about 40 square meters, according to the instructions on the can. She wants to know how many cans of paint she should buy.

Work in groups to discuss the following questions.

[1] **What is the area of the 4 walls and ceiling of Ms. Soong's room?**

[2] a. **Do you suppose she has a door and windows in the room?**
    b. **Do you think she wants to paint the door or doors?**
    c. **Do you think she wants to paint the windows?**
    d. **Does that mean she probably will be painting a smaller area than that suggested by your answer to question 1?**
    e. **If so, how much smaller will the area be?**

[3] a. **Do you think she could "stretch" the paint by thinning it a bit more than the manufacturer expects?**
    b. **Do you think she might use more paint by putting it on a bit more thickly than expected?**

[4] **How many cans would you advise Ms. Soong to buy?**

[5] a. **What is the perimeter (the distance around something) of the room?**
    b. **Could the area of the walls be found by multiplying 14.80 × 2.40?**

[6] **If the paint costs $14.98 for a 4-liter can, how much will the paint for Ms. Soong's room cost?**

What does *one hundred percent* mean?

Usually, one hundred percent is written 100%. The symbol % stands for "percent," or "per hundred." If a cereal is 100% wheat, that means that out of 100 parts, all 100 are wheat. So that cereal is all wheat and nothing but wheat. If another cereal is 1% wheat, that means that out of 100 parts, only 1 is wheat.

1. What does 50% wheat mean? What fraction corresponds to 50 out of 100?

2. What does 25% mean? What fraction corresponds to 25 out of 100?

3. What does 75% mean? What fraction corresponds to 75 out of 100?

A sales tax rate is given in percent. Suppose you must pay a 5% sales tax. This means you must pay 5¢ tax for every 100¢ you spend for something. If the price of an item is $15, you would pay a tax of 15 × 5¢, or 75¢, in addition to the $15.

Each of the following problems shows a price and a sales tax rate. In each case, tell what the sales tax would be.

4. $5, 5% tax
5. $27, 1% tax
6. $27, 2% tax
7. $34, 7% tax
8. $53, 4% tax

9. $20, 3% tax
10. $25, 4% tax
11. $16, 6% tax
12. $23, 2% tax
13. $20, 5% tax

14. $10, 7% tax
15. $10, 8% tax
16. $15, 7% tax
17. $20, 7% tax
18. $34, 6% tax

Percents, Fractions, and Decimals

Percents, fractions, and decimals can all be used to represent the same thing. It often is more natural or easier to use one than another. So we should be able to convert easily from one to another. Since you understand that *percent* means "per hundred," the following rules should seem reasonable to you.

A. To convert from a percent to a decimal, drop the % symbol and move the decimal point (write it in, if necessary) 2 places to the left. Reverse the procedure to convert from a decimal to a percent.

B. To convert a fraction to a percent, take that fraction of 100. To convert a percent to a fraction, drop the % symbol and write the numerical part over 100. Reduce if appropriate.

C. To convert a fraction to a decimal, you divide numerator by denominator. To convert a decimal with n digits at the right of the point to a fraction, write the number without the point over 10^n. Reduce if appropriate.

Copy and complete this table of equivalent decimals, fractions, and percents. Approximate decimals and percents to 3 places.

	Decimal	Fraction	Percent			Decimal	Fraction	Percent
1.	0.333	$\frac{1}{3}$	33.3%	**11.**			$\frac{2}{3}$	
2.	0.25			**12.**	1.5		
3.		$\frac{3}{4}$		**13.**			200%
4.			50%	**14.**		$\frac{1}{10}$	
5.		$\frac{1}{8}$	12.5%	**15.**	2.6		
6.	0.375		37.5%	**16.**	12		
7.	0.625		62.5%	**17.**			650%
8.			87.5%	**18.**	0.20		
9.	0.01		1%	**19.**		$\frac{3}{5}$	
10.			5%	**20.**			80%

How are percents used in these situations?

Can you think of other times when percents are used? You can calculate how much a percent of something is by changing the percent to a decimal and multiplying. This is particularly easy on a calculator.

Example: Calculate 23% of $76.84.
Remember that 23% means 23 per hundred, or $\frac{23}{100}$, or 0.23.
Use a calculator to multiply 0.23 × 76.84.

You'll get 17.6732. Round this to the nearest hundredth (or cent), and the answer is $17.67.

Use whatever procedure you like to do the following. Most can be done in your head.

1. The cost of a $20 book with a 35% discount
2. The cost of a $24.98 item with a 20% discount
3. 5% sales tax on $20
4. 5% sales tax on $19.98
5. 5% sales tax on $25
6. 5% sales tax on $24.98
7. The cost of a $26.25 item with a 20% discount
8. The cost of a $26.23 item with a 20% discount
9. The cost of a $20 item with a 5% discount and 5% sales tax

10. Mr. Brown was visiting his brother in a different state. He bought a tube of toothpaste that had a price tag of $1.78. The clerk charged him $1.87. Assume the clerk was honest and had not made an error.

    a. What could be the cause of this difference?

    b. What do you think the sales tax rate is in this place? (Hint: The clerk probably multiplied the sales tax rate by 1.78 to get the tax. So you should be able to divide the tax [9¢, or $0.09] by 1.78 to get the rate. The clerk also probably rounded to the nearest cent. You should round your answer to an approximate answer.)

11. Ms. Rose bought a book that was marked $9.98. She was charged $10.38. What is the sales tax rate?

12. Miss Sullivan knows her bank pays 5% interest each year. She just got a statement saying she was credited with $23.65 interest last year. She knows she didn't deposit or withdraw money during the year.

    a. How much money did she have in the bank last year (before the $23.65 was added)? This is called the principal. (Hint: The bank multiplied 0.05 times the principal to get 23.65. So you can divide 23.65 by 0.05 to get the principal.)

    b. With the additional interest how much does she have now?

    c. Could your answer be off by 5¢? By 10¢? If all calculations were correct, what is the most your answer could be off by?

Find the missing information in each table. Round your answers appropriately.

13.

	Price	Cost	Sales Tax Rate
a.	$ 2.84	$ 2.95	
b.	$12.78	$13.16	

14.

	Price	Sales Tax	Sales Tax Rate
a.	$4.89	$0.34	
b.	$6.25		5%

15.

	Principal	Interest Rate	Interest
a.		5% per year	$17.50
b.	$160	$5\frac{1}{2}$% per year	
c.		6% per year	$51.36
d.	$180		$11.70

Sometimes percents can be calculated quickly in your head. To figure out how much a tip should be or to check whether the amount of sales tax is correct, it's handy to be able to do percents without paper or pencil.

Examples

10% of $54.00	Simply divide by 10. Just move the decimal point 1 place to the left. $5.4␣00 → $5.40
10% of $53.78	Again divide by 10. Move the point 1 place to the left. $5.3␣78 → $5.378 But this time we'll have to round. Sometimes we round to the lesser cent, sometimes to the next cent. $5.378 rounds to $5.38
20% of $54.00	Divide by 10 as above. Then multiply the answer by 2. $5.4␣00 → $5.40 × 2 = $10.80
20% of $53.78	Divide by 10 and multiply by 2. $5.3␣78 → $5.378 → $5.38 × 2 = $10.76 Sometimes, because of rounding, the answer may be off by a cent or two.
5% of $54.00	Divide by 10, then divide by 2. $5.4␣00 → $5.40 ÷ 2 = $2.70
5% of $53.78	Divide by 10 and then by 2. $5.3␣78 → $5.378 → $5.38 ÷ 2 = $2.69 Again, because of rounding, the answer may be off by a cent or two.
15% of $54.00	Add 10% of $54.00 and 5% of $54.00. $5.40 + $2.70 = $8.10
15% of $53.78	Add 10% of $53.78 and 5% of $53.78. $5.38 + $2.69 = $8.07

Do each calculation in your head. Write only the answer.

1. 10% of $92.00	**5.** 10% of $48.00	**9.** 20% of $4848.00
2. 15% of $92.00	**6.** 20% of $48.00	**10.** 5% of $4848.00
3. 10% of $92.80	**7.** 10% of $4800.00	**11.** 10% of $126.00
4. 15% of $92.80	**8.** 10% of $4848.00	**12.** 15% of $126.00

Do these problems. Use shortcuts when you can.

1. **a.** What is the original price of the glove?
   b. What is the sale price of the glove?
   c. If the sales tax is 4%, what will be the total cost of the glove, including sales tax?

$20 SALE 25% OFF

2. **a.** What is the original price of the camera?
   b. What is the sale price of the camera?
   c. If the sales tax is 6%, what will be the total cost?

$79.98 SALE 20% OFF

3. **a.** What is the original price of the jacket?
   b. What is the sale price of the jacket?
   c. If the sales tax is 5%, what will be the total cost?
   d. Suppose you added the 5% sales tax first and then took 5% off the cost because of the sale. How much would you pay?

$100 SALE 5% OFF

4. **a.** What is the original price of the lamp?
   b. What is the sale price of the lamp? (Read the ad carefully before you answer.)
   c. If the sales tax is 5%, what will be the total cost?
   d. If you added the 5% sales tax first and then subtracted $20, what would you pay?

$59.95 SALE $20 OFF

5. Mr. Millikin gave his class a spelling test with 25 words. Diana got 25 right, Cheryl got 23 right, Cedric got 22 right, and Laurie got 19 right. What percentage did each of these students get right?

6. Bob made the following table for 5 spelling tests. The results show the number of correct words out of the number of words in each test.

Test	Results	Percentage Correct
1	24 out of 25	
2	19 out of 20	
3	47 out of 50	
4	30 out of 32	
5	34 out of 36	

    a. Calculate his percentage of correct answers for each test.
    b. On which test did Bob get the most right?
    c. On which test did Bob get the greatest percentage right?
    d. On which test did Bob get the smallest percentage right?

7. In Betsy's class, you need a 90% average to get an A. She made a table for 5 tests.

Test	Number Correct	Number of Questions	Percentage Correct
1	18	20	
2	38	40	
3	6	10	
4	23	25	
5	36	40	

    a. Calculate the percentage correct on each test.
    b. What is the average of those 5 test scores?
    c. What is the total number of her correct answers on the 5 tests?
    d. What is the total number of questions on the 5 tests?
    e. What is her percentage correct out of the total of 135 questions?
    f. Should Betsy get an A?

TIPS GAME

Players: 2 or more
Materials: Two 0–5 cubes, two 5–10 cubes
Object: To make the most money on tips

Rules

1. Each player is waiting on customers in a restaurant and will get 5 tips. 1 tip will be 10%, 3 tips will be 15%, and 1 tip will be 20%.

2. Roll all 4 cubes. Find the bill for 1 of the customers by making an amount of money in dollars and cents. A `10` can be used anywhere in the amount of money, but it will have to be regrouped if it is not in the place for tens of dollars. For example, if you roll `10` `9` `5` `5`, you could make $109.55 (`10` `9` `5` `5`), $100.55 (`9` `10` `5` `5`), $96.05 (`9` `5` `10` `5`), or several other amounts of money.

3. Decide which tip you'll get from this customer. Then calculate the tip. Keep a record of your tips.

4. After 5 rounds, add the tips.

5. The player with the most money from tips wins.

Sample Game

Round	Tyler Rolled	Made	%	Tip	Jo Rolled	Made	%	Tip
1	8 3 7 3	$ 87.33	15	$13.10	5 3 0 10	$105.30	20	$21.06
2	1 5 5 6	$ 65.51	15	$ 9.83	8 5 8 4	$ 88.54	15	$13.28
3	1 6 4 10	$106.41	20	$21.28	3 9 6 2	$ 96.32	15	$14.45
4	5 8 5 4	$ 85.54	10	$ 8.55	5 10 10 5	$110.55	15	$16.58
5	10 0 8 2	$108.20	15	$16.23	9 0 5 2	$ 95.20	10	$ 9.52
			Total	$68.99			Total	$74.89

Jo was the winner.

Copy and complete this table of equivalent decimals, fractions, and percents. Round decimals and percents to 3 places to the right of the decimal point when necessary.

	Decimal	Fraction	Percent
1.	0.15	■	■
2.	■	$\frac{1}{4}$	■
3.	■	■	37%
4.	■	$\frac{1}{5}$	■
5.	0.28	■	■
6.	■	$\frac{1}{3}$	■
7.	■	■	3%
8.	■	$\frac{1}{6}$	■
9.	0.36	■	■
10.	■	$\frac{2}{3}$	■
11.	■	■	1000%
12.	■	$\frac{2}{9}$	■
13.	1.03	■	■
14.	■	$\frac{3}{2}$	■
15.	■	■	425%
16.	■	$\frac{3}{3}$	■
17.	0.04	■	■
18.	■	$\frac{2}{5}$	■
19.	■	■	$3\frac{1}{2}$%
20.	■	$\frac{6}{5}$	■

Mark had a package of radish seeds that was 15 years old. He wanted to know if the seeds would germinate as well as new seeds. So he did the following experiment:

A. He bought a package of the same brand and variety of new seeds.

B. He counted the number of seeds in each package. There were 324 in the package of old seeds and 135 in the package of new seeds.

C. He made 2 germination trays by placing moist paper towels in the bottom of 2 large baking pans.

D. He saved 3 seeds from each package and sprinkled the rest in the germination trays. He put the old seeds in one tray and the new ones in the other.

E. Each day at about the same time he counted the number of seeds that had germinated (those in which a white root appeared). Then he removed them from the germination trays and planted them in his garden. He recorded his results in a table.

Here is Mark's table.

	New Seeds		Old Seeds	
Day	Number Germinated	Cumulative Number Germinated	Number Germinated	Cumulative Number Germinated
0	0	0	0	0
1	10	10	1	1
2	59	69	38	39
3	45	114	44	83
4	7	121	20	103
5	0	121	11	114
6	1	122	9	123
7	1	123	7	130
8	0	123	4	134
9	0	123	0	134
10	0	123	3	137
11	0	123	1	138
12	0	123	0	138
13	0	123	0	138
14	0	123	0	138
15	0	123	0	138

Use Mark's data to discuss and answer the following questions.

[1] **Do you think a significant number of additional seeds would have germinated had Mark continued his experiment past 15 days?**

[2] **Did more new seeds or old seeds germinate?**

[3] **Which group of seeds, the old or the new, had a higher percentage germination?**

[4] **Which group of seeds, the old or the new, germinated more quickly?**

[5] **If Mark tries to germinate the 3 seeds from each group that he saved, can he be confident that more of the new seeds will germinate and that they will germinate more quickly than the old seeds?**

Mark decided that it would be easier to compare the germination of old and new seeds if he first changed the number germinated in his table to the percentage of seeds that germinated. For the new seeds, he divided the number germinated by 132 (the number of seeds he started with). For the old seeds, he divided by 321. He moved the point 2 places to the right to change these decimals to percents.

Copy and complete Mark's chart. Use a calculator if you have one.

| | New Seeds (132) | | Old Seeds (321) | |
Day	% Germinated	Cumulative % Germinated	% Germinated	Cumulative % Germinated
0	0	0	0	0
1	7.6	7.6	0.3	0.3
2	44.7	52.3	11.8	12.1
3	34.1	▓	▓	▓
4	▓	▓	▓	▓
5	▓	▓	▓	▓
6	▓	▓	▓	▓
7	▓	▓	▓	▓
8	▓	▓	▓	▓
9	▓	▓	▓	▓
10	▓	▓	▓	▓
11	▓	▓	▓	▓
12	▓	▓	▓	▓
13	▓	▓	▓	▓
14	▓	▓	▓	▓
15	▓	▓	▓	▓

Use your new table to discuss and answer the following questions.

[6] **Which data are easier to analyze, those in the table on page 122 or those in your new table? Why?**

[7] **Was it necessary for Mark to use all or almost all of his seeds to find out how each group germinated? For example, could he have used only 1 seed from each group? 5 seeds? 50 seeds? 100 seeds? 150 seeds? More than 150 seeds?**

[8] **If you were going to do an experiment like this one, how could you design it so that you wouldn't have to calculate percentages to get data that are easy to use?**

Compute.

1. 2^6 **2.** 4^3 **3.** 25^3 **4.** 5^7 **5.** 2^{10} **6.** 3^4

Copy and complete these function charts.

7. 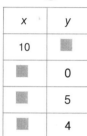 x —⊘4→ y **8.** x —⊗3→ y **9.** x —⊘2→ y **10.** x —⊗4→ n —⊘8→ y

x	y
10	▦
▦	0
▦	5
▦	4

x	y
5	▦
10	▦
▦	9
▦	12

x	y
4	▦
10	▦
▦	3
▦	0

x	y
5	▦
10	▦
▦	0
▦	20

Compute. Round answers to the nearest hundredth.

11. $2.34 + 21.8$ **16.** $0.20 \div 0.4$ **21.** $1 + 0.25$
12. $15.7 - 3.46$ **17.** 0.20×0.4 **22.** 1×0.25
13. $25 - 4.81$ **18.** $0.20 + 0.4$ **23.** $1 \div 0.25$
14. 1.2×0.4 **19.** $0.4 - 0.2$ **24.** $4.2 - 1.68$
15. $1.2 \div 0.4$ **20.** $1 - 0.25$ **25.** $4.2 + 1.68$

For each price and sales tax rate, give the amount of sales tax.

26. \$10 at 5%   **30.** \$25 at 4%   **34.** \$6.23 at 2%
27. \$100 at 7%   **31.** \$25.50 at 4%   **35.** \$6.23 at 4%
28. \$23 at 1%   **32.** \$25.25 at 4%   **36.** \$6.23 at 6%
29. \$23 at 2%   **33.** \$6.23 at 1%   **37.** \$6.23 at 8%

38. Leo and Andy both bought jeans on sale. Here are their tags: Leo's:  Andy's:

Who paid less for jeans?

39. Erica bought an art set that was priced at \$20.00. How much did it cost if the sales tax in her city is 5%?

40. Greta and Edna had dinner with their parents at a restaurant. The bill was \$25.86. Everyone agreed that they should leave a 15% tip. Greta said to leave about \$4. Edna said it should be \$3. Who was right?

Teresa was practicing estimating. She estimated the length of a pencil, the length of her desk, and then the length of the classroom. Each time she was off by just 1 centimeter.

"I guess I am not getting any better at making estimates," she said.

Does Teresa's statement make sense? Try estimating the length of a pencil, a desk, and a classroom. Measure to check.

Here's a way to help get an idea of how good an estimate is:

A. Find out how big the error is. (That is, find the difference between the estimate and the actual amount.)

Teresa estimated that the desk was 65 centimeters long. The length actually was 64 centimeters. She found out how big the error was.

$$65 \text{ cm} - 64 \text{ cm} = 1 \text{ cm}$$

B. Find out what percentage the error is of the actual amount. (That is, divide the difference by the actual amount and multiply by 100.) This is called *percent error*. Sometimes we write *% error*.

Teresa used a calculator to find the percent error.

$$\frac{1}{64} \cdot (100) = 1.5625$$

She rounded this to the nearest percent, getting 1.6% error.

Make an estimate. Then measure the actual amount. Find your percent error. Make a chart like the one below to record your results. Repeat the process. See whether the percent error gets smaller as you practice estimating.

	Estimate	Actual Measurement	Percent Error
Length of classroom			
Width of classroom			
Length of chalkboard			
Weight of piece of chalk			
(Choice of other things)			

Compute.

1. 2^7 **2.** 5^5 **3.** 25^4 **4.** 7^5 **5.** 2^9 **6.** 4^4

Copy and complete these function charts.

7. $x \longrightarrow (+4) \longrightarrow y$ **8.** $x \longrightarrow (-3) \longrightarrow y$ **9.** $x \longrightarrow (\div 2) \longrightarrow y$ **10.** $x \longrightarrow (\times 2) \longrightarrow n \longrightarrow (-10) \longrightarrow y$

x	y
5	▩
10	▩
0	▩
▩	10

x	y
10	▩
▩	0
▩	5
▩	4

x	y
6	▩
12	▩
▩	10
▩	1

x	y
5	▩
10	▩
▩	0
▩	20

Compute. Round answers to the nearest hundredth.

11. $1.23 + 32.9$ **16.** $0.80 \div 0.4$ **21.** $2 + 0.25$
12. $15.8 - 3.58$ **17.** 0.80×0.4 **22.** 2×0.25
13. $35 - 3.02$ **18.** $0.80 + 0.4$ **23.** $2 \div 0.25$
14. 2.4×0.2 **19.** $0.8 - 0.4$ **24.** $2.4 - 1.86$
15. $2.4 \div 0.2$ **20.** $2 - 0.25$ **25.** $2.4 + 1.86$

For each price and sales tax rate, give the amount of sales tax.

26. \$20 at 5%   **30.** \$50 at 6%   **34.** \$8.48 at 2%
27. \$200 at 7%   **31.** \$50.50 at 6%   **35.** \$8.48 at 4%
28. \$42 at 1%   **32.** \$50.50 at 3%   **36.** \$8.48 at 6%
29. \$42 at 2%   **33.** \$8.48 at 1%   **37.** \$8.48 at 8%

38. Manuel bought a pair of jeans that were priced at \$30.00. How much did the jeans cost if the sales tax in his city is 6%?

39. Martha put 21 liters of gasoline at 39¢ a liter in her car. Joan put 19 liters of gasoline at 37¢ a liter in her car. Did Martha or Joan have the larger gasoline bill?

40. Lew took his parents to the Western Wagon Restaurant for dinner. Their bill was \$23.96. Lew said that he'd leave a 15% tip. What would he leave?

    a. 4¢   **b.** 36¢   **c.** \$3.60   **d.** \$6.30

You can use percent error to decide who makes the best approximation when you play the Approximation Game (on page 89). Instead of using the score system described in the game, use a calculator to find the percent error of each approximation. The winner is the player with the smallest percent error.

Sample Game

Problem: 387 × 5964   (Correct answer: 2,308,068)

Player	Guess	Percent Error
Simon	2,000,000	13.3%
Jed	2,400,000	4.0%
Karla	2,300,000	0.3% (less than 1%)
Leah	2,320,000	0.5% (less than 1%)
Jeanette	230,800	90.0%

Karla was the winner, and Leah was next, followed by Jed, Simon, and Jeanette.

Usually, any guess that produces a 1% error or less is very good (or very lucky, or both).

CHAPTER 4
GEOMETRY

If you have to travel from Riverdale to Bellvale, you probably would like to know the *distance* between them. You would also want to know in what *direction* to go.

There are many different ways to describe directions.

From Riverdale, on this map, point C is north. (Many maps have a small arrow pointing to the north like the one between A and B on this map.) So if you know that Bellvale is straight north of Riverdale and that it is also at one of the points shown on this map, then you know that Bellvale is at C.

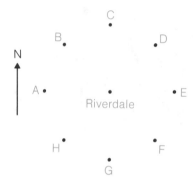

[1] **Which of these points is directly east of Riverdale?**

[2] **Which point is west of Riverdale?**

[3] **Which point is south of Riverdale?**

[4] **Which point is northeast of Riverdale?**

[5] **Which point is southwest of Riverdale?**

[6] **Riverdale is north of which point?**

[7] **Riverdale is south of which point?**

[8] **Riverdale is southwest of which point?**

[9] **Riverdale is northeast of which point?**

Sometimes airplane pilots use an imaginary clock face to describe the relative position of other airplanes or other objects. Something that is straight ahead is "at 12 o'clock." Something that is straight behind is at 6 o'clock, something to the right is at 3 o'clock, and so on.

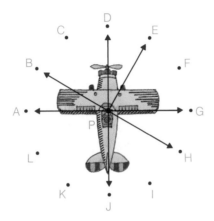

[10] **Which point is at 2 o'clock relative to this airplane?**

[11] **Which point is at 12 o'clock?**

[12] **Which point is at 8 o'clock?**

[13] **How would the pilot describe the direction of point _A_?**

[14] **How would the pilot describe the direction of point _C_?**

[15] **If the plane is flying north, what is the direction of _G_ from the plane?**

[16] **If the plane is flying south, what is the direction of _G_ from the plane?**

From the pilot's point of view, if point _D_ is straight ahead, points _G_ and _A_ are directly to the sides and _J_ is directly behind. We call angles _DPA, DPG, APJ, BPE, HPE,_ and so on _right angles._ Angles _DPJ, APG,_ and _BPH_ are called _straight angles._ _P_ is the _vertex_ of each of these angles.

[17] **Name 2 right angles with _P_ as the vertex and _E_ on one side. You can use the corner of a piece of paper to check to see if an angle is a right angle.**

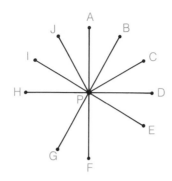

1. There are 9 right angles in the figure. Name all of them. (Note: *IPB* is a right angle, but you may not also count angle *BPI*. Since angle *IPB* and angle *BPI* are the same angle, you should only count it once.)

2. If *A* is north of *P*, what is the direction of
   a. *D* from *P*?   **d.** *P* from *A*?   **g.** *P* from *H*?
   b. *F* from *P*?   **e.** *P* from *D*?   **h.** *D* from *H*?
   c. *H* from *P*?   **f.** *P* from *F*?   **i.** *F* from *A*?

3. Suppose you are the pilot of a plane at *P* going toward *A*. You would say that *A* is "at 12:00 o'clock." Describe each of the following points:
   a. *B*   **d.** *E*   **g.** *H*
   b. *C*   **e.** *F*   **h.** *I*
   c. *D*   **f.** *G*   **i.** *J*

4. The airplane at *P* is headed toward *A*. *A* is north of *P*. What is the direction of
   a. *D* from *P*?   **b.** *F* from *P*?   **c.** *H* from *P*?

5. If *A* is south of *P*, what is the direction of
   a. *D* from *P*?   **b.** *F* from *P*?   **c.** *H* from *P*?

6. If *A* is east of *P*, what is the direction of
   a. *D* from *P*?   **b.** *F* from *P*?   **c.** *H* from *P*?

7. If *A* is west of *P*, what is the direction of
   a. *D* from *P*?   **b.** *F* from *P*?   **c.** *H* from *P*?

Angles are often measured in degrees. When the minute hand on a clock makes 1 complete revolution (as it does every hour), we say that it has turned, or rotated, 360 degrees. We write this as 360°.

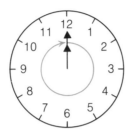

8. How many degrees does the minute hand turn in half an hour? We say there are 180° in a straight angle.

9. How many degrees does the minute hand turn in a quarter of an hour?

10. How many degrees are in a right angle?

11. How many degrees does the minute hand turn in 1 minute?

12. How many degrees does the minute hand turn in 5 minutes?

13. How many degrees does the hour hand turn in 1 hour?

14. How many degrees does the minute hand turn in 10 minutes?

15. How many degrees does the minute hand turn in 20 minutes?

16. How many degrees does the minute hand turn in 45 minutes?

17. How many degrees does the minute hand turn in 40 minutes?

How many degrees does the minute hand turn in 15 minutes?

No matter where the minute hand starts, it rotates 90° in 15 minutes.

At 8:00 P.M. we could say the hour hand has moved, or rotated, 240° since 12:00 o'clock (noon). We could also say it has 120° to go before 12:00 o'clock (midnight). We could even say it has rotated 600° since 12:00 o'clock (midnight last night), and so on.

Each angle could be said to have many different measures. In the clock, the smallest angle between the minute hand and the hour hand is 120°. There is always an angle between the 2 hands that is less than or equal to 180°. For simplicity, we say that this is the angle between the hands.

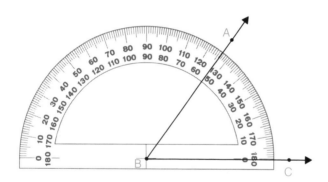

A protractor is an instrument for measuring angles. To measure an angle (∠ABC), place the protractor so that the center dot or hole is over the vertex (B) of the angle and the base line of the protractor is on one side (BC) of the angle. Where the other side (AB) of the angle crosses the scale, you will find the measure of the angle.

In this case, the measure of the angle seems to be between 120° and 130° *or* between 50° and 60°.

[1] Which is correct?

[2] Is the angle greater than or less than a right angle (90°)?

Since it is less than a right angle, the measure of this angle is between 50° and 60°. It is about 54°.

Most protractors have 2 scales. For this reason, you can put the base line of the protractor on either side of an angle and still read the measure easily.

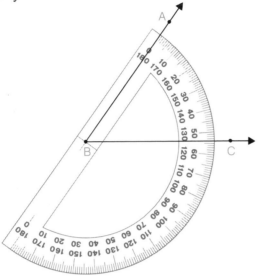

Let's place the base line of the protractor along the other side (*AB*) of angle *ABC*. This time the base line is on side *AB*, and side *BC* crosses the scale at the measure of the angle. Again, the measure of the angle is either between 50° and 60° or between 120° and 130°. We know it is between 50° and 60° because we can see that the angle is less than a right angle. So the measure of ∠*ABC* is about 54°.

Angles that have measures less than 90° are called *acute angles.* Angles with measures between 90° and 180° are called *obtuse angles.* Right angles measure 90°, and straight angles measure 180°.

We use the symbol ∠ to stand for an angle. An angle is named by its vertex or by a point on one side followed by the vertex followed by a point on the other side. The angle on this page could be called ∠*B*, ∠*ABC*, or ∠*CBA*. It could not be called ∠*BAC* or ∠*CAB*.

To make it easier to write or talk about angles, we often say that the angle is the measure of the angle. So we say that angle *ABC* is 54° or, even shorter, ∠*ABC* = 54°.

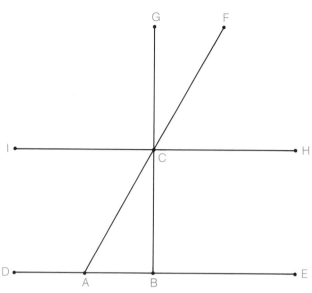

First tell whether each of the following angles is acute, right, obtuse, or straight. Then find the measure of each angle (in degrees).

1. ∠*CAB*
2. ∠*CAD*
3. ∠*CBA*
4. ∠*CBE*
5. ∠*ACB*
6. ∠*GCF*
7. ∠*FCH*

8. ∠*ACI*
9. ∠*DAB*
10. ∠*ICH*
11. ∠*ICG*
12. ∠*HCB*
13. ∠*ICF*
14. ∠*ACH*

Remember

The name of the vertex point is always in the middle.

You have just measured 14 angles. Let's try to find some relationships among some of those angles.

15. What would you expect the sum of angles *CAD* and *CAB* to be? What is the sum of the measures you reported for those angles?

16. Answer the questions in problem 15 for angles *CBA* and *CBE*.

Two angles are called *supplementary angles* if their sum is 180°.

17. Look at the figure. What do you think the sum of angles *ICG*, *GCF*, and *FCH* is? Add your measures for those angles. Is the sum about what you expected?

18. Line *IH* is *parallel* to line *DE*. That is, the lines go in the same direction. What would you expect the relationship between angles *FCH* and *FAE* to be? Check your measurements. What did you find?

19. Answer the questions in problem 18 for angles *GCI* and *GBD*.

20. What would you guess about the relationship between angles *ICA* and *FCH*? Check your measurements. What did you find?

21. Answer the questions in problem 20 for angles *ACB* and *GCF*.

Angles that are formed by 2 intersecting straight lines and are opposite each other are called *vertical angles*.

Angles *ACB* and *GCF* are vertical angles. So are angles *ICA* and *FCH*.

Vertical angles have equal measure. We say they are equal, or *congruent*.

22. Find another pair of vertical angles in the figure. Are they equal?

We sometimes label angles with a single numeral or other symbol so that we can refer to them easily. For example, in the figure below, $\angle CGA$ could also be called $\angle 1$ and $\angle AGD$ could be called $\angle 2$.

1. What is another name for each of the following angles?

   a. $\angle DGB$
   b. $\angle 4$
   c. $\angle AHF$
   d. $\angle 5$
   e. $\angle 8$
   f. $\angle FHB$

2. Which 2 lines in the figure might be parallel?

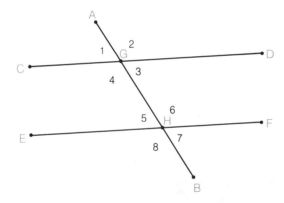

   Lines CD and EF are parallel.

3. What do you think is true about $\angle 2$ and $\angle 6$? Measure to see if you're right.

4. What do you think is true about $\angle 1$ and $\angle 5$? Measure to see if you're right.

When a line crosses 2 other lines, it is called a *transversal*. AB is a transversal of lines CD and EF.

   Angles in corresponding positions when a transversal crosses 2 lines are called *corresponding angles*. $\angle 1$ and $\angle 5$ are corresponding angles. $\angle 4$ and $\angle 8$ are corresponding angles.

5. Name 2 more pairs of corresponding angles.

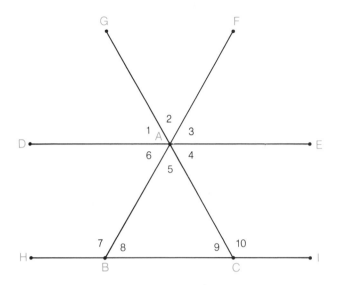

When a transversal crosses parallel lines, the corresponding angles are equal.

In the figure, if *DE* and *HI* are parallel, then $\angle 1 = \angle 9$ (or $\angle GAD = \angle GCH$).

Remember, vertical angles are equal. So, $\angle 1 = \angle 4$. If $\angle 1 = \angle 4$ and $\angle 1 = \angle 9$, what is the relationship between $\angle 4$ and $\angle 9$?

Angles 4 and 9 are called *alternate interior angles*. When a transversal crosses parallel lines, alternate interior angles are equal.

[1] Name 2 angles that are equal to $\angle 8$.

[2] What is the sum of the measures of angles 4, 5, and 6?

[3] Do $\angle 4$ and $\angle 9$ have the same measure?

[4] Do $\angle 6$ and $\angle 8$ have the same measure?

[5] Then what do you think is the sum of angles 9, 5, and 8?

Remember

The sum of the angles of any triangle is 180°.

Draw a large triangle on a sheet of paper. It should be much larger than the ones in our illustrations. Cut out the triangle. (If you don't have scissors, fold the paper along each edge of the triangle. Fold back and forth several times until you have a good crease. Then carefully tear along the crease.) Label the vertices *A*, *B*, and *C*. (*Vertices* is the plural of *vertex*.) If your triangle has one angle that is greater than or equal to 90°, be sure that angle is angle *A*. If all 3 angles are less than 90°, it doesn't matter which you choose to be *A*.

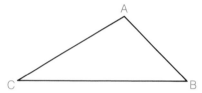

Bring point *C* up to point *A*, and press down on point *X* to form a short crease. *X* is halfway between *A* and *C*. We say *X bisects AC*. Find a crease point *Y* that bisects *AB*. Either draw or fold line *XY*.

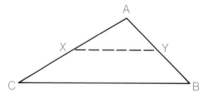

[1] Do you think *XY* is parallel to *BC*? What angles can you measure to check?

Fold the triangle along *XY*. *A* will touch side *CB* at point *A′*; (*A′* is read "*A prime*.") Fold the triangle so that *C* falls on *A′*. You will form line *XX′*. Then fold again so that *B* falls on *A′*. You'll form line *YY′*. Your figure should look like rectangle *XYY′X′*.

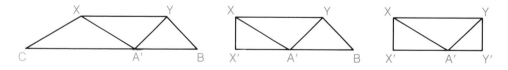

[2] Notice where angles *A*, *B*, and *C* are. From this figure, does it seem that ∠*A* + ∠*B* + ∠*C* = 180°?

The sum of the angles of a triangle is 180°.

If parallel lines are cut by a transversal, corresponding angles are equal and alternate interior angles are equal.

Vertical angles are equal.

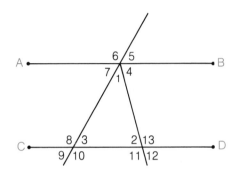

In this figure, *AB* is parallel to *CD*.

Do these problems.

1. If $\angle 1 = 40°$ and $\angle 2 = 80°$, $\angle 3 = ?$
2. If $\angle 1 = 50°$ and $\angle 2 = 75°$, $\angle 3 = ?$
3. If $\angle 1 = 50°$ and $\angle 2 = 75°$, $\angle 9 = ?$
4. If $\angle 12 = 70°$ and $\angle 9 = 30°$, $\angle 1 = ?$
5. If $\angle 1 = 40°$ and $\angle 2 = 80°$, $\angle 5 = ?$
6. If $\angle 4 = 80°$ and $\angle 1 = 60°$, $\angle 7 = ?$
7. If $\angle 4 = 80°$ and $\angle 1 = 60°$, $\angle 9 = ?$
8. If $\angle 4 = 90°$ and $\angle 1 = 65°$, $\angle 8 = ?$
9. If $\angle 2 = 80°$, $\angle 11 = ?$
10. If $\angle 2 = 80°$, $\angle 1 + \angle 3 = ?$
11. If $\angle 11 = 100°$, $\angle 1 + \angle 3 = ?$
12. If $\angle 8 = 140°$, $\angle 1 + \angle 2 = ?$

Draw a triangle with 2 sides that are the same length. (For simplicity, we often say that 2 sides are equal when they are the same length.) Cut out your triangle. Label its vertices *ABC* so that *AB* = *AC*.

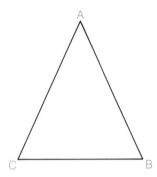 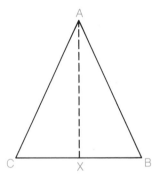

Fold your triangle so that *B* falls on *C*. The fold line, *AX*, bisects *BC*.

From your folded triangle, you can see that ∠*AXB* = ∠*AXC*.

What is the measure in degrees of ∠AXB?

If the angle between 2 lines is a right angle (90°), we say that the lines meet at right angles or are *perpendicular*.

Since *AX* bisects *BC* and is perpendicular to *BC*, *AX* is called the *perpendicular bisector* of *BC*.

With your triangle still folded, notice that ∠*B* = ∠*C*. A triangle with 2 sides equal is an *isosceles triangle*. Triangle *ABC* is an isosceles triangle. Angles *B* and *C* are called the *base angles* of isosceles triangle *ABC*.

Remember

An isosceles triangle has 2 equal sides.

The base angles of an isosceles triangle are equal.

A triangle with 2 equal angles is an isosceles triangle.

The sum of the angles of a triangle is 180°.

If parallel lines are cut by a transversal, corresponding angles are equal.

Vertical angles are equal.

The base angles of an isosceles triangle are equal.

Do the following problems.

1. Triangle *ABC* is isosceles, with *AB* = *AC*.

   a. If ∠*B* = 80°, ∠*C* = ? *A* = ?
   b. If ∠*B* = 75°, ∠*A* = ?
   c. If ∠*A* = 28°, ∠*B* = ?
   d. If ∠*A* = 34°, ∠*B* = ?

2. In triangle *DEF*, *DE* = *EF* = *DF*.

   a. What is the relationship between ∠*E* and ∠*F*?
   b. What is the relationship between ∠*D* and ∠*E*?
   c. What is the relationship between ∠*D* and ∠*F*?
   d. ∠*E* = ?

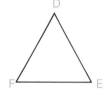

A triangle in which all 3 sides are equal is an *equilateral triangle*.

If all 3 sides of a triangle are equal, its 3 angles are also equal.

A triangle with all 3 angles equal is an *equiangular triangle*.

An equilateral triangle is also an equiangular triangle.

3. A figure with 4 sides is a *quadrilateral*.

   a. ∠1 + ∠3 + ∠*G* = ?
   b. ∠2 + ∠4 + ∠*I* = ?
   c. ∠1 + ∠2 + ∠3 + ∠4 + ∠*G* + ∠*I* = ?
   d. Does ∠*J* = ∠1 + ∠2?
   e. Does ∠*H* = ∠3 + ∠4?
   f. ∠*J* + ∠*H* + ∠*G* + ∠*I* = ?

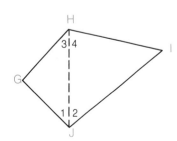

Multiply or divide.

1. 63×100
2. $63 \times 10,000$
3. $63 \div 100$
4. $63 \div 10,000$
5. 10×480

6. 1000×480
7. $48 \div 10$
8. $480 \div 1000$
9. 123×10
10. 123×1000

11. $123 \times 1,000,000$
12. $321 \div 10$
13. $321 \div 1000$
14. $321 \div 1,000,000$
15. $7 \times 100,000$

16. $70 \times 10,000$
17. 700×1000
18. 7000×100
19. $70,000 \times 10$
20. $700,000 \times 1$

21. $800,000 \div 1$
22. $80,000 \div 10$
23. $8000 \div 100$
24. $800 \div 1000$
25. $80 \div 10,000$

26. $8 \div 100,000$
27. $9 \div 1$
28. $90 \div 10$
29. $900 \div 100$
30. $9000 \div 1000$

31. $90,000 \div 10,000$
32. $900,000 \div 100,000$
33. 246×1000
34. $246 \div 1000$
35. 2460×1000

36. $2460 \div 1000$
37. 6×100
38. $6 \div 100$
39. $69 \div 100$
40. 60×100

Compute. Any number, except zero, raised to the zeroth power is 1.
$7^0 = 1$, $5^0 = 1$, $750^0 = 1$, and so on.

41. 2^3
42. 3^2
43. 4^3
44. 3^4
45. 2^4
46. 1^2
47. 1^{10}
48. 2^1
49. 2^{10}
50. 10^2

51. 5^3
52. 5^2
53. 5^1
54. 5^0
55. 8^2
56. 8^1
57. 8^0
58. 3^4
59. 3^2
60. 3^0

You've probably noticed that we have used some words and ideas quite often in this chapter. To say that lines have equal length, that angles have equal measure, and that lines are parallel, we use the same words many times.

So, for convenience, mathematicians decided to use symbols for these words and ideas. Some of these are shown below. We'll be using them in this book, and we hope that you will too.

Symbol	**Meaning**
$\triangle ABC$	Triangle ABC
$\angle A$	Angle A
$\angle BAC$	Angle BAC (A is the vertex, B is a point on one side of the angle, and C is a point on the other side of the angle.)
$\angle A = 37°$	The measure of angle A is $37°$.
$\angle A = \angle D$	The measure of angle A is equal to the measure of angle D.
AB	Side AB, or line segment AB
$AB = 10$ cm	The length of side AB (or segment AB) is 10 centimeters.
$AB = CD$	The length of side AB (or segment AB) is equal to the length of side CD (or segment CD).
$AB \parallel CD$	Line segment AB is parallel to line segment CD.
$AB \perp CD$	Line segment AB is perpendicular to line segment CD.
$\triangle ABC \cong \triangle DEF$	Triangle ABC is congruent to triangle DEF (point A corresponds to point D, point B to point E, and point C to point F).
$\triangle ABC \sim \triangle DEF$	Triangle ABC is similar to triangle DEF (here too point A corresponds to point D and so on).

Remember

The sum of the angles of a quadrilateral is 360°.

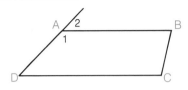

AB ∥ *CD*

1. If ∠1 = 110°, ∠2 = ?
2. If ∠2 = 60°, ∠D = ?
3. If ∠1 = 115°, ∠D = ?
4. If ∠C = 90°, ∠B = ?

5. If ∠C = 95°, ∠B = ?
6. If ∠B = 90° and ∠D = 60°, ∠1 = ?
7. If ∠C = 90°, ∠1 + ∠D + ∠B = ?
8. If ∠2 = 50°, ∠B + ∠C + ∠D = ?

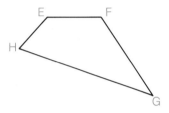

9. If ∠E = 120°, ∠F = 90°, and ∠G = 70°, ∠H = ?
10. If ∠H = ∠G and ∠E + ∠F = 220°, ∠H = ?
11. If ∠E = ∠H = 180°, what is true of lines *EF* and *HG*?

KL ∥ *MN*

12. ∠K + ∠N = ?
13. If ∠L = 70°, ∠M = ?
14. If ∠N = ∠M = 180°, what is true of lines *KN* and *LM*?

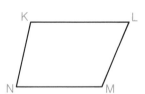

Remember

A quadrilateral with exactly 1 pair of sides parallel is a *trapezoid*.
A quadrilateral with 2 pairs of sides parallel is a *parallelogram*.

15. Draw a trapezoid.
16. Draw a parallelogram.
17. Draw a quadrilateral that is neither a trapezoid nor a parallelogram.

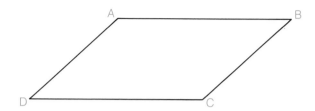

Quadrilateral *ABCD* is a parallelogram.

1. If $\angle A = 120°$, $\angle B = ?$
2. If $\angle A = 120°$, $\angle D = ?$
3. If $\angle A = 120°$, $\angle C = ?$
4. If $\angle A = 100°$, $\angle B = ?$ $\angle C = ?$ $\angle D = ?$
5. If $\angle A = 90°$, $\angle B = ?$ $\angle C = ?$ $\angle D = ?$

6. Measure sides *AB* and *CD* of parallelogram *ABCD*. What is true of them?

7. Measure sides *AD* and *BC* of parallelogram *ABCD*. What is true of them?

8. Try to draw a parallelogram in which opposite sides are not equal in length.

9. If a parallelogram has 1 right angle, what is the measure of each of its other angles? Then how many right angles does it have altogether?

Remember

A *rectangle* is a parallelogram with 1 right angle.

A *rhombus* is a parallelogram with all 4 sides equal

A *square* is a rhombus with 1 right angle.

---

10. Draw a rhombus.

11. Define a square as a special kind of rectangle (instead of a special kind of rhombus).

3 QUESTIONS GAME

Players: 2
Materials: Paper, pencil
Object: After asking 3 questions, to guess what figure the other player has drawn.

Rules

1. The first player draws a figure and writes the name of it on a sheet of paper, making sure the second player cannot see it. The figure must be one of these: triangle, isosceles triangle, equilateral triangle, right triangle, isosceles right triangle, quadrilateral, trapezoid, parallelogram, rectangle, square, or rhombus.

2. The figure may not have any extra properties that are not indicated by its name. For example, a quadrilateral with 1 right angle is not allowed, nor could you say that a figure with 2 sets of parallel sides is a trapezoid.

3. The second player asks 3 questions, 1 at a time, to which the first player must answer yes or no truthfully.

4. The second player tries to name the figure that the first player has drawn.

5. To win the round, the second player must correctly describe the figure as completely as possible. For example, if the figure is a rhombus and the second player says it is a parallelogram, the statement is true but not complete. So the second player would not win the round. The first player would.

Sample Game

Lena drew a trapezoid.

Harvey said:	Lena said:
Does it have 4 sides?	Yes.
Does it have 2 pairs of parallel sides?	No.
Does it have 1 pair of parallel sides?	Yes.
It's a trapezoid.	That's right.

Harvey won the round.

Compute. Use shortcuts when you can.

1. 10% of 8800
2. 20% of 8800
3. 30% of 8800
4. 40% of 8800
5. 50% of 8800

6. 10% of $18.00
7. 5% of $18.00
8. 1% of $18.00
9. 6% of $18.00
10. 16% of $18.00

11. 50% of $4000
12. 25% of $4000
13. 10% of $4000
14. 35% of $4000
15. 5% of $4000

16. 10% of 14,000
17. 20% of 14,000
18. 30% of 14,000
19. 40% of 14,000
20. 50% of 14,000

21. 50% of $12,000
22. 5% of $12,000
23. 0.5% of $12,000
24. 5.5% of $12,000
25. 55.5% of $12,000

26. 20% of 800
27. 2% of 800
28. 18% of 800
29. 4% of 800
30. 16% of 800

Solve for x.

31. $x\%$ of $100 = 5$
32. $x\%$ of $200 = 5$
33. $x\%$ of $50 = 5$
34. $x\%$ of $40 = 8$
35. 10% of $x = 10$
36. 10% of $x = 20$
37. 10% of $x = 5$
38. 10% of $x = 73$
39. 6% of $x = 15$
40. $x\%$ of $48 = 24$

41. $\frac{1}{2} = x\%$
42. $\frac{1}{4} = x\%$
43. $0.74 = x\%$
44. $3.02 = x\%$
45. $0.0003 = x\%$
46. $1000 = x\%$
47. $\frac{1}{8} = x\%$
48. $x\% = \frac{3}{8}$
49. $x\% = \frac{7}{8}$
50. $x\% = 1$

You learned how to bisect a line segment on pages 140 and 142. Remember, *bisect* means to cut into halves. You did that by folding the paper so that one end of the line segment fell exactly on the other. You can do this with a line segment drawn on a sheet of paper.

  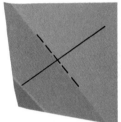

Fold back at one end of the line segment.

Make that end fall on the other end. Fold the paper.

The fold line bisects the line segment.

You can also bisect an angle by folding paper.

Fold the paper back on one side of the angle.

Make that side fall on the other side. Fold the paper.

The fold line bisects the angle.

Since the lengths of the sides of the angle don't matter, you should not try to get the end points of the sides on top of each other.

Constructions

1. Draw an angle on a sheet of paper. Bisect the angle by paper folding. Measure the original angle and the smaller angles. Are the smaller angles half the size of the larger one?

2. Bisect a straight angle.
   a. Is this fold like the fold for constructing a perpendicular bisector of a line segment?
   b. How is it different?

3. Use your figure from problem 2 to construct a 45° angle.

4. Now construct a $22\frac{1}{2}°$ angle.

5. Find or make 3 lengths the same size. These can be 3 equal strips of paper, 3 unsharpened pencils, 3 rulers, or 3 other objects. Put them together to form an equilateral triangle. Hold them very steady and draw 1 of the angles formed by the objects. What should the measure of the angle be? Measure with your protractor to see if it is.

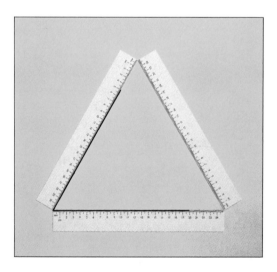

6. Start with a 60° angle and construct a 30° angle.

7. Then construct a 15° angle.

8. Finally construct a $7\frac{1}{2}°$ angle.

Play the 3 Questions Game.

Congruent Figures

For this activity, you will need wax paper, tracing paper, or some other paper you can see through easily and draw on. You will also need a ruler or other straightedge.

2 figures are said to be *congruent* if 1 can be made to fit exactly on the other.

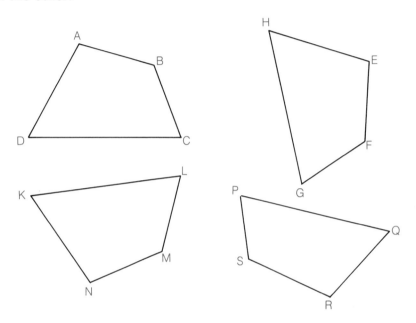

Which of these figures are congruent to figure *ABCD*? To answer the question, follow the steps below. If 1 figure fits exactly over another figure, the 2 figures are congruent. You may turn the wax paper over. Figures are congruent even if they have to be flipped to make them fit. If it is impossible to make the 2 figures fit, they are not congruent.

A. Trace figure *ABCD* on a piece of wax paper. Hold the paper very steady as you draw.

B. Hold your wax paper copy of *ABCD* over *EFGH*. Turn or move the wax paper to see if you can make the copy of *ABCD* fit exactly on *EFGH*.

C. Repeat step B with figure *KLMN*.

D. Repeat with *PQRS*.

Now can you say which are congruent to figure *ABCD*?

You can use wax paper or tracing paper to copy figures. Here's a way to copy figure *ABCDE*. Carefully trace the figure on a piece of wax paper. Put the traced figure on a sheet of paper where you want to make the copy. Use a ruler to keep the lines straight, and press hard as you trace over the figure on your wax paper. That will leave marks on the paper underneath. Then retrace the lines to make them as dark as you like. You may also do this by first sticking a pin through each of the vertices (holding the paper steady) and then connecting the pinholes.

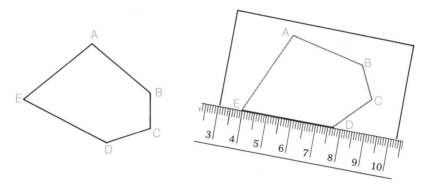

You can draw parallel lines and construct other figures by copying angles and line segments.

For example, to construct a line parallel to line *AB* through point *P*, draw any line through *P* that crosses *AB*. This will form ∠1.

Then copy ∠1 so that the vertex of the new angle is at *P*. The new angle (∠2) is a corresponding angle to ∠1, and the line *CD* is parallel to *AB*.

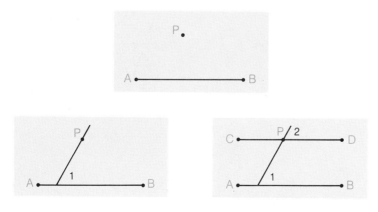

Use wax paper or tracing paper to copy each of these figures onto a different sheet of paper.

1. Isosceles right triangle *ABC*

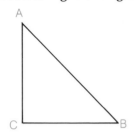

2. Rhombus *DEFG*

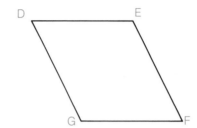

3. Trapezoid *HIJK*

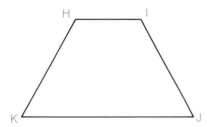

4. Equilateral triangle *LMN*

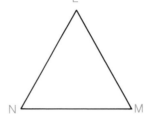

5. Parallelogram *OPQR*

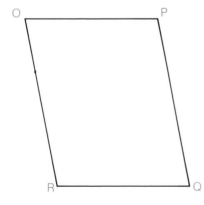

6. Isosceles triangle *STU*

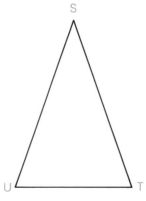

Work in small groups. Use a straightedge, wax paper or tracing paper, and a pencil to construct each of the following figures. Write down the steps you use for each construction.

1. On a sheet of paper, draw a line AB and mark a point P not on the line. Construct a line parallel to AB through P.

2. Construct a square. (Hint: Fold the wax paper to make a right angle. Choose any length for a side. Copy that side for the other sides.)

3. Construct an isosceles triangle.

4. Construct a right triangle.

5. Construct an isosceles right triangle.

6. Construct a trapezoid.

7. Construct a parallelogram.

8. Construct a rhombus.

9. Construct a rectangle.

We often want to make a copy of something that looks just like
the original but is smaller or bigger. A road map is a small model
of the real roads it shows. A blueprint is a small picture of a
building or other object. A statue is a model of a real person or
thing that may be smaller or larger.

We say that 2 figures are *similar* when they look alike but are
different sizes.

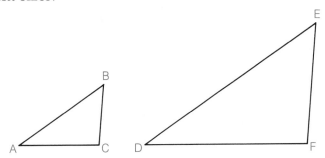

Triangles *ABC* and *DEF* are similar. The sides of triangle *DEF* are 2
times as long as the corresponding sides of triangle *ABC*.

**[1] Are the angles of triangle *DEF* the same size as those of triangle
ABC? (Use wax paper or tracing paper to check.)**

You can construct a polygon that is similar to another if you are
given the ratio of the lengths of the sides. Just copy the angles and
make the sides the necessary length.

To make a triangle *GHI* similar to *ABC* but with sides 3 times as
long, copy angle *A* (at *G*). Either mark off length *AC* 3 times along
GI or measure the length necessary to make *GI* 3 times *AC*. Next,
copy angle *C* at *I*.

[2] Do you have to continue tripling sides and copying angles?

[3] Have you already determined triangle *GHI* by this much work?

Remember

Two figures are similar if the corresponding angles are equal
when their vertices are matched up. In similar figures, the lengths
of corresponding sides are proportional.

---

1. Triangle *ABC* has sides that are 3 centimeters (*BC*), 4 centimeters (*AC*), and 5 centimeters (*AB*) long. Make a similar triangle on your paper with sides 3 times as long.

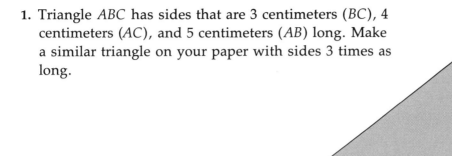

2. Gene wanted to know how tall a certain flagpole was. He held a meterstick upright on the ground and measured its shadow. The shadow was 140 centimeters long. He then measured the shadow of the flagpole. It was 28 meters long.

    a. Can you use similar triangles to decide how tall the flagpole is?
    b. How tall is the flagpole?

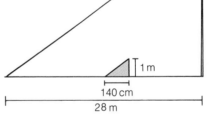

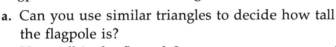

3. Marie wanted to know how tall an apartment building was. She walked away from it down the street until the top of the building made an angle of $22\frac{1}{2}°$ with the ground. The distance from the point where she measured the angle to the building was 175 meters. About how tall was the building? (Hint: Do you remember how to make a $22\frac{1}{2}°$ angle? Mark off a distance of 175 millimeters to the line that represents the building.)

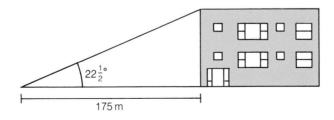

1. Use a protractor and a ruler to draw a triangle that has a 30° angle between sides that are 4 centimeters and 6 centimeters in length.

2. Try to draw a second triangle that has a 30° angle between sides that are 4 centimeters and 6 centimeters but that is *not* congruent to the triangle in problem 1. Is this possible?

3. Draw a triangle that has a 5-centimeter side between angles of 30° and 70°. Is it possible to draw another triangle that has a 5-centimeter side between angles of 30° and 70° but is *not* congruent to the first triangle?

4. Draw a triangle that has sides of length 4 centimeters, 6 centimeters, and 8 centimeters. You may have to experiment a bit. For example, draw the 8-centimeter side, then draw several light 4-centimeter sides from one end and 6-centimeter sides from the other until they fit. (If you have a compass for drawing circles, it will help.)

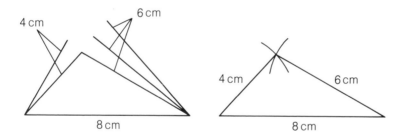

5. Is it possible to draw a triangle that is not congruent to the triangle you drew in problem 4 but that has sides of 4 centimeters, 6 centimeters, and 8 centimeters?

6. Try to draw a triangle with sides 10 centimeters, 4 centimeters, and 5 centimeters. What happened?

7. Draw a triangle that has angles of 50°, 60°, and 70°. Can you draw another triangle with angles of 50°, 60°, and 70° that is not congruent to your first one?

TRIANGLE GAME

Players: 2 or more
Materials: Two 0–5 cubes, two 5–10 cubes
Object: To make as many triangles as possible

Rules

1. Take turns rolling all 4 cubes.
2. Each number rolled stands for a number of centimeters.
3. Think of as many triangles made from combinations of these lengths as you can. Make a list.
4. The other players may challenge any of your triangles. If they do, you must draw it to show that it really is a triangle.
5. The player who makes the most triangles wins the round.

Sample Game

Jennifer rolled:

Ruby rolled:

Jennifer could make 4 triangles:

    8, 7, 5
    8, 7, 4
    8, 5, 4
    7, 5, 4

Jennifer won this round.

Ruby could not make any triangles.

Do the following calculations in your head. Just write the answer.

1. 10% of $72.00
2. 5% of $72.00
3. 15% of $72.00
4. 20% of $72.00
5. 25% of $72.00

6. 10% of $72.80
7. 5% of $72.80
8. 15% of $72.80
9. 20% of $72.80
10. 25% of $72.80

11. 10% of $7200.00
12. 5% of $7200.00
13. 15% of $7200.00
14. 20% of $7200.00
15. 25% of $7200.00

16. 10% of $7272.00
17. 5% of $7272.00
18. 15% of $7272.00
19. 20% of $7272.00
20. 25% of $7272.00

21. 10% of $5000.00
22. 20% of $5000.00
23. 50% of $5000.00
24. 70% of $5000.00
25. 90% of $5000.00

26. 10% of $630.00
27. 5% of $630.00
28. 50% of $630.00
29. 55% of $630.00
30. 60% of $630.00

31. 5% of $28.00
32. 1% of $28.00
33. 6% of $28.00
34. 7% of $28.00
35. 10% of $28.00

36. 5% of $6.40
37. 1% of $6.40
38. 2% of $6.40
39. 3% of $6.40
40. 4% of $6.40

41. 10% of $108.00
42. 5% of $108.00
43. 1% of $108.00
44. 6% of $108.00
45. 9% of $108.00

46. 10% of $840.00
47. 20% of $840.00
48. 2% of $840.00
49. 18% of $840.00
50. 12% of $840.00

Many people enjoy doing problems like these for fun. Try them. Work alone or in small groups.

1. Joe's 3 cousins, Trudy, Dan, and Leona, live in different states: California, Wisconsin, and Virginia. They all have different jobs: one teaches, one is a doctor, and one is a farmer. Leona doesn't live in California. Dan doesn't live in Wisconsin. The cousin in California is not a farmer. The cousin in Wisconsin is a doctor. Dan is not a teacher.

   a. Where does Trudy live?
   b. What does she do?

2. Mrs. Root was talking about numerals to her math class. She said, "Numerals are just symbols for the digits 0, 1, 2, 3, 4, 5, 6, 7, 8, and 9. We could use other symbols for the digits. Here's a problem for you. ER is the square of R, and $ETRT$ is the square of RE." She turned and wrote this on the blackboard:

$$\begin{array}{r} E\,R\,R \\ +\ T\,R\,E\,E \\ \hline \end{array}$$

   Then she said, "You can use my symbols to tell me what this sum is."

   a. What is the answer in Mrs. Root's symbols?
   b. What is the answer in numerals?

3. Rafael, Louise, Norman, Harriet, and Taku call themselves the Five Friends for Fitness. They get together every day after school to exercise for an hour. They decided to have a contest with 5 events: swimming 2 kilometers, running 3 kilometers, doing sit-ups, doing push-ups, and a 100-meter dash. Points were awarded for each event (5 for first place, 4 for second, 3 for third, 2 for fourth, and 1 for fifth) and totaled to find the winner.

   Louise won easily, with 24 points. There were no ties, either in events or in totals. Norman took second place. Taku was third and very consistent, since he had the same number of points in 4 events. Rafael was fourth. We won't mention who was last, but she did take first place in running 3 kilometers and third place in swimming 2 kilometers.

   a. Who was last overall in the contest?
   b. What place did Norman take in the 3-kilometer run?

Start with a long strip of paper (2 centimeters wide or a bit wider and at least 20 centimeters long).

A. Hold the end, fold the strip up, and crease the fold.

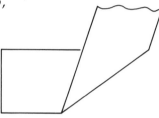

B. Unfold it.

C. Fold the long end down so that the top is along the first fold. Crease well.

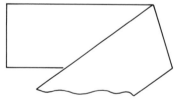

D. Unfold.

E. Fold the long end up so that the bottom of the strip is along the second fold.

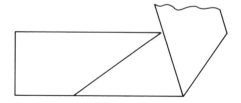

F. Unfold.

G. Fold down.

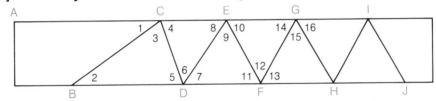

H. Unfold. Fold up. Unfold. Fold down. Unfold. Continue folding and unfolding.

[1] What do you notice about the triangles?

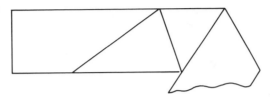

[2] With your first fold (*BC*), you made ∠*ACB* and ∠*BCE*. With your second fold (*CD*), you bisected one of those angles. Which one?

[3] With your third fold (*DE*), you bisected an angle. Which angle?

Suppose ∠1 is 44°.

1. ∠2 = ?
2. ∠*BCE* = ?
3. ∠3 = ∠4 = ?
4. Are ∠4 and ∠5 alternate interior angles of parallel lines?

5. ∠5 = ?   7. ∠6 = ∠7 = ?   9. ∠*DEG* = ?
6. ∠*CDF* = ?   8. ∠8 = ?   10. ∠9 = ∠10 = ?

11. What is the difference between

    a. 60° and ∠1?   **c.** 60° and ∠7?
    b. 60° and ∠4?   **d.** 60° and ∠10?

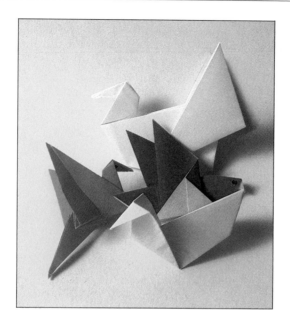

When you did the paper folding on pages 162 and 163, each time you made a fold the difference between your new angle and 60° was half what it was before.

If we don't count fold *BC* (because it created angles 1 and 2), we could say it takes 4 folds (*CD*, *DE*, *EF*, and *FG*) to get the angles of the triangle within 1° of 60° ($\angle 13 = 59°$) when angle 1 is 44°.

1. Suppose $\angle 1 = \angle 2 = 50°$. How many folds would it take to be within 1° of 60°? (After 1 fold, we'd be 5° off; after 2, we'd be $2\frac{1}{2}°$ off; after 3, we'd be off by $1\frac{1}{4}°$, which is not quite close enough; and so on.)

2. Suppose $\angle 1$ was 30°. How many folds would it take to be within 1° of 60°?

3. Suppose $\angle 1$ was 10°. How many folds would it take to be within 1° of 60°?

4. No matter how far from 60° the first angle is, what is the largest number of folds it should take to be within 1° of 60°?

If you start the paper folding with an angle that is close to 60°, after 2 or 3 folds the angles you fold will be very close to 60°.

After you have folded several triangles, check whether your angles are close to 60°. They will be close to 60° when you can't see any difference between 2 triangles next to each other. Then fold 10 more triangles. Cut out the piece with these 10 triangles. Cut it in half so that you have 2 short strips with 5 triangles each.

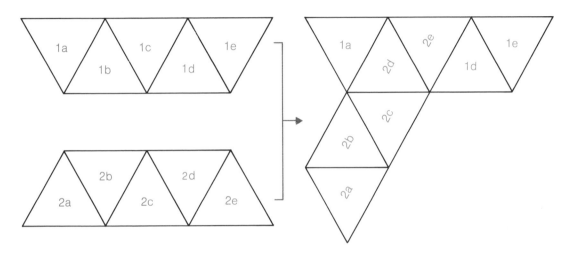

Overlap the 2 strips as shown (strip 2 is on top). Fold the bottom (strip 1) up toward you so that it makes a pyramid (the triangles marked 1a and 1e will overlap).

If this is hard to do, try to make the pyramid several times with strip 1. Then put strip 2 back in as shown.

When you fold the 2 strips, strip 2 has 2 triangles (2d and 2e) caught inside the pyramid. Wrap the other triangles around the pyramid, but tuck the last triangle (2a) into the pyramid. This should hold the pyramid together.

A pyramid made of 4 equilateral triangles is called a *regular tetrahedron*.

In this figure, the pilot of an airplane flying north is at point P. You may use your protractor to solve problems 1–11.

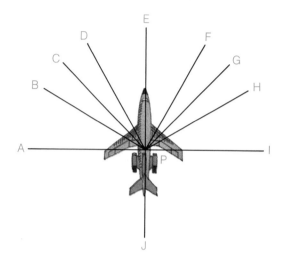

1. What point would the pilot say is at 1 o'clock?
2. What point would the pilot say is at 10 o'clock?
3. What point is east of the pilot?
4. Tell whether each of the following angles is acute, right, obtuse, or straight.

   a. $\angle APH$ **b.** $\angle APJ$ **c.** $\angle EPI$ **d.** $\angle EPF$ **e.** $\angle EPJ$

5. What is the measure, in degrees, of $\angle GPI$?
6. What is the measure, in degrees, of $\angle HPI$?
7. What is the measure, in degrees, of $\angle BPF$?
8. What is the measure, in degrees, of $\angle APH$?
9. What angle is a supplementary angle of $\angle BPA$?
10. Is there a line in the figure that is parallel to line AI? If so, name the line.
11. Is there a line in the figure that is perpendicular to line AI? If so, name the line.

In the figure, *AB* is parallel to *CD*.

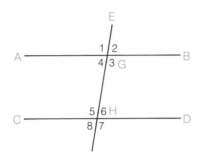

12. If ∠1 = 100°, what is the measure of each of the following angles?

    a. ∠2   **b.** ∠5   **c.** ∠7   **d.** ∠*CHE*   **e.** ∠*CHD*

Use this figure to answer 13–16.

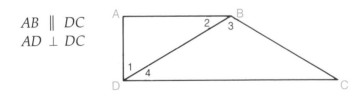

$AB \parallel DC$
$AD \perp DC$

13. ∠*A* = ?
14. If ∠1 = 60°, ∠2 = ?
15. If ∠4 = 40°, ∠2 = ?
16. If ∠1 = 50° and ∠3 = 110°, ∠*C* = ?
17. Draw an isosceles triangle.
18. Draw a trapezoid.
19. Draw a rhombus.
20. Draw an isosceles right triangle.
21. Is it possible for an isosceles right triangle to be congruent to an equilateral triangle?
22. Is it possible for a rhombus in which one angle measures 60° to be congruent to a rhombus in which one angle measures 120°?

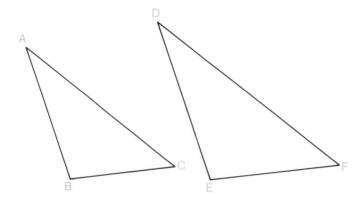

23. Triangle *ABC* is similar to triangle *DEF*. If *AB* = 3 centimeters, *BC* = 2 centimeters, and *EF* = 6 centimeters, how long is *DE*?

24. Triangle *ABC* is similar to triangle *DEF*. If *BC* = 2 centimeters, *EF* = 6 centimeters, and *DF* = 15 centimeters, how long is *AC*?

25. Is it possible to draw a triangle with the following lengths of sides?

    a. 5 centimeters, 5 centimeters, and 5 centimeters

    b. 3 centimeters, 4 centimeters, and 5 centimeters

    c. 6 centimeters, 10 centimeters, and 20 centimeters

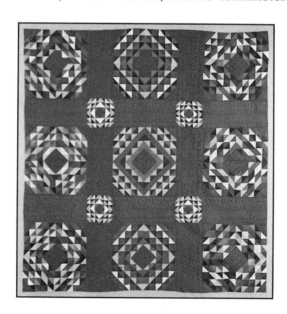

You will need paper and glue, paste, or tape for this activity.

Take a strip of paper about 25 to 30 centimeters long and about 3 centimeters wide. Twist it half a turn and then bring the ends together. Glue, paste, or tape them to form a continuous strip.

The strip you have made is called a Möbius strip. It has only 1 side. If you try to draw a line down the middle of 1 side, you will find yourself on the "other side" of the strip without crossing an edge.

1. If you cut the strip down the middle, how many strips do you expect to get?
2. Try it. How many do you actually get?
3. How is the strip twisted?
4. If you now cut it down the middle, what do you think you'd get?

Make another Möbius strip. Cut it $\frac{1}{3}$ of the way from 1 edge.

5. What happens?

Experiment with Möbius strips. Möbius strips are named for August Ferdinand Möbius (sometimes his last name will be spelled *Moebius*).

In this figure, the pilot of an airplane flying north is at point *P*. You may use your protractor to solve problems 1–11.

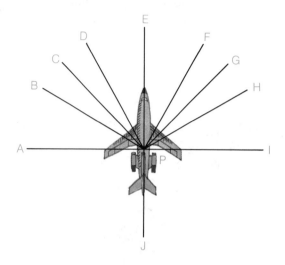

1. What point would the pilot say is at 2 o'clock?

2. What point would the pilot say is at 11 o'clock?

3. What point is south of the pilot?

4. Tell whether each of the following angles is acute, right, obtuse, or straight.

   a. ∠*APG*   **b.** ∠*APE*   **c.** ∠*DPG*   **d.** ∠*EPG*   **e.** ∠*API*

5. What is the measure, in degrees, of ∠*FPI*?

6. What is the measure, in degrees, of ∠*APB*?

7. What is the measure, in degrees, of ∠*DPG*?

8. What is the measure, in degrees, of ∠*BPI*?

9. What angle is a supplementary angle of ∠*DPE*?

10. Is there a line in the figure that is parallel to line *EJ*? If so, name the line.

11. Is there a line in the figure that is perpendicular to line *EJ*? If so, name the line.

In the figure, *AB* is parallel to *CD*.

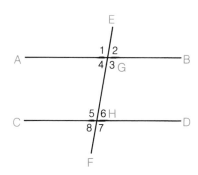

12. If $\angle 1 = 110°$, what is the measure of each of the following angles?

    a. $\angle 2$ **b.** $\angle 5$ **c.** $\angle 7$ **d.** $\angle CHE$ **e.** $\angle CHD$

Use this figure to answer 13–16.

$$AB \parallel DC$$
$$AD \perp DC$$

13. $\angle A = ?$

14. If $\angle 1 = 70°$, $\angle 2 = ?$

15. If $\angle 4 = 50°$, $\angle 2 = ?$

16. If $\angle 1 = 60°$ and $\angle 3 = 100°$, $\angle C = ?$

17. Draw an equilateral triangle.

18. Draw a parallelogram.

19. Draw a square.

20. Draw a right triangle.

21. Is it possible for a right triangle to be congruent to an equilateral triangle?

22. Is it possible for a rhombus in which one angle measures 50° to be congruent to a rhombus in which one angle measures 130°?

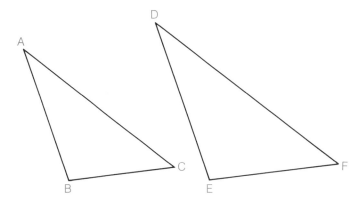

23. Triangle *ABC* is similar to triangle *DEF*. If *AB* = 4 centimeters, *BC* = 3 centimeters, and *EF* = 9 centimeters, how long is *DE*?

24. Triangle *ABC* is similar to triangle *DEF*. If *BC* = 3 centimeters, *EF* = 9 centimeters, and *DF* = 18 centimeters, how long is *AC*?

25. Is it possible to draw a triangle with sides of the following lengths?

   a. 6 centimeters, 6 centimeters, and 6 centimeters
   b. 4 centimeters, 5 centimeters, and 6 centimeters
   c. 3 centimeters, 9 centimeters, and 13 centimeters

A. Make a square from a rectangular piece of paper.

First fold one corner up like this: Then fold the end over like this:

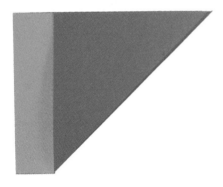

Cut on the second fold line to make a square.

B. Fold the square 4 times. Make 2 diagonal folds and 2 folds that cut the sides in half. Each fold should be a "valley fold." (The sides go up from a valley fold.)

To help you see how to hold the paper, we'll call this corner *L*.

L

C. Kite fold every corner. A kite fold is really 2 folds—each fold bisects the angle on each side of the diagonal. The first fold looks like this:

The whole kite fold looks like this:

After you kite fold all 4 corners, the folded square looks like this. We are going to label the midpoints of the sides *A*, *B*, *C*, and *D*.

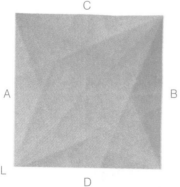

D. Fold on *AB* and tuck in the end triangle. Both *A* and *B* are tucked inside. Unfold before you make the next fold.

E. Fold on *CD* and tuck in the end triangles. Now *C* and *D* will be tucked inside. Unfold before you do the next part.

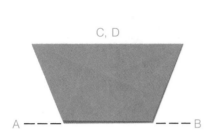

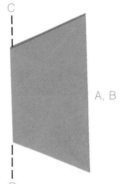

F. Push in on the 4 places you just tucked in.

G. Bring the 4 corners together to form a polyhedron.

H. Tape or glue these corners together. This polyhedron is sometimes called a German bell.

Now answer these questions about the German bell. Work with a friend.

1. How many right triangles, of all sizes, can you find?
2. How many isosceles triangles, of all sizes, can you find?
3. How many triangles, of all sizes, can you find?

CHAPTER 5
FRACTIONS

5

When he was 9 years old, Zerah Colburn hesitated when asked to square 4395 (multiply 4395 by itself), but he gave the correct answer (19,316,025) when the question was repeated. When someone asked why he had hesitated, he admitted he didn't like to multiply a 4-digit number by another 4-digit number. He explained, "I found out another way; I multiplied 293 by 293 and then multiplied twice by the number 15." (Look back at page 78 if you don't remember who Zerah Colburn was.)

Use a calculator. Check whether $293 \times 293 \times 15 \times 15$ is the same as 4395^2.

Calculating wonders like Zerah Colburn sometimes had great difficulty explaining to other people how they did their calculations. All of them appear to have had a remarkable memory for and interest in numbers. Several seem to have relied on certain rules they discovered, and at least some relied on factoring large numbers to make them easier to handle.

Remember

To factor a number means to find 2 or more numbers whose product is that number.

1 is a factor of every number. Every number is a factor of itself.

Once Zerah Colburn was asked to multiply 21,734 × 543. He said that he did it by changing the problem to 65,202 × 181. Apparently, he factored numbers whenever possible. He could very quickly give the factors of any numbers less than 1,000,000. Three numbers that he factored instantly at one session are 247,483; 171,395; and 36,083. He did this so quickly that the person who gave him the numbers to factor didn't have time to write down the factors.

Learning to factor quickly will probably not make you a calculating wonder. And even if it did, there are computers that could probably calculate more efficiently. But there are times when factoring helps.

One of the most common uses of factoring is to help with the manipulation of fractions. Factoring is also useful as a check on calculations. If you know that 525 is divisible by 25, then you know that the product of 525 times any other number is also divisible by 25.

You probably know several rules that should help you find factors of numbers. You have already learned why the rules listed in the table on page 180 work. For example, you know that a number ending in 0 is divisible by 2 because 10 is divisible by 2. In the same way, a number ending in 00 is divisible by 4 because 10 × 10, or 100, is divisible by 2 × 2, or 4.

Here are some divisibility rules.

Divisor	Divisibility Rule	Example
2	If the last digit is even, the number is divisible by 2.	37,516 6 is even.
3	If the sum of the digits is divisible by 3, the number is divisible by 3.	15,351 The sum is 15.
4	If the last 2 digits make a number divisible by 4, the number is divisible by 4.	21,372 72 ÷ 4 = 18
5	If the last digit is 0 or 5, the number is divisible by 5.	6135 27,230
6	If the number is divisible by both 2 and 3, it is divisible by 6.	3774 4 is even, and the sum is 21.
7	There are rules for divisibility by 7. But the simplest way to find out is simply to divide.	1673 Try 7.
8	If the last 3 digits make a number divisible by 8, the number is divisible by 8.	25,384 384 ÷ 8 = 48
9	If the sum of the digits is divisible by 9, the number is divisible by 9.	2367 Sum is 18.
10	If the last digit is 0, the number is divisible by 10.	379,940

For each rule it is also true that if the condition does *not* hold, then the number is *not* divisible by the divisor. This is important too.

Let's check whether 2898 has 2, 3, 4, 5, 6, 7, 8, 9, or 10 as factors.

2898 has a factor of 2 (because it ends with an 8) but not 4 (because 98 is not divisible by 4) or 8 (because if it doesn't have a factor of 4, it won't have a factor of 8).

It has a factor of 9 (because $2 + 8 + 9 + 8 = 27$, and 27 is divisible by 9), and therefore it also has a factor of 3.

2898 is not divisible by 5 or 10 (since the last digit is neither 0 nor 5).

But it is divisible by 6 (since it is divisible by both 2 and 3).

2898 is divisible by 7 (just divide to get 414).

So 2, 3, 6, 7, and 9 are factors of 2898, and 4, 5, 8, and 10 are not factors of 2898.

Check whether each of these numbers has 2, 3, 4, 5, 6, 7, 8, 9, or 10 as factors.

1. 128	**7.** 360	**13.** 2521	**19.** 7560
2. 98	**8.** 43	**14.** 361	**20.** 7561
3. 100	**9.** 77	**15.** 2519	**21.** 490
4. 72	**10.** 125	**16.** 91	**22.** 720
5. 144	**11.** 5796	**17.** 48	**23.** 1440
6. 315	**12.** 2520	**18.** 57	**24.** 430

[1] Did you find that 2520 is divisible by all the numbers—2, 3, 4, 5, 6, 7, 8, 9, and 10?

[2] Since 2520 is divisible by 2, 3, 4, 5, 6, 7, 8, 9, and 10, could 2521 be divisible by any of them?

[3] What is a 3-digit number that has 7, 8, and 9 as factors?

You know that different but equivalent fractions can be used to represent a certain part of a whole. Look at the circles below. They are divided into 4, 8, 12, and 16 equal parts.

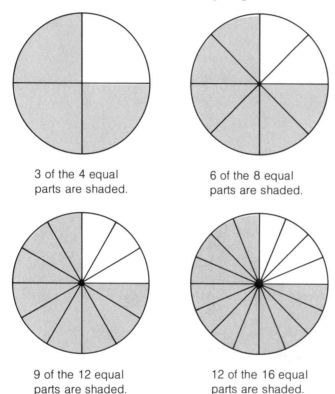

3 of the 4 equal
parts are shaded.

6 of the 8 equal
parts are shaded.

9 of the 12 equal
parts are shaded.

12 of the 16 equal
parts are shaded.

[1] Does it seem that the same portion of each circle is shaded?

[2] Do $\frac{3}{4}$, $\frac{6}{8}$, $\frac{9}{12}$, and $\frac{12}{16}$ all represent the same part of the circle?

We say the 4 fractions are equivalent, and we write $\frac{3}{4} = \frac{6}{8}$, $\frac{3}{4} = \frac{9}{12}$, $\frac{6}{8} = \frac{12}{16}$, and so on.

Notice that multiplying both the numerator (top) and the denominator (bottom) of $\frac{3}{4}$ by 2 is like cutting each of the original 4 equal parts into halves (so that we now have 8 equal parts) and doubling the number of parts shaded (so that we now have 6 shaded parts).

$$\frac{2 \times 3}{2 \times 4} = \frac{6}{8}$$

(The same thing happens if you multiply the top and bottom of $\frac{3}{4}$ by any other number.) You can reverse this process by dividing the top and bottom of $\frac{6}{8}$ by 2.

$$\frac{6 \div 2}{8 \div 2} = \frac{3}{4}$$

(The same thing happens if you divide both parts of $\frac{9}{12}$ by 3 or both parts of $\frac{12}{16}$ by 4.)

So both the top and the bottom of any fraction can be multiplied by any number (as long as it's the same number) to get an equivalent fraction. And if there is a common factor in both the top and bottom of a fraction, both can be divided by that common factor to get an equivalent fraction.

Multiplying or dividing both parts of a fraction by the same number will change the fraction, but it will not change the number that the fraction represents. That number is called a *rational number*. (The term *rational number* comes from the word *ratio*.)

Usually, but not always, people prefer to work with fractions that have small numerators and denominators. Most people would rather work with $\frac{3}{4}$ than with $\frac{12}{16}$. But many people do find $\frac{64}{100}$ simpler than $\frac{16}{25}$ to understand and deal with.

Often when you are working with a fraction, you want to find an equivalent fraction with numerator and denominator smaller than the fraction you have. The process you use is sometimes called *simplifying the fraction* (although the resulting fraction is not necessarily simpler), or *reducing the fraction* (although the part represented by the fraction is no smaller).

We will call the process *reducing the fraction*. When there is no equivalent fraction with smaller numerator and denominator, we will say the fraction has been *completely reduced* or *reduced to lowest terms*.

Remember

We do not make the rational number represented by the fraction smaller when we *reduce* a fraction. Only the numerator and denominator have become smaller.

Example: Completely reduce $\frac{135}{315}$.

Both numerator and denominator end in 5. So you know they are divisible by 5 (135 ÷ 5 = 27; 315 ÷ 5 = 63).

You may keep a record of what you do this way:

$$\frac{135}{315} \quad \rightarrow \quad \frac{\overset{27}{\cancel{135}}}{\underset{63}{\cancel{315}}}$$

The sum of the digits of both 27 and 63 tells us that they are divisible by 9 (27 ÷ 9 = 3; 63 ÷ 9 = 7).

Continue your record keeping this way:

$$\begin{array}{c} 27 \\ \cancel{135} \\ \cancel{315} \\ 63 \end{array} \qquad \begin{array}{c} \overset{3}{\cancel{27}} \\ \cancel{135} \\ \cancel{315} \\ \underset{7}{\cancel{63}} \end{array}$$

So $\frac{135}{315} = \frac{3}{7}$.

When you reduce a fraction, always remember to write in both the new numerator and the new denominator. Sometimes people forget to write the 1 when the numerator can be completely reduced to 1.

Completely reduce each of the following fractions.

1. $\frac{9}{12}$ 8. $\frac{4}{6}$ 15. $\frac{60}{100}$ 22. $\frac{8}{64}$

2. $\frac{3}{12}$ 9. $\frac{18}{81}$ 16. $\frac{73}{73}$ 23. $\frac{81}{243}$

3. $\frac{12}{243}$ 10. $\frac{4}{64}$ 17. $\frac{12}{50}$ 24. $\frac{147}{588}$

4. $\frac{108}{243}$ 11. $\frac{36}{36}$ 18. $\frac{12}{18}$ 25. $\frac{125}{625}$

5. $\frac{126}{189}$ 12. $\frac{7}{21}$ 19. $\frac{216}{252}$ 26. $\frac{100}{350}$

6. $\frac{54}{162}$ 13. $\frac{6}{16}$ 20. $\frac{140}{504}$ 27. $\frac{17}{64}$

7. $\frac{7}{56}$ 14. $\frac{75}{100}$ 21. $\frac{24}{36}$ 28. $\frac{12}{30}$

We usually think of fractions in relation to 1 or more parts of something.

Example: Think of a whole as 1.

$\frac{1}{5}$ means 1 of 5 equal parts of the whole.

$\frac{3}{5}$ means 3 of 5 equal parts of the whole.

We can also think of fractions of numbers.

Examples: What is $\frac{1}{5}$ of 30?

Divide 30 into 5 equal parts.   Take 1 of those parts.

So $\frac{1}{5}$ of 30 is 6.

What is $\frac{3}{5}$ of 15?

There are 2 ways to think about this.

Divide 15 into 5 equal parts.   Take 3 of those parts.

Or take 15 3 times.   Divide that into 5 equal parts.   Take 1 of those parts.

So $\frac{3}{5}$ of 15 is 9.

Sometimes it is useful to take a fraction of a fraction. How this works may be easier to understand if we think about cutting up a piece of fabric in the following way. (However, it's not likely that you would ever have to share fabric this way.)

Elizabeth had $\frac{3}{7}$ of a piece of fabric. She gave someone $\frac{5}{6}$ of her part of the fabric. Now she wants to know what fraction of the original piece of fabric that was.

First imagine the original piece of fabric divided into sevenths. Elizabeth had 3 of the sevenths of the piece of fabric.

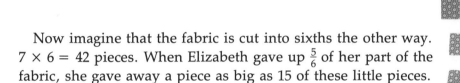

Now imagine that the fabric is cut into sixths the other way. $7 \times 6 = 42$ pieces. When Elizabeth gave up $\frac{5}{6}$ of her part of the fabric, she gave away a piece as big as 15 of these little pieces.

$$\frac{5}{6} \text{ of } \frac{3}{7} = \frac{5 \times 3}{6 \times 7} = \frac{15}{42}$$

Because of this we sometimes write $\frac{5}{6}$ of $\frac{3}{7}$ as $\frac{5}{6} \times \frac{3}{7}$ and say we are *multiplying the fractions*.

Of course, you could reduce $\frac{15}{42}$ to $\frac{5}{14}$. In fact, you would save some arithmetic by noticing that $\frac{5 \times 3}{6 \times 7}$ has a factor of 3 in both numerator and denominator. You could divide the top and the bottom by 3:

$$\frac{5 \times \overset{1}{\cancel{3}}}{\underset{2}{\cancel{6}} \times 7} = \frac{5}{14}$$

Remember

To find $\frac{a}{b}$ of $\frac{c}{d}$, you calculate $\frac{a \times c}{b \times d}$.

Do these problems. Reduce your answers completely.

1. $\frac{1}{3}$ of 60   **11.** $\frac{1}{3} \times 60$ **21.** $\frac{3}{7}$ of $\frac{5}{6}$

2. $\frac{2}{3}$ of 60   **12.** $\frac{2}{3} \times 60$ **22.** $\frac{5}{6}$ of $\frac{3}{7}$

3. $\frac{1}{5}$ of 40   **13.** $\frac{1}{7}$ of 14   **23.** $\frac{3}{5}$ of $\frac{3}{8}$

4. $\frac{3}{5}$ of 40   **14.** $\frac{3}{7} \times 14$ **24.** $\frac{3}{8}$ of $\frac{3}{5}$

5. $\frac{5}{5}$ of 40   **15.** $\frac{5}{8} \times 40$ **25.** $\frac{2}{3} \times \frac{3}{4}$

6. $\frac{1}{6}$ of 72   **16.** $\frac{1}{3}$ of $\frac{1}{4}$ **26.** $\frac{3}{4} \times \frac{2}{3}$

7. $\frac{5}{6}$ of 72   **17.** $\frac{2}{3}$ of $\frac{1}{4}$ **27.** $\frac{1}{6} \times \frac{1}{3}$

8. $\frac{4}{6}$ of 72   **18.** $\frac{1}{4}$ of $\frac{2}{3}$ **28.** $\frac{1}{3} \times \frac{1}{6}$

9. $\frac{2}{3}$ of 72   **19.** $\frac{3}{4}$ of $\frac{2}{3}$ **29.** $\frac{3}{10} \times \frac{5}{9}$

10. $\frac{3}{7}$ of 49   **20.** $\frac{2}{3}$ of $\frac{3}{4}$ **30.** $\frac{5}{9} \times \frac{3}{10}$

Solve for n. Look for shortcuts.

31. $\frac{100 \times 100}{10 \times 10} = n$

32. $\frac{5 \times (3 + 4)}{7} = n$

33. $\frac{4 \times 4 \times 3}{16 \times 3} = n$

34. $\frac{1 - (6 \times 3 \times 0)}{25} \times 25 = n$

35. $\frac{45 \times 20}{(9 \times 5) \times 10} = n$

36. $\frac{(74 \times 36) \times \left(\frac{5}{5} - 1 \right)}{37 \times 2} = n$

37. $\frac{5 \times 5 \times 5 \times 5}{10 \times 10 \times 10 \times 10} \times \frac{10 \times 10 \times 10 \times 10}{5 \times 5 \times 5 \times 5} = n$

38. $\frac{75 \times 75 \times 75}{25 \times 25 \times 25} = n$

39. $\frac{(3 + 7) \times (4 + 6) \times (20 - 10)}{1 \times 1 \times 1 \times 1 \times 1 \times 1} = n$

40. $\frac{49 \times (35 + 6)}{7 \times 7} = n$

Work in pairs. Roll a 0–5 cube the number of times suggested in problems 1, 2, and 3. Keep records. Compare your results with your predictions. See how the results from other pairs compare with the predictions.

1. Suppose you roll a 0–5 cube 300 times.
   a. About what fraction of those times would you expect it to land with 0 up?
   b. How many times is that?
   c. Do you think that you would get exactly that many?

2. Suppose you roll a 0–5 cube 100 times.
   a. About what fraction of those times would you expect an even number (0, 2, or 4) to be up?
   b. How many times is that?
   c. Do you think that you would get exactly that many?

3. Suppose you roll a 0–5 cube 120 times.
   a. About what fraction of those times would you expect a number divisible by 3 (0 or 3) to be up?
   b. How many times is that?
   c. Do you think that you would get exactly that many?

Improper Fractions and Mixed Numbers

Some fractions have numerators that are greater than or equal to their denominators. Here are some examples:

$$\frac{7}{3}, \frac{5}{5}, \frac{9}{4}, \frac{15}{11}$$

Such fractions are called *improper fractions* because they are not really parts of a whole.

By dividing, we can change an improper fraction to a whole number or to a mixed number (a whole number mixed with a proper fraction). Here's an example:

$$\frac{7}{3} \rightarrow 3\overline{)7}\,{}^{2 \text{ R}1}; \text{ so } \frac{7}{3} = 2\frac{1}{3}$$

We can also change a mixed number to an improper fraction.

$$2\frac{1}{3} = \frac{6}{3} + \frac{1}{3} = \frac{7}{3}$$

The denominator is the same as the original fraction. The numerator is the product of the denominator and the whole number part *plus* the original numerator: $(3 \times 2) + 1 = 7$.

Change each improper fraction to a mixed or a whole number.

1. $\frac{5}{3}$ 4. $\frac{8}{5}$ 7. $\frac{10}{9}$ 10. $\frac{7}{2}$ 13. $\frac{25}{6}$ 16. $\frac{8}{8}$ 19. $\frac{83}{10}$

2. $\frac{10}{3}$ 5. $\frac{10}{5}$ 8. $\frac{20}{9}$ 11. $\frac{11}{4}$ 14. $\frac{8}{7}$ 17. $\frac{53}{8}$ 20. $\frac{4}{2}$

3. $\frac{6}{3}$ 6. $\frac{13}{5}$ 9. $\frac{30}{9}$ 12. $\frac{13}{6}$ 15. $\frac{25}{7}$ 18. $\frac{13}{10}$ 21. $\frac{9}{2}$

Change each mixed number to an improper fraction.

22. $1\frac{1}{2}$ 25. $3\frac{2}{7}$ 28. $5\frac{3}{8}$ 31. $4\frac{2}{3}$ 34. $4\frac{7}{9}$ 37. $5\frac{1}{2}$ 40. $3\frac{5}{6}$

23. $3\frac{1}{3}$ 26. $5\frac{1}{6}$ 29. $1\frac{3}{4}$ 32. $3\frac{3}{8}$ 35. $2\frac{7}{10}$ 38. $2\frac{1}{5}$ 41. $6\frac{9}{10}$

24. $2\frac{5}{7}$ 27. $4\frac{1}{8}$ 30. $5\frac{1}{4}$ 33. $1\frac{5}{9}$ 36. $8\frac{3}{10}$ 39. $4\frac{3}{5}$ 42. $1\frac{1}{10}$

Multiply. Change improper fractions to whole or mixed numbers.
Reduce all answers.

43. $\frac{3}{5}$ of 20

44. $\frac{1}{3}$ of 15

45. $\frac{1}{2} \times 4$

46. $\frac{3}{7} \times 21$

47. $\frac{2}{3} \times \frac{4}{7}$

48. $\frac{3}{7} \times \frac{14}{15}$

49. $\frac{2}{3} \times \frac{6}{8}$

50. $\frac{7}{8} \times 16$

51. $\frac{1}{3} \times \frac{1}{9}$

52. $\frac{2}{3} \times \frac{3}{4}$

53. $\frac{2}{3} \times 10$

54. $\frac{3}{4} \times 30$

55. $\frac{4}{7} \times 28$

56. $\frac{1}{6} \times \frac{6}{7}$

57. $\frac{6}{7} \times \frac{1}{6}$

What does the commutative law for multiplication say?

The commutative law for multiplication is true for fractions as well as for whole numbers.

$$\frac{3}{7} \times \frac{11}{13} = \frac{3 \times 11}{7 \times 13}$$

Since 3, 11, 7, and 13 are whole numbers and the commutative law of multiplication is true for whole numbers, $3 \times 11 = 11 \times 3$ and $7 \times 13 = 13 \times 7$. So

$$\frac{3}{7} \times \frac{11}{13} = \frac{3 \times 11}{7 \times 13} = \frac{11 \times 3}{13 \times 7} = \frac{11}{13} \times \frac{3}{7}.$$

Multiply. Look for shortcuts. Cancel when you can. Change improper fractions to whole or mixed numbers. Reduce all answers.

58. $\frac{12}{49} \times \frac{21}{27}$

59. $\frac{21}{27} \times \frac{12}{49}$

60. $\frac{9}{16} \times 12$

61. $12 \times \frac{9}{16}$

62. $\frac{7}{15} \times \frac{5}{14}$

63. $\frac{5}{14} \times \frac{7}{15}$

64. $\frac{1}{6}$ of 20

65. $\frac{5}{6}$ of 20

66. $\frac{3}{7} \times \frac{5}{9}$

67. $\frac{3}{4} \times \frac{16}{21}$

68. $\frac{3}{10} \times \frac{5}{9}$

69. $\frac{2}{5} \times \frac{16}{25}$

70. $\frac{16}{25} \times \frac{2}{5}$

71. $\frac{1}{2} \times \frac{4}{7}$

72. $\frac{2}{3} \times \frac{9}{16}$

73. $\frac{4}{5} \times \frac{15}{16}$

74. $\frac{5}{6} \times \frac{12}{35}$

75. $\frac{7}{12} \times \frac{6}{7}$

3 friends, Mrs. Ritchie, Mrs. Baronoff, and Mrs. Brady, each had 3 children. They agreed that each would leave $\frac{2}{5}$ of her money to her oldest child, $\frac{1}{3}$ to her middle child, and the rest to her youngest child.

1. Mrs. Ritchie left $24,000.
   a. How much money should her oldest child get?
   b. How much money should her middle child get?
   c. How much money should her youngest get?
   d. What fraction (reduced completely) of the money should her youngest get?

2. Mrs. Baronoff left $30,000.
   a. How much money should her oldest child get?
   b. How much money should her middle child get?
   c. How much money should her youngest get?
   d. What fraction (reduced completely) of the money should her youngest get?

3. Mrs. Brady left $15.
   a. How much money should her oldest child get?
   b. How much money should her middle child get?
   c. How much money should her youngest get?
   d. What fraction (reduced completely) of the money should her youngest get?

4. A bread recipe calls for $\frac{1}{2}$ cup of oatmeal, $\frac{2}{3}$ cup of cornmeal, and 2 eggs (among other things). Jerome wants to make half the recipe.
   a. How much oatmeal should he use?
   b. How much cornmeal should he use?
   c. How many eggs should he use?

5. Captain Elsworth was flying at half the speed of sound (mach $\frac{1}{2}$). The control tower told her to reduce her speed to $\frac{1}{3}$ of what it was. What is the mach number for her new speed? (A mach number is the ratio of the speed of a body to the speed of sound in a fluid medium, such as air. It is named for Ernst Mach, an Austrian physicist.)

6. A plane was flying at a speed of mach $\frac{3}{4}$. Its speed was reduced to $\frac{2}{3}$ of what it had been. What is its new mach number?

7. If you roll a 0–5 cube, you expect it to land with 1 or 2 up $\frac{1}{3}$ of the time. If you toss a coin, you expect it to land with the head up $\frac{1}{2}$ of the time. If you roll the cube and toss the coin at the same time, what fraction of the time would you expect 1 or 2 up on the cube and the head up on the coin?

4 authors got together to write a book. They agreed to split their royalties this way: $\frac{2}{5}$ for Mr. Salisby, $\frac{1}{4}$ for Ms. Ryder, $\frac{1}{5}$ for Ms. Lopez, and the rest for Dr. Kita.

8. The total royalties for the first year were $5000.
   a. How much money from royalties did Mr. Salisby get?
   b. How much money from royalties did Ms. Ryder get?
   c. How much money from royalties did Ms. Lopez get?
   d. How much money from royalties did Dr. Kita get?
   e. What *fraction* of the royalties did Dr. Kita get the first year? (Reduce your answer completely.)
   f. Mr. Salisby had some help from Mr. Hyatt in writing his part of the book. He agreed to pay Mr. Hyatt $\frac{1}{4}$ of his royalties. What fraction of the total royalties is that? How much money is that?

9. The total royalties for the second year were $20,000. Answer questions a–f from problem 8 for the second year.

Suppose you roll two 0–5 cubes 360 times.

[1] About what fraction of the time would you expect the first 0–5 cube to land with 0 up?

[2] How many times is that?

[3] About what fraction of those 60 times would you expect the second cube to land with a 0 up as well?

[4] How many times is that?

[5] Of the 360 times you roll the two 0–5 cubes, would you expect to get two 0s up about $\frac{1}{6}$ of $\frac{1}{6}$, or $\frac{1}{36}$, of the time?

Try the experiment. Work in pairs. One person should keep track of the total number of rolls. The other keeps track of the number of double 0s rolled.

Do you get about 10 double 0s in 360 rolls? Some pairs will get 9 or 8 or 7 double 0s, and some will get 11 or 12 or 13 double 0s. But in your class, there should be few pairs that get more than 20 double 0s or fewer than 3 double 0s.

1. Suppose you roll two 0–5 cubes. What fraction of the time would you expect to get
    a. 0 on the first cube and 0 on the second cube?
    b. 0 on the first and 5 on the second cube?
    c. 1 on the first and 4 on the second?
    d. 2 on the first and 3 on the second?
    e. 3 on the first and 2 on the second?
    f. 4 on the first and 1 on the second?
    g. 5 on the first and 0 on the second?
    h. 6 on the first and 0 on the second? (Be careful.)
    i. 5 as the sum of the numbers on the 2 cubes?
       (Hint: Is the sum 5 only when you get 1 of the combinations in b–g?)

2. Suppose you flip 2 coins. What fraction of the time would you expect
    a. the first coin to show heads?
    b. the first coin to show heads and the second coin to show heads?
    c. the first coin to show heads and the second coin to show tails?
    d. the first coin to show tails and the second coin to show heads?
    e. the first coin to show tails and the second coin to show tails?
    f. exactly 1 of the coins to show heads?

3. Suppose you flip 2 coins 100 times.
    a. What fraction of the time would you expect exactly 1 to land heads?
    b. About how many times is that?

Try the experiment in problem 3. Compare your results to what you predicted.

[6] Do you get 1 head exactly 50 times?
[7] Do you get 1 head about 50 times?

Practice with Probability

The *probability* of an event is the fraction representing the number of times the event would be expected to occur in a large number of trials.

Action	Event	Probability
Flipping a fair coin	heads	$\frac{1}{2}$
Rolling a 0–5 cube	0	$\frac{1}{6}$
Rolling two 0–5 cubes	double 0	$\frac{1}{36}$

1. Suppose you flip 2 coins. What is the probability of getting
   a. 2 heads?
   b. 2 tails?
   c. 1 head and 1 tail?

You have just found the probabilities of getting 2, 0, and 1 heads when flipping 2 coins. Use these answers to help you answer the next question.

2. Suppose you flip 2 coins. What is the probability of getting
   a. 1 or 2 heads?
   b. 0, 1, or 2 heads?

3. Suppose you roll two 0–5 cubes. What is the probability of rolling two 0s?

4. Suppose you roll two 0–5 cubes. What is the probability of these events:

	First Cube	Second Cube
a.	0	1
b.	1	0

5. Suppose you roll two 0–5 cubes. What is the probability of these events:

	First Cube	Second Cube
a.	0	2
b.	1	1
c.	2	0

6. Suppose you roll two 0–5 cubes. What is the probability of these events:

	First Cube	Second Cube
a.	0	3
b.	1	2
c.	2	1
d.	3	0

7. Suppose you roll two 0–5 cubes. What is the probability of rolling each of the following sums? Don't reduce your answers. Leave them with 36 as the denominator.

   a. 0 (See problem 3.)
   b. 1 (See problem 4.)
   c. 2 (See problem 5.)
   d. 3
   e. 4
   f. 5 (Try to guess. Then check.)
   g. 6 (Be careful. Remember they are 0–5 cubes.)
   h. 7
   i. 8
   j. 9
   k. 10

Sum	Number of Times
0	II
1	II
2	III
3	HHT I
4	HHT
5	HHT II
6	HHT II
7	IIII
8	III
9	II
10	I

8. What *would you expect* the sum of all the probabilities for problem 7 to be? That is, if you roll two 0–5 cubes, what will be the probability of getting a number from 0 through 10 when you add the 2 numbers?

9. What is the sum of the probabilities in problem 7?

10. Work with a partner. Roll two 0–5 cubes. Add the 2 numbers. Keep a record of the sums. Use a form like this one. Roll the cubes 360 times. Compare your results with your answers to problem 7.

In the last lesson, you had to add

$$\frac{1}{36} + \frac{2}{36} + \frac{3}{36} + \frac{4}{36} + \frac{5}{36} + \frac{6}{36} + \frac{5}{36} + \frac{4}{36} + \frac{3}{36} + \frac{2}{36} + \frac{1}{36}.$$

If you had reduced each fraction, you would have had to add

$$\frac{1}{36} + \frac{1}{18} + \frac{1}{12} + \frac{1}{9} + \frac{5}{36} + \frac{1}{6} + \frac{5}{36} + \frac{1}{9} + \frac{1}{12} + \frac{1}{18} + \frac{1}{36}.$$

[1] How would you do each of these problems?

[2] Which problem is easier?

Adding fractions is like adding measurements. The denominators of fractions are like the units of measurements. If you wanted to add 17 inches and 2 feet, you would change both measurements to the same units. You'd probably use inches in this case. The answer would be 17 inches + 24 inches, or 41 inches.

To add $\frac{1}{36}$ and $\frac{1}{18}$, change $\frac{1}{18}$ to $\frac{2}{36}$ and add:

$$\frac{1}{36} + \frac{2}{36} = \frac{3}{36}$$

To make both denominators the same is easy when one denominator is a factor of the other. In this case, since 18 is a factor of 36, just multiply top and bottom of $\frac{1}{18}$ by 2 to get $\frac{2}{36}$. Notice that this is like changing measurements in feet to measurements in inches.

When one denominator is not a factor of the other, you usually must change both denominators.

Examples: $\frac{1}{6} + \frac{2}{9} = \frac{3}{18} + \frac{4}{18} = \frac{7}{18}$

$\frac{2}{3} + \frac{1}{4} = \frac{8}{12} + \frac{3}{12} = \frac{11}{12}$

Here are the ways to handle all the possible situations for adding fractions:

A. If the fractions have the same denominator, just add the numerators.

Example: $\frac{2}{36} + \frac{3}{36} = \frac{5}{36}$

B. If the fractions have different denominators, first change them to equivalent fractions that have the same denominator as described below. Then add the numerators.

1. When one fraction has a denominator that is a factor of the other, multiply top and bottom of that fraction by the number that will make the denominators the same.

   Example: $\frac{5}{12} + \frac{5}{36} = \frac{15}{36} + \frac{5}{36} = \frac{20}{36} = \frac{5}{9}$ (reduced)

2. When you can see that both denominators are factors of the same number, you can make both denominators the same.

   Example: $\frac{5}{12} + \frac{7}{18} = \frac{15}{36} + \frac{14}{36} = \frac{29}{36}$

3. When you can't find any other way, you can always multiply the 2 denominators. This will give a number that you can use as the same denominator for both fractions.

   Example: $\frac{2}{7} + \frac{3}{8} = \frac{8 \times 2}{8 \times 7} + \frac{7 \times 3}{7 \times 8} = \frac{16}{56} + \frac{21}{56} = \frac{37}{56}$

   You will get the same answer using this procedure as you will using the other 2 ways. It just takes longer.

   Examples

   $$\frac{5}{12} + \frac{5}{36} = \frac{36 \times 5}{36 \times 12} + \frac{12 \times 5}{12 \times 36} = \frac{180}{432} + \frac{60}{432} = \frac{240}{432} = \frac{5}{9}$$

   $$\frac{5}{12} + \frac{7}{18} = \frac{18 \times 5}{18 \times 12} + \frac{12 \times 7}{12 \times 18} = \frac{90}{216} + \frac{84}{216} = \frac{174}{216} = \frac{29}{36}$$

   (Note: A more detailed explanation of the method in B3 can be found on page 202.)

Add. Reduce your answers completely.

1. $\frac{1}{5} + \frac{3}{5}$ 8. $\frac{1}{4} + \frac{1}{3}$ 15. $\frac{1}{6} + \frac{1}{3}$

2. $\frac{3}{10} + \frac{5}{10}$ 9. $\frac{3}{4} + \frac{1}{8}$ 16. $\frac{1}{2} + \frac{1}{2}$

3. $\frac{1}{36} + \frac{5}{36}$ 10. $\frac{2}{7} + \frac{4}{7}$ 17. $\frac{1}{3} + \frac{2}{3}$

4. $\frac{3}{36} + \frac{4}{36}$ 11. $\frac{6}{36} + \frac{5}{36}$ 18. $\frac{1}{2} + \frac{1}{3}$

5. $\frac{1}{12} + \frac{1}{9}$ 12. $\frac{1}{6} + \frac{5}{36}$ 19. $\frac{1}{2} + \frac{1}{5}$

6. $\frac{1}{12} + \frac{1}{4}$ 13. $\frac{1}{8} + \frac{1}{4}$ 20. $\frac{3}{5} + \frac{2}{5}$

7. $\frac{7}{36} + \frac{5}{12}$ 14. $\frac{1}{2} + \frac{1}{4}$ 21. $\frac{2}{5} + \frac{3}{5}$

To subtract fractions, you use the same procedures as for adding fractions, except that you subtract the numerators.

Examples: $\frac{5}{7} - \frac{2}{7} = \frac{3}{7}$

$$\frac{5}{12} - \frac{11}{36} = \frac{15}{36} - \frac{11}{36} = \frac{4}{36} = \frac{1}{9}$$

$$\frac{2}{9} - \frac{1}{6} = \frac{4}{18} - \frac{3}{18} = \frac{1}{18}$$

$$\frac{1}{3} - \frac{1}{4} = \frac{4}{12} - \frac{3}{12} = \frac{1}{12}$$

Subtract. Reduce your answers completely.

22. $\frac{1}{2} - \frac{1}{4}$ 27. $\frac{1}{6} - \frac{1}{36}$ 32. $\frac{5}{10} - \frac{4}{10}$

23. $\frac{5}{7} - \frac{3}{7}$ 28. $\frac{3}{8} - \frac{2}{8}$ 33. $\frac{1}{2} - \frac{2}{5}$

24. $\frac{1}{3} - \frac{1}{6}$ 29. $\frac{3}{8} - \frac{1}{4}$ 34. $\frac{1}{6} - \frac{1}{12}$

25. $\frac{5}{8} - \frac{1}{8}$ 30. $\frac{1}{3} - \frac{1}{4}$ 35. $\frac{5}{6} - \frac{17}{36}$

26. $\frac{6}{36} - \frac{1}{36}$ 31. $\frac{3}{4} - \frac{2}{3}$ 36. $\frac{1}{4} - \frac{1}{6}$

MAKE $\frac{1}{2}$ GAME

Players: 2 or more
Materials: Two 0–5 cubes, two 5–10 cubes
Object: To make a problem with the answer closest to $\frac{1}{2}$

Rules

1. Take turns rolling all 4 cubes.

2. Make 2 fractions that are both less than 1.

3. Make an addition or subtraction problem that gives an answer close to $\frac{1}{2}$. Don't calculate the answer yet.

4. The player whose problem has an answer closest to $\frac{1}{2}$ wins the round. You don't need to calculate the answers unless you can't tell by looking.

Sample Game

Oralee rolled: $\boxed{0}$ $\boxed{4}$ $\boxed{5}$ $\boxed{7}$ Bryant rolled: $\boxed{3}$ $\boxed{5}$ $\boxed{6}$ $\boxed{7}$

She made: $\frac{4}{7} + \frac{0}{5}$ He made: $\frac{5}{6} - \frac{3}{7}$

They couldn't tell who was closer to $\frac{1}{2}$ without calculating.

Oralee: $\frac{4}{7} + \frac{0}{5} = \frac{4}{7}$

Bryant: $\frac{5}{6} - \frac{3}{7} = \frac{35}{42} - \frac{18}{42} = \frac{17}{42}$

They changed $\frac{4}{7}$ to $\frac{24}{42}$. When both fractions had the same denominator, it was easy for them to see which fraction was closer to $\frac{1}{2}$, or $\frac{21}{42}$. $\frac{24}{42}$ is closer to $\frac{21}{42}$, or $\frac{1}{2}$, than $\frac{17}{42}$ is.

Oralee won this round.

On page 199, one of the ways for finding a denominator to use when adding fractions was to multiply the denominators. You can *always* add 2 fractions if you do that.

Here are the steps you use:

Step 1   The denominator of the sum is $\frac{3}{7} + \frac{5}{11} = \frac{}{77}$
           the product of the denominators.

           $7 \times 11 = 77$

Step 2   The numerator of the sum is found $\frac{3}{7} + \frac{5}{11} = \frac{33 + 35}{77} = \frac{68}{77}$
           by multiplying each numerator
           by the opposite denominator
           and adding the products.

           $3 \times 11 = 33, 7 \times 5 = 35$

Step 3   Reduce the answer if appropriate.

Some people refer to the multiplications in the second step as "cross multiplying" because you cross to the other fraction to multiply.

$$\frac{3}{7} \bigtimes \frac{5}{11}$$

To subtract fractions, use the same steps but subtract in the second step. You must write the product of the *first* numerator and the second denominator *first*.

Example

Step 1 $\frac{3}{5} - \frac{2}{7} = \frac{}{35}$ $(5 \times 7 = 35)$

Step 2 $\frac{3}{5} - \frac{2}{7} = \frac{21 - 10}{35} = \frac{11}{35}$ $(3 \times 7 = 21; 2 \times 5 = 10)$

Step 3   Reduce if appropriate.

Remember, there may be simpler ways to compute the answers, but this system will always work.

Practice with Fractions

Add or subtract. Reduce completely. Change improper fractions to whole or mixed numbers.

1. $\frac{3}{8} + \frac{5}{9}$

2. $\frac{1}{3} + \frac{1}{4}$

3. $\frac{3}{7} + \frac{2}{7}$

4. $\frac{1}{3} + \frac{1}{6}$

5. $\frac{7}{10} + \frac{5}{10}$

6. $\frac{2}{3} + \frac{1}{4}$

7. $\frac{1}{2} + \frac{2}{3}$

8. $\frac{1}{3} + \frac{5}{12}$

9. $\frac{3}{4} + \frac{1}{2}$

10. $\frac{2}{5} + \frac{3}{4}$

11. $\frac{5}{6} - \frac{1}{7}$

12. $\frac{1}{3} - \frac{1}{4}$

13. $\frac{5}{6} - \frac{1}{3}$

14. $\frac{7}{10} - \frac{3}{10}$

15. $\frac{1}{8} - \frac{1}{9}$

16. $\frac{1}{2} - \frac{1}{3}$

17. $\frac{3}{5} - \frac{5}{10}$

18. $\frac{3}{5} - \frac{6}{10}$

19. $\frac{1}{4} - \frac{1}{5}$

20. $\frac{7}{11} - \frac{1}{3}$

21. $\frac{5}{8} + \frac{7}{8}$

22. $\frac{7}{8} - \frac{5}{8}$

23. $\frac{1}{5} + \frac{1}{6}$

24. $\frac{1}{5} - \frac{1}{6}$

25. $\frac{5}{6} + \frac{4}{5}$

26. $\frac{5}{6} - \frac{4}{5}$

27. $\frac{1}{3} - \frac{2}{9}$

28. $\frac{3}{8} - \frac{1}{4}$

29. $\frac{3}{8} + \frac{1}{4}$

30. $\frac{1}{3} + \frac{2}{9}$

Solve for n. Look for shortcuts.

31. $\frac{5}{6} \times \frac{4}{5} \times \frac{3}{4} \times \frac{2}{3} \times \frac{1}{2} = n$

32. $\left(\frac{5}{6} \times \frac{4}{5} \times \frac{3}{4} \times \frac{2}{3} \times \frac{1}{2} \right) + \frac{5}{6} = n$

33. $\frac{5}{6} - \left(\frac{5}{6} \times \frac{4}{5} \times \frac{3}{4} \times \frac{2}{3} \times \frac{1}{2} \right) = n$

34. $\frac{1}{6} + \frac{2}{6} + \frac{3}{6} + \frac{4}{6} + \frac{5}{6} = n$

35. $\frac{2}{5} \times \left(\frac{1}{6} + \frac{2}{6} + \frac{3}{6} + \frac{4}{6} + \frac{5}{6} \right) = n$

36. $\frac{1}{6} + \frac{1}{3} + \frac{1}{2} + \frac{2}{3} + \frac{5}{6} = n$

37. $\frac{2}{3} \times \frac{3}{2} = n$

38. $\frac{2}{3} \times \frac{2}{3} \times \frac{2}{3} \times \frac{2}{3} \times \frac{3}{2} \times \frac{3}{2} \times \frac{3}{2} \times \frac{3}{2} = n$

39. $\frac{1}{21} + \frac{2}{21} + \frac{3}{21} + \frac{4}{21} + \frac{5}{21} + \frac{6}{21} = n$

40. $n = \frac{1}{15} + \frac{2}{15} + \frac{3}{15} + \frac{4}{15} + \frac{5}{15}$

More Practice with Fractions

Do these problems. Watch the signs. Reduce answers completely.
Change improper fractions to whole or mixed numbers.

1. $\frac{5}{8} - \frac{1}{10}$ 11. $\frac{7}{10} \times \frac{2}{3}$ 21. $\frac{3}{6} - \frac{2}{8}$

2. $\frac{5}{8} + \frac{1}{10}$ 12. $\frac{7}{10} + \frac{2}{3}$ 22. $\frac{4}{5} - \frac{3}{10}$

3. $\frac{5}{8} \times \frac{1}{10}$ 13. $\frac{1}{5} - \frac{0}{6}$ 23. $\frac{4}{5} \times \frac{3}{10}$

4. $\frac{6}{5} - \frac{4}{5}$ 14. $\frac{1}{5} + \frac{0}{6}$ 24. $\frac{4}{5} + \frac{3}{10}$

5. $\frac{6}{5} + \frac{4}{5}$ 15. $\frac{1}{5} \times \frac{0}{6}$ 25. $\frac{5}{6} \times \frac{3}{10}$

6. $\frac{6}{5} \times \frac{4}{5}$ 16. $\frac{4}{7} \times \frac{3}{8}$ 26. $\frac{5}{6} + \frac{3}{10}$

7. $\frac{7}{10} + \frac{1}{3}$ 17. $\frac{4}{7} - \frac{3}{8}$ 27. $\frac{5}{6} - \frac{3}{10}$

8. $\frac{7}{10} - \frac{1}{3}$ 18. $\frac{4}{7} + \frac{3}{8}$ 28. $\frac{3}{8} - \frac{1}{8}$

9. $\frac{7}{10} \times \frac{1}{3}$ 19. $\frac{2}{8} + \frac{3}{6}$ 29. $\frac{3}{8} + \frac{1}{8}$

10. $\frac{7}{10} - \frac{2}{3}$ 20. $\frac{3}{6} \times \frac{2}{8}$ 30. $\frac{3}{8} \times \frac{1}{8}$

31. A doctor told a nurse to give the patient a $\frac{1}{4}$-grain tablet of medicine. There were no $\frac{1}{4}$-grain tablets. So the nurse gave the patient two $\frac{1}{2}$-grain tablets.
    a. Did the nurse do the right thing?
    b. How much medicine did the nurse give the patient?
    c. How many times more medicine did the nurse give the patient than the doctor ordered?
    d. What would you have done if you had been the nurse? (There are only $\frac{1}{2}$-grain tablets available, and you can't contact the doctor.)

32. A cook was doubling a recipe. The recipe called for $\frac{1}{4}$ cup of milk. So the cook used $\frac{1}{8}$ cup of milk.
    a. Was that the right thing to do?
    b. Why do you think the cook did that?
    c. How much milk should the cook have used?

33. Phineas and Phyllis Arrback gave all of their prize-winning goldfish to their 3 grandchildren. The oldest, Philip, was to get $\frac{1}{2}$ of the goldfish; the next oldest, Phoebe, was to get $\frac{1}{4}$ of the goldfish; and the youngest, Phemie, was to get $\frac{1}{6}$ of the goldfish. The Arrbacks had 11 goldfish.

a. How many goldfish should each child get?

b. Is the total of your answers 11?

The grandchildren argued about how to divide up the goldfish. Nobody wanted to kill any of the valuable goldfish. A wise friend came to visit and asked what the trouble was.

When they told her, she said: "I'll solve your problem. I just bought a goldfish at the pet store. We'll put my goldfish in with your 11. So we'll have 12 goldfish. Now Philip gets 6 goldfish, Phoebe gets 3 goldfish, Phemie gets 2 goldfish, and I'll take my goldfish and be on my way."

c. Did the grandchildren get their 11 goldfish?

d. Why was it possible for their friend to solve the problem this way?

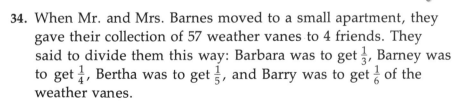

34. When Mr. and Mrs. Barnes moved to a small apartment, they gave their collection of 57 weather vanes to 4 friends. They said to divide them this way: Barbara was to get $\frac{1}{3}$, Barney was to get $\frac{1}{4}$, Bertha was to get $\frac{1}{5}$, and Barry was to get $\frac{1}{6}$ of the weather vanes.

a. Would any of the friends get a whole number of weather vanes with this arrangement? How many friends? Who?

b. Suppose you are a wise friend who happens to visit and you want to solve the problem so that each of the friends gets a whole number of weather vanes. How many weather vanes would you want to bring with you?

c. What is the sum of the 4 fractions $\frac{1}{3}$, $\frac{1}{4}$, $\frac{1}{5}$, and $\frac{1}{6}$?

d. Why is it possible for you to solve the problem this way?

One way to think about division is to think about functions.
Here is a function rule:

$$x \xrightarrow{\times 2} y$$

[1] If x is 5, what is y?

There are 2 ways to show how you can go from y back to x:

A. $y \xrightarrow{\div 2} x$ B. $y \xrightarrow{\times \frac{1}{2}} x$

[2] If y = 10, do both rules work to give x = 5?

We can do the same thing with fractions.
Let's look at this function rule:

$$x \xrightarrow{\times \frac{2}{3}} y$$

We can use either of these 2 rules to go from y to x:

C. $y \xrightarrow{\div \frac{2}{3}} x$ D. $y \xrightarrow{\times \frac{3}{2}} x$

These 2 function charts will help you see how this works. Copy
and complete the function charts.

$$x \xrightarrow{\times \frac{2}{3}} y \qquad y \xrightarrow{\times \frac{3}{2}} x$$

x	y
3	
6	
12	
1	
$\frac{1}{2}$	

y	x
2	
4	
8	
$\frac{2}{3}$	
$\frac{1}{3}$	

Compare the 2 function charts on page 206.

[3] Does the rule —$\left(\times \frac{3}{2}\right)$→ **"undo" the rule** —$\left(\times \frac{2}{3}\right)$→ ?

We say that $\frac{3}{2}$ is the *multiplicative inverse* of $\frac{2}{3}$.

Remember

For any fraction $\frac{d}{b}$, where d and b are whole numbers and are not equal to zero, $\frac{b}{d}$ is the multiplicative inverse of $\frac{d}{b}$. Multiplying by $\frac{b}{d}$ is equivalent to dividing by $\frac{d}{b}$.

Examples: $\frac{4}{7} \div \frac{2}{7} = \frac{4}{7} \times \frac{7}{2} = \frac{28}{14} = 2$

$\frac{3}{8} \div \frac{3}{4} = \frac{3}{8} \times \frac{4}{3} = \frac{12}{24} = \frac{1}{2}$

$\frac{3}{7} \div \frac{2}{9} = \frac{3}{7} \times \frac{9}{2} = \frac{27}{14}$

Another way to think about dividing fractions is to think about dividing measurements.

If the units are the same, dividing measurements is just like dividing numbers. For example, to find out how many suits can be made out of a piece of cloth 36 meters long if each suit requires a piece of cloth 2 meters long, you divide the measurements. The answer is 36 meters ÷ 2 meters = 18. Notice, however, that the units do not appear in the answer. The answer is 18 *suits,* not 18 meters.

Dividing fractions can be done the same way. If the denominators are the same, the quotient of the fractions is the quotient of their numerators.

Examples: $\frac{4}{7} \div \frac{2}{7} = 2$

$\frac{3}{8} \div \frac{3}{4} = \frac{3}{8} \div \frac{6}{8} = \frac{3}{6} = \frac{1}{2}$

$\frac{3}{7} \div \frac{2}{9} = \frac{27}{63} \div \frac{14}{63} = \frac{27}{14}$

Compare these examples with those using the multiplicative inverse.

Divide. Use either method. Reduce all fractions.

1. $\frac{3}{5} \div \frac{4}{5}$ 6. $\frac{3}{36} \div \frac{4}{36}$ 11. $\frac{1}{6} \div \frac{1}{12}$

2. $\frac{6}{7} \div \frac{2}{7}$ 7. $\frac{1}{12} \div \frac{1}{9}$ 12. $\frac{1}{2} \div \frac{2}{5}$

3. $\frac{1}{3} \div \frac{1}{4}$ 8. $\frac{3}{4} \div \frac{2}{3}$ 13. $\frac{3}{8} \div \frac{1}{4}$

4. $\frac{6}{36} \div \frac{2}{36}$ 9. $\frac{9}{12} \div \frac{8}{12}$ 14. $\frac{5}{6} \div \frac{1}{2}$

5. $\frac{1}{6} \div \frac{1}{18}$ 10. $\frac{3}{10} \div \frac{7}{10}$ 15. $\frac{1}{4} \div \frac{1}{6}$

16. 1 tablespoon of flour is the same as $\frac{1}{16}$ cup of flour. How many tablespoons of flour are there in $\frac{3}{4}$ cup of flour?

17. The road into the Walnut Wilderness Campground is $\frac{7}{8}$ mile long. The owner wants to plant walnut trees every $\frac{1}{16}$ of a mile along both sides of the road. There already are walnut trees on both sides of the front gate. How many walnut trees should she buy?

ROLL A FRACTION GAME

Players: 2 or more
Materials: Two 0–5 cubes, two 5–10 cubes, calculators
Objects: To make the fraction closest to the goal

Rules

1. Pick a simple fraction between 0 and 1 as a goal—for example,

$$\frac{1}{3}, \frac{1}{4}, \frac{2}{3}, \frac{3}{4}, \frac{2}{5}, \text{ or } \frac{3}{5}.$$

2. Take turns rolling all 4 cubes. If you roll a **10**, roll again.

3. Make two 2-digit numbers. Use them to form a fraction as close to the goal as you can. (You may use zero as the tens digit to make a number like 08.)

4. The player with the fraction closest to the goal wins the round. (If you can't tell just by looking or by reducing the fractions, use a calculator to change the fractions to decimals to see which is closest to the goal.)

Sample Games

Chris and Rita chose $\frac{2}{3}$ as the goal.

Chris rolled: **3** **5** **7** **9**   Rita rolled: **1** **2** **7** **8**

He made: $\frac{53}{79}$ She made: $\frac{18}{27}$

Rita won this round. Both players knew that Rita had $\frac{2}{3}$ exactly.

Joe and Winnie chose $\frac{1}{2}$ as the goal.

Joe rolled: **0** **3** **7** **8**   Winnie rolled: **1** **4** **5** **8**

He made: $\frac{37}{80}$ She made: $\frac{41}{85}$

They couldn't tell who was closer to $\frac{1}{2}$, so they used a calculator. After rounding:

Joe had 0.46.   Winnie had 0.48.

Winnie was the winner of this round.

1. Lorraine is going to make Special Green Salad. Here is the list of what she needs to make it for 4 people.

1   head lettuce
½   bunch spinach
½   cup green peas
½   cup cooked lima beans
¼   cup toasted sunflower seeds

   a. How much spinach is needed to make enough salad for 2 people?
   b. What amount of sunflower seeds is needed to make enough salad for 12 people?

2. Bonnie is making draft stoppers for the doors and windows in her house. She needs $\frac{1}{9}$ yard of fabric to make each one. She bought a $\frac{2}{3}$-yard fabric remnant for 84¢.

   a. How many draft stoppers can she make?
   b. How much did the fabric for 1 draft stopper cost Bonnie?

3. There are 24 students in Mel's class. He said that $\frac{1}{2}$ are boys, $\frac{1}{3}$ have brown eyes, $\frac{1}{4}$ are girls, $\frac{1}{5}$ are wearing jeans today, and $\frac{1}{6}$ are left-handed.

   a. Which of Mel's statements make sense?
   b. Which of Mel's statements don't make sense?

4. Ted found this recipe:

French Dressing
½   cup oil
2   tablespoons lemon juice
2   tablespoons cider vinegar
¼   teaspoon salt
¼   teaspoon mustard powder
¼   teaspoon paprika
⅛   teaspoon pepper
Shake together in a jar.

a. About how much salad dressing does this recipe make?
(Hint: 3 teaspoons = 1 tablespoon; 1 tablespoon = $\frac{1}{16}$ cup)

b. Is the amount of salt, mustard, paprika, and pepper
altogether more than 1 teaspoon?

5. Suppose you roll two 0–5 cubes. What is the probability that
the sum of the 2 numbers rolled will be 6 or more? (Hint: Add
the probabilities for 6, 7, 8, 9, and 10.)

6. Suppose you roll two 0–5 cubes. What is the probability that
the sum of the numbers rolled will be 3 or less?

7. Vera and Mike are playing Total Throw. They roll two 0–5
cubes. Mike wins if the total showing is 0, 1, 2, 8, 9, or 10.
Vera wins if the total showing is 3, 4, 5, 6, or 7.

a. What is the probability that Mike will win on a given
throw?

b. What is the probability that Vera will win on a given
throw?

8. Suppose you flip 3 coins. What is the probability of getting

a. 3 heads?   **c.** 2 heads and 1 tail?

b. 1 head and 2 tails?   **d.** 3 tails?

9. Work with somebody else and play Total Throw (see problem 7)
100 times.

a. About how many times out of 100 would you expect the
player who wins with 0, 1, 2, 8, 9, or 10 to win?

b. How many times did that player actually win?

10. Suppose you flip 3 coins 200 times. About how many times
would you expect to get:

a. 3 heads?   **c.** 2 heads and 1 tail?

b. 1 head and 2 tails?   **d.** 3 tails?

Try the experiment in problem 10. Work with a partner and
compare your results with those you predicted and with those of
others doing the experiment.

1. 412 × 3.12
2. 4.12 × 3.12
3. 4120 × 0.312
4. 0.412 × 31,200
5. 312 × 4.12

6. 729 ÷ 0.3
7. 7.29 ÷ 0.3
8. 7.29 ÷ 3
9. 7290 ÷ 0.03
10. 72.9 ÷ 0.03

11. 3141 × 221
12. 31.41 × 2.21
13. 3.141 × 0.221
14. 2.21 × 0.3141
15. 22,100 × 3.141

16. 663 ÷ 2.21
17. 66.3 ÷ 2.21
18. 6.63 ÷ 2.21
19. 0.663 ÷ 2.21
20. 66.3 ÷ 0.221

21. 202 × 11
22. 20.2 × 11
23. 2.02 × 11
24. 2020 × 0.11
25. 1.1 × 2.02

26. 9.36 ÷ 3.12
27. 93.6 ÷ 0.312
28. 0.936 ÷ 0.312
29. 93.6 ÷ 3.12
30. 9360 ÷ 3.12

31. 2.345 × 1.11
32. 23.45 × 0.111
33. 2.345 × 0.0111
34. 0.2345 × 11.1
35. 234.5 × 11.1

36. 6.363 ÷ 0.707
37. 63.63 ÷ 7.07
38. 636.3 ÷ 70.7
39. 0.6363 ÷ 0.707
40. 63.63 ÷ 70.7

41. 2.002 × 33.3
42. 20.02 × 33.3
43. 200.2 × 33.3
44. 2.002 × 0.333
45. 200.2 × 0.0333

46. 98.2 ÷ 49.1
47. 0.0982 ÷ 4.91
48. 0.982 ÷ 0.491
49. 9.82 ÷ 4.91
50. 9.82 ÷ 49.1

EXPONENT GAME

Players: 2 or more
Materials: 0–5 cubes, 5–10 cubes, a calculator
Object: To make the largest number

Rules

1. Each player rolls two 0–5 cubes and uses the numbers rolled to make a number with an exponent. If you roll 2 zeros, roll again.

2. The player who has the largest number wins. Try to decide whose number is largest by estimating. Use the calculator if you have to.

Variation: Roll one 0–5 and one 5–10 cube.

Remember: Raising 0 to any power gives 0.

$$0^5 = 0$$
$$0^9 = 0$$

Raising any number to the zeroth power gives 1.

$$5^0 = 1$$
$$9^0 = 1$$

You *cannot* make 0^0.

Sample Game

Luisa and Audrey played with two 0–5 cubes.

Luisa's Roll	Her Number	Its Value	Audrey's Roll	Her Number	Its Value	Winner of Round
3 0	3^0	1	4 5	5^4	625	Audrey
1 2	1^2	1	1 2	2^1	2	Audrey
2 4	2^4	16	2 4	4^2	16	tie
4 5	4^5	1024	3 4	4^3	64	Luisa

Audrey won the game.

Kate is working on a project to find ways to conserve energy. She decided to find out how much electricity she used in her room at home. Kate made a chart that shows how she used electricity on a typical day.

Electricity Used on a Typical Day

Name of Electric Appliance	Watts (listed on appliance)	Number of Hours Used Each Day	Watt-Hours of Use Each Day
Radio	8	1	8
Electric clock	2	24	48
Reading lamp	100	2	200
Ceiling lamp (2 bulbs)	75 per bulb; 150 total	3	450

Kate knows that electric companies charge customers for the amount of electricity they use. The cost is usually given in cents per kilowatt-hour. Another way to say that is the number of cents for each 1000 watt-hours. A watt-hour is the amount of electricity needed to use 1 watt continuously for 1 hour. The electric company in Kate's city charges 15¢ per kilowatt-hour for electricity used in homes.

Work in small groups to discuss these questions.

1. About how many watt-hours of electricity are used in Kate's room on a typical day?

2. On a typical day, about how much money does the electricity Kate uses in her room cost?

3. On a typical day, about how much money could Kate save
   a. by not playing the radio?
   b. by using only one 75-watt bulb in the ceiling lamp instead of two?

4. How much does the electricity for Kate's clock cost in 1 year?

5. How much money could Kate save in a year if she used 60-watt bulbs in her ceiling lamp?

Work on these questions at home with your family. Discuss the answers later with the class.

6. Make a chart for the electricity you use at home. First decide whether you want to cover only your room or the whole house in your chart.

7. Find out how much 1 kilowatt-hour of electricity costs where you live. Check whether your estimated use and cost is in rough agreement with your family's electric bill. If you considered only your room, you'll have to estimate what your share of the whole family's electricity use is.

8. Make a list of ways you can conserve electricity without imposing hardships on yourself or your family.

9. By following your suggestions, about how much money can your family save
   a. in 1 month?
   b. in 1 year?

$$\frac{3}{10} \quad \frac{8}{10} \quad \frac{73}{100} \quad \frac{80}{100} \quad \frac{53}{1000}$$

Certain fractions, such as the ones above, are special because they have denominators that are powers of 10. They can also be written as decimals:

$\frac{3}{10} = 0.3$ (Both $\frac{3}{10}$ and 0.3 may be read as "three-tenths.")

$\frac{8}{10} = 0.8$ (eight-tenths)

$\frac{73}{100} = 0.73$ (seventy-three–hundredths)

$\frac{80}{100} = 0.80$ (eighty-hundredths)

$\frac{53}{1000} = 0.053$ (fifty-three–thousandths)

There are other correct ways to read both decimals and fractions. For example, $\frac{53}{1000}$ is sometimes read "fifty-three over one thousand" and 0.053 may be read "zero point zero five three" or "point zero five three."

There are decimal equivalents of other fractions as well. But only fractions that have equivalent fractions with denominators that are powers of 10 have decimal equivalents.

On the meter stick shown below, you can see that $\frac{1}{2}$ meter corresponds to 50 centimeters or 0.5 meter. So $\frac{1}{2}$ is equivalent to 0.5, and we write $\frac{1}{2} = 0.5$ or $\frac{1}{2} = 0.50$. In the same way, $\frac{3}{4} = 0.75$. But $\frac{1}{3}$ can only be approximated by a decimal, since there is no equivalent fraction for $\frac{1}{3}$ that has a power of 10 as a denominator. So $\frac{1}{3}$ is approximately 0.333 and is actually a bit more than 0.333.

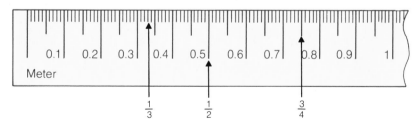

We could get the same results by dividing the numerator of each fraction by the denominator. This can be done either on paper or with a calculator.

Examples

For $\frac{1}{2}$, $2\overline{)1.000}$ with 0.500 above; so $\frac{1}{2} = 0.5$.

For $\frac{3}{4}$, $4\overline{)3.000}$ with 0.750 above; so $\frac{3}{4} = 0.75$.

For $\frac{1}{3}$, $3\overline{)1.000}$ with 0.333 above; so $\frac{1}{3}$ is about 0.333.

For $\frac{1}{3}$, notice that however long we go on dividing by 3, there is always a remainder. So there is no exact decimal equivalent of $\frac{1}{3}$. But we say that the decimal approximation of $\frac{1}{3}$ is about 0.333.

One important reason for changing fractions to decimal equivalents or decimal approximations is to be able to carry out calculations on a calculator. Beyond that, decimals are easier to add and to compare than are fractions with different denominators. For example, most people find it difficult to tell whether $\frac{7}{9}$ or $\frac{19}{25}$ is greater, but they have no trouble seeing that 0.778 $\left(\frac{7}{9}\right)$ is greater than 0.76 $\left(\frac{19}{25}\right)$.

Even if you are using a calculator, knowing some of the easy decimal equivalents can be helpful. This is true especially when you already have some numbers entered in the calculator and you don't want to lose them just to calculate a decimal equivalent.

Fraction-Decimal Equivalents

Copy and complete the following list. Carry out computations to 4 places and round to 3 places where necessary. Try to remember as many of the fraction-decimal equivalents and approximations as you can. Save the list. It will be helpful in playing the Up to 1 Game.

1. $\frac{1}{2} = 0.5$ 16. $\frac{1}{7} =$ 31. $\frac{3}{9} =$

2. $\frac{1}{3} = 0.333$ 17. $\frac{2}{7} =$ 32. $\frac{4}{9} =$

3. $\frac{2}{3} = 0.667$ 18. $\frac{3}{7} =$ 33. $\frac{5}{9} =$

4. $\frac{1}{4} =$ 19. $\frac{4}{7} =$ 34. $\frac{6}{9} =$

5. $\frac{2}{4} =$ 20. $\frac{5}{7} =$ 35. $\frac{7}{9} =$

6. $\frac{3}{4} =$ 21. $\frac{6}{7} =$ 36. $\frac{8}{9} =$

7. $\frac{1}{5} =$ 22. $\frac{1}{8} =$ 37. $\frac{1}{10} =$

8. $\frac{2}{5} =$ 23. $\frac{2}{8} =$ 38. $\frac{2}{10} =$

9. $\frac{3}{5} =$ 24. $\frac{3}{8} =$ 39. $\frac{3}{10} =$

10. $\frac{4}{5} =$ 25. $\frac{4}{8} =$ 40. $\frac{4}{10} =$

11. $\frac{1}{6} =$ 26. $\frac{5}{8} =$ 41. $\frac{5}{10} =$

12. $\frac{2}{6} =$ 27. $\frac{6}{8} =$ 42. $\frac{6}{10} =$

13. $\frac{3}{6} =$ 28. $\frac{7}{8} =$ 43. $\frac{7}{10} =$

14. $\frac{4}{6} =$ 29. $\frac{1}{9} =$ 44. $\frac{8}{10} =$

15. $\frac{5}{6} =$ 30. $\frac{2}{9} =$ 45. $\frac{9}{10} =$

UP TO 1 GAME

Players: 2 or more
Materials: Four 0–5 cubes
Object: To be the last player to get 1

Rules

1. Take turns rolling all four 0–5 cubes.

2. On your turn, use any 2 of the numbers you roll to make a fraction or a decimal less than 1. For example, if you roll [2] [3] [2] [1] , you could make $\frac{1}{3}$, $\frac{2}{3}$, $\frac{1}{2}$, or any of these decimals: .12, .21, .22, .23, .32, .13, .31.

3. Keep a record of the amount you make on each turn. Write the amount as a decimal. If you make a fraction, write the decimal equivalent or an approximation.

4. On each turn, you must write an amount greater than the amount you made on your previous turn. But you cannot make an amount of 1 or greater.

5. On any turn, if you cannot write an amount less than 1 but greater than your previous turn, then you are out.

6. The last player to go out wins.

Sample Game

Turn	Hilda's Record Numbers Rolled	Amount Made	Ben's Record Numbers Rolled	Amount Made
1	[3] [2] [0] [3]	.00 $\left(\frac{0}{2}\right)$	[3] [2] [5] [2]	.22
2	[2] [3] [3] [4]	.23	[1] [0] [3] [5]	.30
3	[1] [2] [0] [5]	.25	[1] [3] [0] [5]	.333 $\left(\frac{1}{3}\right)$
4	[1] [2] [2] [5]	.40 $\left(\frac{2}{5}\right)$	[1] [0] [4] [5]	.41
5	[2] [2] [0] [3]	.667 $\left(\frac{2}{3}\right)$	[3] [0] [3] [5]	.50
6	[2] [2] [0] [5]	Can't go.	[5] [5] [2] [3]	.52

Ben won.

We compare numbers for many reasons and in several different ways.

If you were told that Rick is 178 centimeters tall and his brother Stan is 172 centimeters tall, you would be able to tell who is taller and about how much taller he is. This is an obvious way to report data for comparison. Simply state the data and let the reader or listener think about it.

Sometimes, depending on what we believe someone wants to know or should know, we report data in other ways.

One thing we might do is to say, "Rick is 6 centimeters taller than Stan." We have now lost some information, but we have made it easier for someone to draw certain kinds of conclusions. We reported the actual difference in their heights. Reporting a difference is another way to report data for comparison.

If Rick's younger sister, Rosie, is only 89 centimeters tall, we might compare her height to Rick's by saying, "Rick is twice as tall as Rosie" or "Rosie is half as tall as Rick." In this case, we have compared the data by dividing. Such a comparison is called a *ratio*.

> The ratio of Rick's height to Rosie's is 2 to 1.
> The ratio of Rosie's height to Rick's is 1 to 2.

Sometimes the *to* is replaced by a colon (:). So we would write $2:1$ and $1:2$. Or, since a ratio is simply a rational number, we could write $\frac{2}{1}$ and $\frac{1}{2}$, or even 2 and $\frac{1}{2}$.

We often reduce ratios. The ratio $8:4$ can be reduced to $2:1$. In each case, find the completely reduced ratio of the first to the second number.

1. 100 to 20	**4.** 75 to 123	**7.** 6 to 4	**10.** 10 to 100
2. 75 to 150	**5.** 13 to 91	**8.** 100 to 25	**11.** 100 to 1000
3. 60 to 80	**6.** 13 to 92	**9.** 73 to 100	**12.** 9 to 90

13. Mr. Segal drove 300 kilometers in 5 hours. If he continues at that rate, how long will he take altogether to complete a 1200-kilometer trip?

14. Ms. Howe drove 400 kilometers in 5 hours. If she continues at that rate, how long will she take altogether to complete a 1200-kilometer trip?

Rates are special kinds of ratios. We usually use the word *per* in reporting rates, and the units involved are usually different. Generally the second number or the denominator is 1 in a rate.

Examples

Gasoline costs 42¢ per liter at Jake's Service Station. Five liters of gasoline will cost Martha $2.10 (5 × 42 = 210).

Pilar can run 3 kilometers in 12 minutes. She runs an average of 4 minutes per kilometer (12 ÷ 3). You can say that she runs at an average rate of 1 kilometer per 4 minutes, or $\frac{1}{4}$ kilometer per minute. To find her average rate per hour, multiply by 60 to get 15 kilometers per hour.

15. Hamburger costs $2.50 per kilogram at the local market. How much will 3 kilograms of hamburger cost?

16. At Gertrude's Gas Station, gasoline costs 39¢ per liter. How much will 10 liters of gasoline cost?

17. Mr. Martinez's car usually averages about 6 kilometers per liter of gasoline.
    a. About how far can he go on 10 liters of gas?
    b. About how far can he go on 20 liters of gas?
    c. If the tank holds 85 liters, about how far can he go on 1 tankful of gas?

18. Ms. Josephson drove 400 kilometers after filling the gas tank in her car. Then it took 40 liters of gasoline to fill the tank again. What was the average number of kilometers per liter of gasoline for that trip?

19. When Mrs. Pulaski filled the gas tank in her car, she put 20 liters of gasoline into it. She then drove 255 kilometers in 3 hours. She stopped at a gas station and filled the tank again, this time with 30 liters of gas.
    a. What was her average speed for the trip?
    b. On the average, how many kilometers did she drive per liter of gasoline?
    c. At that rate, how far could she go on 10 liters of gas?
    d. How far could she go on 40 liters of gas at that rate?

Rates are also used to compute interest. If your bank pays 5% interest per year, it pays you 5¢ for every dollar you leave in the bank for a year, or $5 for every $100.

Simple interest means the bank pays interest only on the money you put into the bank. (The money you put in is called the *principal*).

Example 1: If you deposit $100 for 2 years at 6% interest, you get $6 interest at the end of the first year and another $6 interest at the end of the second year, or a total of $12 interest.

Use this formula to compute simple interest: $I = prt$

where $I =$ the total interest paid
     $p =$ the principal
     $r =$ the rate per year
     $t =$ the time in years the money is invested

Example 2: Using the formula to do example 1:
$$I = prt = 100 \times 0.06 \times 2 = 12.$$

Example 3: What is the simple interest on $73 invested for $2\frac{1}{2}$ years at $8\frac{1}{2}$% interest?
$$I = prt = 73 \times 0.085 \times 2.5 = 15.5125$$
Rounded to the nearest cent, the interest is $15.51.

Example 4: What is the simple interest on $83.50 invested for 3 months at 6%? (Assume that 3 months $= \frac{3}{12} = \frac{1}{4}$ of a year.)
$$I = prt = 83.5 \times 0.06 \times \frac{1}{4} = 1.2525$$
Rounded to the nearest cent, the interest is $1.25.

Compute the simple interest on the following investments. Use a calculator.

1. $100 at 4% for 5 years
2. $100 at 4% for 6 months
3. $1000 at 10% for 10 years
4. $500 at 12% for 4 years
5. $200 at 6% for 3 months

6. $2000 at 8% for 12 years
7. $6000 at 8% for 20 days
8. $10,000 at 7% for 25 days
9. $2000 at 6% for 60 days
10. $10,000 at 10% for 1 year

Most banks and other institutions compute *compound interest* rather than simple interest. In compound interest, the bank records your interest as soon as it's earned and then calculates interest on your interest. *Compounded annually* means the investor is given credit annually, or at the end of a year.

Example 5

What is the interest on $100 at 5% for 4 years compounded annually?

Interest and Principal

at start: $100
after 1 year: $100 + (100 × 0.05 × 1) = 100 + 5 = $105
after 2 years: $105 + (105 × 0.05 × 1) = 105 + 5.25 = $110.25
after 3 years: $110.25 + (110.25 × 0.05 × 1) = 110.25 + 5.5125 = $115.76 (rounded)
after 4 years: $115.76 + (115.76 × 0.05 × 1) = 115.76 + 5.788 = $121.55 (rounded)

So compounding the interest produced a final total of $121.55 for interest of $21.55 ($1.55 more than simple interest would be).

A different way to calculate the answer to example 5 is to multiply by 1.05 for each year.

Interest and Principal

at start: $100
after 1 year: $100 × 1.05 = $105
after 2 years: $100 × 1.05 × 1.05 = $110.25
after 3 years: $100 × 1.05 × 1.05 × 1.05 = $115.7625
after 4 years: $100 × 1.05 × 1.05 × 1.05 × 1.05 = $121.55062

Round to 121.55, and the interest earned is $21.55

Compute the interest on the following compounded annually. Compare answers with your answers for similar problems on page 222.

11. $100 at 4% for 5 years
12. $1000 at 10% for 10 years
13. $500 at 12% for 4 years
14. $2000 at 8% for 12 years

15. $10,000 at 10% for 1 year
16. $1000 at 8% for 9 years
17. $1000 at 12% for 6 years
18. $1000 at 5% for 14 years

Check whether each of these numbers has 2, 3, 4, 5, 6, 7, 8, 9, or 10 as factors.

1. 390 **2.** 945 **3.** 2160 **4.** 2519 **5.** 192

Completely reduce each of the following fractions.

6. $\frac{7}{14}$ **7.** $\frac{24}{27}$ **8.** $\frac{15}{25}$ **9.** $\frac{192}{390}$ **10.** $\frac{200}{450}$

Calculate. Watch the signs. Write answers as reduced fractions.

11. $\frac{1}{3}$ of 24 **13.** $\frac{4}{7} - \frac{2}{7}$ **15.** $\frac{4}{7} \times \frac{2}{7}$ **17.** $\frac{1}{2} - \frac{1}{3}$ **19.** $\frac{3}{4} \times \frac{1}{9}$

12. $\frac{4}{7} + \frac{2}{7}$ **14.** $\frac{4}{7} \div \frac{2}{7}$ **16.** $\frac{1}{2} + \frac{1}{3}$ **18.** $\frac{3}{4} + \frac{1}{9}$ **20.** $\frac{3}{4} \div \frac{1}{9}$

21. If you toss 2 coins, what is the probability of getting 2 tails?

22. If you roll two 5–10 cubes, what is the probability of getting two 7s?

23. Suppose you roll two 5–10 cubes 720 times.

    a. About how many times would you expect to get two 7s?
    b. Would you be surprised if you didn't get exactly that number?
    c. Why or why not?

24. Mrs. Suzuki says that $\frac{1}{5}$ of the students in the orchestra play percussion instruments, $\frac{1}{4}$ play brass, $\frac{1}{3}$ play woodwinds, and the rest play strings.

    a. Is this possible?
    b. If so, how many students might be in the orchestra?

25. Dave and some friends are making kite kits. Dave is cutting out cloth tails. Each tail is 3 inches $\left(\frac{1}{12} \text{ yard}\right)$ across. How many tails can be cut from $\frac{5}{6}$ of a yard of cloth?

For each fraction, give a decimal equivalent or approximation correct to 3 places.

26. $\frac{1}{2}$ **27.** $\frac{2}{5}$ **28.** $\frac{2}{7}$ **29.** $\frac{5}{8}$ **30.** $\frac{7}{10}$

31. Ms. Preston drove 400 kilometers in 6 hours. If she continues at that rate, how long will it take her altogether to complete a 700-kilometer trip?

CONSTANT COMPARISON

Players: 2
Materials: Two 0–5 cubes, two 5–10 cubes
Object: To make the greater score

Rules

1. Take turns rolling all 4 cubes a total of 10 times. (Each player rolls 5 times.)

2. On each roll, the player who rolled the cubes chooses 2 of the numbers to compare by division. The other player chooses 2 of the numbers to compare by subtraction. (They may choose the same pair of numbers.)

3. Each player writes the 2 numbers chosen and the ratio or difference on a score sheet like those below.

4. At the end of the game, award points this way:

	Whole numbers:	Fractions:
2 of a kind	20 points	30 points
3 of a kind	30 points	40 points
4 of a kind	50 points	70 points

5. The winner is the player with the highest score.

Sample Game

Numbers rolled:

0 5	0 1	3 3	3 4	0 5	3 4	1 4	1 5	1 5	0 5
5 7	5 7	5 7	6 7	7 8	5 7	5 10	8 9	6 9	9 10

Doug									
First number	5	1	3	7	0	4	5	9	5	10
Second number	5	0	3	6	5	3	10	8	1	5
Comparison	1	1	1	1	0	1	$\frac{1}{2}$	1	5	5

Bea									
First number	5	0	3	3	5	3	10	1	6	5
Second number	5	5	3	6	0	5	5	5	1	10
Comparison	0	0	0	$\frac{1}{2}$	5	$\frac{3}{5}$	5	$\frac{1}{5}$	5	$\frac{1}{2}$

Doug's score:

Six 1s may count as 4 and 2 of a kind (70 points) or 3 and 3 (60 points) or 2, 2, and 2 (60 points). So Doug would take 70 points, plus 20 points for two 5s, for a total of 90 points.

Bea's score:

Bea takes three 0s (30 points), two $\frac{1}{2}$s (30 points), and three 5s (30 points), for a total of 90 points.

The game is a tie.

Chapter Test

Check whether each of these numbers has 2, 3, 4, 5, 6, 7, 8, 9, or 10 as factors.

1. 392   **2.** 360   **3.** 3717   **4.** 1024   **5.** 343

Completely reduce each of the following fractions.

6. $\frac{8}{12}$ **7.** $\frac{21}{24}$ **8.** $\frac{10}{25}$ **9.** $\frac{360}{392}$ **10.** $\frac{100}{250}$

Calculate. Watch the signs. Write answers as reduced fractions.

11. $\frac{1}{3}$ of 21   **13.** $\frac{3}{7} - \frac{2}{7}$ **15.** $\frac{3}{7} \times \frac{2}{7}$ **17.** $\frac{1}{3} - \frac{1}{4}$ **19.** $\frac{3}{4} \times \frac{1}{6}$

12. $\frac{3}{7} + \frac{2}{7}$ **14.** $\frac{3}{7} \div \frac{2}{7}$ **16.** $\frac{1}{3} + \frac{1}{4}$ **18.** $\frac{3}{4} + \frac{1}{6}$ **20.** $\frac{3}{4} \div \frac{1}{6}$

21. If you toss 2 coins, what is the probability of getting 2 heads?

22. If you roll two 5–10 cubes, what is the probability of getting two 10s?

23. Suppose you roll two 5–10 cubes 360 times.
  a. About how many times would you expect to get two 10s?
  b. Would you be surprised if you didn't get exactly that number?
  c. Why or why not?

24. Mrs. Duhamel says that on the last test $\frac{1}{5}$ of her students got As, $\frac{1}{3}$ got Bs, $\frac{1}{3}$ got Cs, $\frac{1}{10}$ got Ds, and the rest failed.
  a. Is this possible?
  b. If so, how many students are in the class?

25. Rosario needs 2 inches $\left(\frac{1}{18}$ of a yard$\right)$ of material to make a ribbon. She ties these ribbons around trees that she wants to cut down. How many ribbons can she make with $\frac{2}{3}$ of a yard of material?

For each fraction, give a decimal equivalent or approximation correct to 3 places.

26. $\frac{1}{5}$ **27.** $\frac{3}{5}$ **28.** $\frac{2}{9}$ **29.** $\frac{1}{7}$ **30.** $\frac{8}{10}$

31. Mr. Halfacre drove 300 kilometers in 4 hours. If he continues at that rate, how long will it take him altogether to complete a 500-kilometer trip?

Mrs. Ferguson's new car averages about 7 kilometers per liter in city driving and about 14 kilometers per liter in highway driving. The car's gasoline tank holds 45 liters.

1. Mrs. Ferguson just filled the tank with gasoline. Can she drive 140 kilometers in the city and then take a 200-kilometer trip on the highway?

2. Several trips combining city and highway driving are shown in this table. For each one, tell whether Mrs. Ferguson could make the trip with 1 full tank of gasoline.

Trip	Kilometers (in city)	(on highway)	Is Trip Possible with 1 Tank of Gasoline?
A	50	500	
B	100	300	
C	140	200	
D	200	100	
E	300	50	
F	300	100	
G	500	50	

3. Mrs. Ferguson uses her car to drive to and from work 5 days a week, and she usually fills her tank once a week.

   a. Could she work 100 kilometers from home?
   b. Could she work 75 kilometers from home?
   c. Could she work 50 kilometers from home?
   d. Could she work 25 kilometers from home?

CHAPTER 6
MEASUREMENT
MIXED NUMBERS
SIGNED NUMBERS

Two systems of measurement are commonly used in the United States. The first, which we will call the "traditional system," has as units inches, feet, miles, quarts, gallons, acres, ounces, pounds, tons, degrees Fahrenheit, and so on. The second, which we will call the "metric system," has as units centimeters, meters, kilometers, milliliters, liters, hectares, milligrams, grams, kilograms, degrees Celsius, and so on.

Almost all developed countries in the world except the United Kingdom and the United States use only the metric system of measurement. By international agreement in 1960, the metric system known as SI (from its French name, *Système International d'Unités*) became the standard international measurement system.

Throughout your life you will certainly often use both metric units and traditional units. In this chapter we will review both the traditional and the metric systems of measurement.

Because everyone uses the same units for measuring time, let's start by discussing time.

[1] How long is a second?

Work in pairs. Use a watch or clock with a second hand (or a digital watch or clock that shows seconds). Try to count to yourself at the same rate that seconds go by. Have your partner say, "Start." Count 10 seconds. See how close you can come to saying "10" when 10 seconds have passed. Then let your partner try.

Try counting 60 seconds (or 1 minute).

Try counting 100 seconds.

See how close you can come to the correct number of seconds that have passed.

[2] What is your pulse rate?

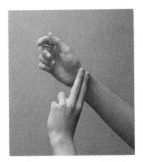

Hold the fingers of one hand on the wrist of the other hand—just below the thumb. Move your fingers around until you feel a beating. This beating is your pulse.

Each time your heart beats, a surge of blood goes through your arteries. There are several places on your body where you can feel this increase and decrease of pressure.

Move your fingers on your wrist until you can feel each beat clearly. Don't squeeze too hard. If you do, the flow will be blocked and you won't feel the pulse.

Count your pulse for 1 minute (60 seconds). What is your pulse rate per minute?

[3] If you count pulse beats for only 15 seconds, what do you have to do to get the rate per minute?

[4] If you count pulse beats for 20 seconds, what do you do to get the rate per minute?

1. James counts 18 pulse beats in 15 seconds. What is his pulse rate per minute?

2. Sue's pulse beats 35 times in 30 seconds. What is her pulse rate?

3. What is Sam's pulse rate if his pulse beats 96 times in $1\frac{1}{2}$ minutes?

4. What is Lee's pulse rate if his pulse beats 42 times in 40 seconds?

5. What is Kara's pulse rate if her pulse beats 117 times in $1\frac{1}{2}$ minutes?

[5] How many seconds are there in 1 minute?

[6] How many minutes in 1 hour?

[7] How many hours in 1 day?

[8] What are some other common units of time?

Time of day is usually divided into time before noon (A.M.) and time after noon (P.M.). A.M. stands for *ante meridiem*, which means "before midday," "before noon," or "before the sun reaches its highest point in the sky." P.M. stands for *post meridiem*, which means "after noon." 12:00 M. means 12:00 noon.

Some people use 12:00 M. to stand for midnight. This is incorrect, but it is common enough that you should probably spell out "noon" and "midnight" to avoid confusion.

[9] If the time now is 10:30 A.M., what time will it be

    a. 1 hour from now?
    b. $1\frac{1}{2}$ hours from now?
    c. 2 hours from now?
    d. 12 hours from now?
    e. 13 hours from now?
    f. $13\frac{1}{2}$ hours from now?
    g. 14 hours from now?

[10] If today is Monday and the time is 10:30 A.M., what day will it be 14 hours from now?

There are 60 minutes in an hour. So we often refer to 15 minutes as a quarter of an hour $\left(\frac{1}{4} \text{ hour}\right)$ and 30 minutes as half an hour $\left(\frac{1}{2} \text{ hour}\right)$. An hour and a half, or $1\frac{1}{2}$ hours, is 90 minutes, and so on.

You can see that $\frac{1}{3}$ of an hour is 20 minutes, $\frac{2}{5}$ of an hour is 24 minutes, and so on, but people seldom use these fractions of an hour.

6. How many seconds are there in 2 minutes?

7. How many seconds are there in $2\frac{1}{2}$ minutes?

8. How many minutes are there in 2 hours?

9. How many minutes are there in $2\frac{1}{2}$ hours?

10. How many hours are there in 2 days?

11. How many hours are there in $2\frac{1}{2}$ days?

12. How many days are there in 3 weeks?

13. How many days are there in 1 month?
    (Have you considered all possibilities?)

14. How many days are there in 1 year? (Be careful.)

15. **a.** How many whole weeks are there in 1 year?
    b. How many extra days are there?

16. How many months are there in 1 year?

17. For each of the following problems, assume it is now 9:00 A.M.
    on Monday. Tell what time and day it will be (or it was).

a. in 2 hours	**j.** in 48 hours	**s.** 2 hours ago
b. in 5 hours	**k.** in 72 hours	**t.** 9 hours ago
c. in $3\frac{1}{2}$ hours	**l.** in 96 hours	**u.** 12 hours ago
d. in 12 hours	**m.** in $99\frac{1}{2}$ hours	**v.** $1\frac{1}{2}$ hours ago
e. in $15\frac{1}{2}$ hours	**n.** in 84 hours	**w.** $13\frac{1}{2}$ hours ago
f. in 24 hours	**o.** in $87\frac{1}{2}$ hours	**x.** 24 hours ago
g. in $27\frac{1}{2}$ hours	**p.** in $1\frac{3}{4}$ hours	**y.** $25\frac{1}{2}$ hours ago
h. in 36 hours	**q.** in $73\frac{3}{4}$ hours	**z.** $37\frac{1}{2}$ hours ago
i. in $39\frac{1}{2}$ hours	**r.** in $13\frac{3}{4}$ hours	

18. How many days are there in 1 century? (Hint: Years divisible
    by 100, such as 1700, 1800, and 1900, are *not* leap years unless
    they are also divisible by 400, as is 2000.)

You don't need to know everything about a measurement system in order to use it easily and effectively. For example, most people who have grown up with the traditional measurement system do not know how many inches are in a mile, how long a rod is, or how many square feet are in an acre. We just remember those things that we use often. Most people do know how many inches are in a foot and how long a yard is.

The most commonly used measures of length in the metric system are the meter, the centimeter, the millimeter, and the kilometer. A typical door is about 2 meters high, and your schoolroom door is probably about 1 meter wide.

Just as a cent is $\frac{1}{100}$ of a dollar, a centimeter is $\frac{1}{100}$ of a meter. So there are 100 centimeters in a meter. The line segment shown here is 1 centimeter long.

|——————|

1 centimeter

One of your fingernails is likely to be about 1 centimeter wide. It's a good idea to check this so that you'll have a handy way to measure this distance. Of course, this may change as you grow.

A millimeter is $\frac{1}{1000}$ of a meter, or $\frac{1}{10}$ of a centimeter. The centimeter segment shown here is divided into millimeters.

|‖‖‖‖‖‖‖‖‖|

10 millimeters

A kilometer is 1000 meters long. If you walk very fast, you could probably walk a kilometer in about 10 minutes. Good athletes can run 1000 meters (or 1 kilometer) in about $2\frac{1}{2}$ minutes.

[1] Find the current world's record for running 1000 meters.

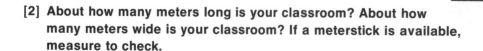

[2] About how many meters long is your classroom? About how many meters wide is your classroom? If a meterstick is available, measure to check.

The meter is the basic unit of length in the metric system. The following table shows some metric units of length:

Unit	Symbol	Relationship to the Meter	Number of Meters
kilometer	km	one thousand meters	1000
meter	m	one meter	1
centimeter	cm	one-hundredth of a meter	0.01
millimeter	mm	one-thousandth of a meter	0.001

Complete each of the following. Write the symbol for an appropriate metric unit.

1. This book is about 20 ___ wide and 24 ___ tall.
2. I can walk a distance of 5 ___ in an hour.
3. I can walk a distance of about 85 ___ in a minute.
4. My finger is about 16 ___ wide and about 75 ___ long.
5. Notebook paper is about 22 ___ wide and 28 ___ long.
6. A tall basketball player might be about 2 ___ tall.
7. A new pad of paper with 50 sheets is about 1 ___ thick.
8. A 1-story house is about 6 ___ high.
9. To drive from Seattle, Washington, to Miami, Florida, is about 5475 ___.
10. An unsharpened pencil is about 19 ___ long.

You can change from one metric unit of length to another by moving the decimal point (and maybe writing or dropping extra zeros).

Example: 73 m = ? km
Move the decimal point 3 places to the left.
Write in the zeros. .073
73 m = 0.073 km

Copy and complete the following.

11. 25 m = ▓ cm
12. 642 cm = ▓ mm
13. 25,000 m = ▓ km

14. 86 mm = ▓ cm
15. 642 cm = ▓ m
16. 25 km = ▓ m

Other commonly used metric units include those for area and volume. These too are based on the meter. The following tables show some metric units of area and volume.

Unit of Area	Symbol	Is the Area of a Square with Sides	Is About the Area Of
square kilometer	km²	1 km	a large farm
hectare	ha	100 m	2 football fields
square meter	m²	1 m	the top of a table
square centimeter	cm²	1 cm	the top of a thumbtack

Unit of Volume	Symbol	Is the Volume of a Cube with Sides	Is About the Volume Of
cubic meter	m³	1 m	an automatic washing machine
liter	L	10 cm	a head of lettuce
cubic centimeter	cm³	1 cm	a small cube of sugar
milliliter	mL	1 cm	20 drops of water

[1] What do you notice about the volume of cubic centimeters and milliliters?

[2] What is the relation between 1 L and 1 mL?

The base unit of weight in the metric system is the *kilogram*. The following table shows some metric units of weight.

Unit	Symbol	Is the Weight Of	Is About the Weight Of
metric ton	t	1000 kg	a small car
kilogram	kg	1000 g	1 liter of water
gram	g	$\frac{1}{1000}$ kg	2 paper clips
milligram	mg	$\frac{1}{1000}$ g	7 crystals of table salt

Temperature in the metric system is measured in degrees Celsius. The symbol is °C.

Complete each of the following. Write the symbol for an appropriate metric unit.

1. Some people believe you should drink about 2 ___ of water every day.
2. A grown woman might reasonably weigh 60 ___ .
3. I took a 250-___ tablet of vitamin C this morning.
4. William worked on a farm that had 80 ___ of pasture land.
5. Melissa grew enough vegetables for her family in a garden that was 50 ___ .
6. The area of 1 side of a sheet of paper is about 600 ___ .
7. It's very hot today. The temperature is 35___ .
8. In Mr. Martin's swimming pool there are about 40 ___ of water.
9. A bottle of rubber cement has a volume of 120 ___ .
10. The area of Alaska is about 1,525,000 ___ , but that of Rhode Island is only about 3150 ___ .
11. A letter and envelope together weigh about 9 ___ .
12. No trucks that weigh more than 5 ___ are allowed on the bridge.
13. The volume of a small bottle of eye drops is 15 ___ .

Choose the most reasonable number.

14. Bashir, a normal 12-year-old boy, weighs ▨ kilograms.
    a. 2   b. 20   c. 44   d. 120

15. Bashir is ▨ centimeters tall.
    a. 1.5   b. 16   c. 60   d. 157

16. The average temperature in St. Louis for the month of December is ▨ °C.
    a. 2   b. 25   c. 53   d. 86

17. 2 liters of orange juice weigh about ▨ kilograms.
    a. 0.4   b. 2   c. 12   d. 150

18. A fairly tall oak tree is about ▨ meters tall.
    a. 0.02   b. 0.5   c. 20   d. 500

You will not ordinarily do arithmetic with measurements in different units, since the person doing the measuring would probably have used the same units. If you want to compare the heights of 2 people, both heights are likely to be given in centimeters. So you won't have to convert from one unit to another.

Occasionally you will need to do arithmetic with measurements that are given in different units. Generally you should convert them to the same units before going on.

Example

Karin weighs 63.7 kilograms, and she has a jar of cranberry juice that contains 1422 grams. How much would Karin weigh if she could right now drink all the juice in the jar?

Since there are 1000 grams in a kilogram, the juice weighs 1.422 kilograms. $63.7 + 1.422 = 65.122$. However, Karin's weight almost certainly was not correct to the nearest thousandth of a kilogram. So reporting the answer to the nearest thousandth gives a false sense of precision. The answer should be rounded to the nearest tenth of a kilogram and reported as 65.1 kilograms.

One of the advantages of the metric system is that measurements are easy to convert, because the units are related by powers of 10.

The 3 most commonly used prefixes in the metric system are *kilo-* (meaning "thousand"), *centi-* ("one-hundredth"), and *milli-* ("one-thousandth"). So a kilometer is 1000 meters, a centimeter is one-hundredth of a meter, and a millimeter is one-thousandth of a meter.

In working with volumes and areas, you will have to be careful, because the units are multiplied.

Examples: $1 \text{ m } = 100 \text{ cm}$
$1 \text{ m}^2 = 10{,}000 \text{ cm}^2 \ (100^2 = 10{,}000)$
$1 \text{ m}^3 = 1{,}000{,}000 \text{ cm}^3 \ (100^3 = 1{,}000{,}000)$

As the size of the *unit* gets bigger, the *number* of units needed to measure the same thing gets smaller. As the size of the unit gets smaller, the number needed to measure the same thing gets bigger.

→ To convert from one unit to another in this direction →
multiply the number of units by 10 (move the decimal point 1 place to the right) for each unit.

kilometer   hectometer   decameter   meter   decimeter   centimeter   millimeter

← To convert from one unit to another in this direction ←
divide the number of units by 10 (move the decimal point 1 place to the left) for each unit.

Since units of length are squared for measures of area, you multiply and divide by 100 to change from unit to unit.

→ To convert units in this direction →
multiply by 100 (move point 2 places to the right) for each unit.

km²   hectare   dam²   m²   dm²   cm²   mm²

← To convert units in this direction ←
divide by 100 (move point 2 places to the left) for each unit.

Since units of length are cubed for measures of volume, you multiply and divide by 1000 to change from unit to unit.

→ To convert units in this direction →
multiply by 1000 (move point 3 places to the right) for each unit.

km³   hm³   dam³   m³   dm³   cm³   mm³

← To convert units in this direction ←
divide by 1000 (move point 3 places to the left) for each unit.

Examples

37,042 mg = ? kg   Move point 6 places to the left. So 37,042 mg = 0.037042 kg.

17 cm² = ? m²   Move point 4 places to the left. So 17 cm² = 0.0017 m².

Convert each of the following.

1. 7564 m = ▨ km
2. 7564 g = ▨ kg
3. 486 cm = ▨ m
4. 8956 mL = ▨ L
5. 8956 mg = ▨ g
6. 72.560 km = ▨ m

7. 72.560 kg = ▨ g
8. 6.581 m = ▨ cm
9. 37.492 L = ▨ mL
10. 37.492 g = ▨ mg
11. 3 m = ▨ km
12. 3 m = ▨ cm

13. 3 m = ▨ mm
14. 3 L = ▨ mL
15. 3 g = ▨ mg
16. 5 km^2 = ▨ m^2
17. 5 m^2 = ▨ mm^2
18. 5 m^2 = ▨ cm^2

19. 8 km^3 = ▨ m^3
20. 8 m^3 = ▨ cm^3
21. 8 m^3 = ▨ mm^3
22. 1 day = ▨ hours
23. 1 day = ▨ minutes
24. 1 day = ▨ seconds

25. Mr. Anderson bought 2 jars of honey. The label on one jar of honey says it contains 0.8 kilograms of honey. The label on the other says it contains 500 grams of honey.

    a. Which one contains more?
    b. How much more?
    c. How much honey did he buy?
    d. He is going to use the honey in a recipe calling for 1250 grams of honey. How much more honey did he buy than he needed?

26. A roll of film is 35 millimeters wide and about 100 centimeters long. What is the approximate area of the film?

Look back at questions 22–24. Is converting as easy with units of time as with other metric units?

Convert the following.

27. 7 m = ▨ cm

28. 7 m² = ▨ cm²

29. 7 m³ = ▨ cm³

30. 2 kg = ▨ g

31. 2 L = ▨ mL

32. 143 km = ▨ m

33. 8 km = ▨ m

34. 0.8 kg = ▨ g

35. 1 km² = ▨ ha (hm²)

36. 1 km² = ▨ m²

37. 1 km³ = ▨ m³

38. 8 km³ = ▨ m³

39. 1 m = ▨ mm

40. 1 m² = ▨ mm²

41. 1 m³ = ▨ mm³

42. 1 km³ = ▨ mm³

43. 83.4 km³ = ▨ mm³

44. 1 ha = ▨ cm²

45. 73 ha = ▨ cm²

46. 830 g = ▨ kg

47. Mr. Kantowski weighs 45 kilograms and is 1.51 meters tall.

   a. Is this big or small for a grown man?

   b. Since he would like to be bigger, he tells his weight in grams and his height in centimeters. How does he tell his weight and height?

   c. Does telling his weight and height this way actually make him bigger?

48. Lana just ran 2 kilometers in 7 minutes. She thinks it would be fun to report this in centimeters and seconds so that it would seem she had run farther and for a longer time. How would she describe her run?

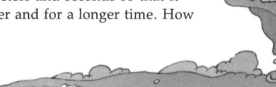

49. Harold is going to use small ceramic tiles that are 1 centimeter square to tile a table that is $\frac{1}{2}$ meter wide and 1 meter long. About how many tiles will he need?

50. Cecile was told to take 2 grams of vitamin C every day. She has a bottle of tablets that contain 500 mg of vitamin C each. How many of these tablets should she take every day?

51. A recipe calls for 500 milliliters of milk. You have a 1-liter bottle of milk. About what fraction of that will you need to use?

The Traditional System of Measure

The traditional measurement system is now used only in the United Kingdom and the United States. The following tables show some of the commonly used units of measure in this system.

Unit of Length	Abbreviation	Relation to Other Units	Relation to Objects or Events
inch	in	$\frac{1}{12}$ ft	is this long: _____
foot	ft	12 in	about as long as a grown man's foot
yard	yd	36 in 3 ft	the distance between the nose and the fingertip for many adults
mile	mi	63,360 in 5280 ft 1760 yd	about the distance you can walk in 20 minutes at a reasonable pace

Unit of Area	Abbreviation	Relation to Other Units	Relation to Objects or Events
square inch	in²	$\frac{1}{144}$ ft²	is this big: (sides are 1 in long)
square foot	ft²	144 in²	the area of a square with sides 1 foot long
square yard	yd²	1296 in² 9 ft²	the area of a square with sides 1 yard long
acre	A	43,560 ft² 4840 yd²	about the area of a square with sides 209 feet long
square mile	mi²	640 A	the area of a square with sides 1 mile long

Unit of Volume	Abbreviation	Relation to Other Units	Relation to Objects or Events
cubic inch	in³	$\frac{1}{1728}$ ft³	the volume of a cube with sides of 1 inch
cubic foot	ft³	1728 in³	the volume of a cube with sides of 1 foot
cubic yard	yd³	46,656 in³ 27 ft³	the volume of a cube with sides of 1 yard

Unit of Liquid Volume (capacity)	Abbreviation	Relation to Other Units	Relation to Objects or Events
teaspoon	tsp	$\frac{1}{3}$ tbs	about the amount that fits in an ordinary teaspoon
tablespoon	tbs	3 tsp $\frac{1}{2}$ fl oz $\frac{1}{16}$ c	about the amount that fits in a large soup spoon
fluid ounce	fl oz	2 tbs $\frac{1}{8}$ c	1 fluid ounce of water weighs about 1 ounce
cup	c	16 tbs 8 fl oz	about the size of an ordinary drinking glass
pint	pt	2 c 16 fl oz	about the size of a milkshake container
quart	qt	2 pt 4 c 32 fl oz	one-*quart*er of a gallon
gallon	gal	4 qt 8 pt 16 c	the size of a large container of milk

Unit of Dry Measure (capacity)	Abbreviation	Relation to Other Units	Relation to Objects or Events
pint	pt	$\frac{1}{2}$ qt	The volumes of the dry measure pint and quart are about 16% larger than the liquid measures with the same names.
quart	qt	2 pt	
peck	pk	8 qt	a small fruit basket
bushel	bu	4 pk	a large fruit basket

Unit of Weight	Abbreviation	Relation to Other Units	Relation to Objects or Events
ounce	oz	$\frac{1}{16}$ lb	9 pennies weigh about 1 ounce.
pound	lb	16 oz	the weight of 1 pint of water
ton	T	2000 lb	about the weight of a small delivery truck

Unit of Temperature	Symbol	Example	Relation to Objects or Events
degrees Fahrenheit	°F	32°F	water freezes
		68°F	in ordinary clothes, people are comfortably cool
		77°F	in ordinary clothes, people are comfortably warm
		212°F	water boils

Work in small groups to do this activity:

Use whatever measuring equipment is necessary. Estimate various measures and then check by measuring. Do your estimates improve with practice? These are some things you might measure: the length of the room, the weight of a classmate, the volume of a wastebasket, and so on.

Complete each of the following. Write the abbreviation for an appropriate traditional unit of measure.

1. Some people believe you should drink about 8 ___ of water a day.

2. A grown woman might reasonably weigh about 130 ___.

3. Matthew worked on a farm that had 120 ___ of pasture land.

4. It is very hot today. The temperature is about 95 ___.

5. Billie Sue is 64 ___ tall.

6. This book is about $8\frac{1}{2}$ ___ wide and 11 ___ tall.

7. A letter with its envelope ordinarily weighs a little less than 1 ___.

8. A fairly tall oak tree is about 65 ___ tall.

9. The area of the floor in Isabel's room is about 110 ___.

10. Eleanor ran 5 ___ in 37 minutes.

11. Sidney ran 440 ___ in 1 minute.

12. The area of a 5–10 number cube is about $3\frac{3}{8}$ ___.

13. Ms. Barton's gas tank holds 20 ___ of gas.

14. The recipe for cookies calls for $\frac{1}{2}$ ___ of vanilla.

15. A ___ of water weighs about 1 pound.

16. Josie's brother weighed about 7 ___ when he was born.

17. Yesterday when we were ice-skating on the pond, the temperature was about 28 ___.

18. They delivered 1 ___ of coal to the school storage area.

19. The baker made 20 pies from 1 ___ of apples.

20. There is about 36 ___ of storage space in the hall closet.

Solve. Reduce answers completely. Change improper fractions to mixed numbers.

1. $\frac{1}{3} + \frac{1}{5}$ 16. $\frac{1}{2} - \frac{1}{4}$ 31. $\frac{5}{8} + \frac{1}{3}$

2. $\frac{1}{3} \times \frac{1}{5}$ 17. $\frac{1}{2} \div \frac{1}{4}$ 32. $\frac{5}{8} \div \frac{1}{3}$

3. $\frac{1}{3} - \frac{1}{5}$ 18. $\frac{1}{2} + \frac{1}{4}$ 33. $\frac{5}{8} \times \frac{1}{3}$

4. $\frac{1}{3} \div \frac{1}{5}$ 19. $\frac{5}{6} + \frac{1}{9}$ 34. $\frac{1}{3} \times \frac{5}{8}$

5. $\frac{2}{3} - \frac{3}{5}$ 20. $\frac{5}{6} \div \frac{1}{9}$ 35. $\frac{5}{8} - \frac{1}{3}$

6. $\frac{2}{3} + \frac{3}{5}$ 21. $\frac{5}{6} \times \frac{1}{9}$ 36. $\frac{3}{2} + \frac{2}{3}$

7. $\frac{2}{3} \div \frac{3}{5}$ 22. $\frac{5}{6} - \frac{1}{9}$ 37. $\frac{3}{2} \times \frac{2}{3}$

8. $\frac{2}{3} \times \frac{3}{5}$ 23. $\frac{13}{14} + \frac{5}{7}$ 38. $\frac{3}{2} \div \frac{2}{3}$

9. $\frac{3}{4} + \frac{1}{6}$ 24. $\frac{5}{7} \div \frac{13}{14}$ 39. $\frac{2}{3} \times \frac{3}{2}$

10. $\frac{3}{4} - \frac{1}{6}$ 25. $\frac{13}{14} - \frac{5}{7}$ 40. $\frac{3}{2} - \frac{2}{3}$

11. $\frac{3}{4} \times \frac{1}{6}$ 26. $\frac{5}{7} \times \frac{13}{14}$ 41. $\frac{4}{5} - \frac{3}{4}$

12. $\frac{1}{6} \times \frac{3}{4}$ 27. $\frac{13}{14} \div \frac{5}{7}$ 42. $\frac{4}{5} \div \frac{3}{4}$

13. $\frac{3}{4} \div \frac{1}{6}$ 28. $\frac{14}{13} \div \frac{5}{7}$ 43. $\frac{4}{5} \times \frac{3}{4}$

14. $\frac{1}{6} \div \frac{3}{4}$ 29. $\frac{13}{14} \times \frac{5}{7}$ 44. $\frac{4}{5} + \frac{3}{4}$

15. $\frac{1}{2} \times \frac{1}{4}$ 30. $\frac{14}{13} \times \frac{5}{7}$ 45. $\frac{3}{4} \times \frac{4}{5}$

Here are some tables from a 120-year-old arithmetic book. Notice how some units of measure are different from those in common use today.

TABLES OF DENOMINATE NUMBERS

LINEAR MEASURE.

TABLE.

12 inches	make	1 foot, marked *ft.*
3 feet	- - -	1 yard, - - *yd.*
5½ yards or 16½ feet -	-	1 rod, - *rd.*
40 rods	- -	1 furlong, - - *fur.*
8 furlongs or 320 rods	-	1 mile, - - *mi.*
3 miles - - -	-	1 league, - - *L.*
69¼ statute miles, or	}	1 degree on the } *deg.* or °.
60 geographical miles, -	-}	equator, - }
360 degrees - -	-	a circumference of the earth.

AVOIRDUPOIS WEIGHT.

TABLE.

16 drams, *dr.* make	1 ounce, marked	*oz.*
16 ounces - -	1 pound, - -	*lb.*
25 pounds -	1 quarter, - -	*qr.*
4 quarters -	1 hundred weight,	*cwt.*
20 hundred weight	1 ton, - -	*T.*

DRY MEASURE.

TABLE.

2 pints, *pt.* make	1 quart, marked	*qt.*
8 quarts - -	1 peck, - -	*pk.*
4 pecks - -	1 bushel, - -	*bu.*
36 bushels -	1 chaldron, -	*ch.*

LIQUID MEASURE.

TABLE.

4 gills, *gi.* make	1 pint, marked	*pt.*
2 pints - - -	1 quart, - -	*qt.*
4 quarts - -	1 gallon, - -	*gal.*

UNITED STATES MONEY.

TABLE.

10 Mills make	1 Cent, marked	*ct.*
10 Cents - -	1 Dime, - -	*d.*
10 Dimes - -	1 Dollar, - -	*$.*
10 Dollars - -	1 Eagle, - -	*E.*
20 Dollars - -	2 Eagles, -	2 *E.*

Work in small groups to discuss these questions.

[1] **What units in these tables do you recognize?**

[2] **What units in these tables seem strange to you?**

[3] **If you were a teacher 120 years ago, how would you teach linear measure to a seventh-grade class?**

[4] **What units of measure do you think might be in common use 120 years from now?**

You will sometimes want to convert from one unit to another in traditional units. Because of the differing relationships among the units, this is somewhat harder than converting units within the metric system. It is common to use fractions with traditional measures but natural and much more common to use decimals with metric units.

Convert. Use the information on pages 242–244 to help you.

1. 3 mi = ▨ yd
2. 15,840 ft = ▨ mi
3. 204 in = ▨ ft
4. 21 fl oz = ▨ tsp

5. 3 c = ▨ fl oz
6. 1 gal = ▨ c
7. $3\frac{1}{2}$ gal = ▨ c
8. 72 c = ▨ gal

9. 1 ft² = ▨ in²
10. 1 ft³ = ▨ in³
11. 3 yd³ = ▨ ft³
12. 162 ft³ = ▨ yd³

13. 7 lb = ▨ oz
14. $1\frac{1}{2}$ tsp = ▨ tbs
15. 24 tsp = ▨ fl oz
16. 8 tbs = ▨ c

17. A recipe for bread calls for $\frac{1}{2}$ cup sugar, $\frac{1}{4}$ pound butter, and $3\frac{1}{2}$ cups whole-wheat flour. A chart in the back of the recipe book shows that $2\frac{1}{4}$ cups sugar = 1 pound sugar and $4\frac{1}{2}$ cups flour = 1 pound flour. If you have about half of a 5-pound bag of sugar, a pound of butter, and half of a 5-pound bag of whole-wheat flour, do you have enough of everything to double the recipe?

18. A 12-ounce can of frozen orange juice is to be mixed with 3 cans of water. How many quarts of orange juice will this make?

19. There are $16\frac{1}{2}$ feet in a rod. How many rods are in a mile?

20. A developer is selling building lots that are 300 feet by 300 feet. About how many acres are in each lot?

MATCH THE MEASURE

Players: 2
Materials: Measuring tools (rulers, metersticks, and so on)
Object: To find an object that has the same number of units of length as a given number

Rules

1. The first player picks any number from 1 through 1000.

2. The second player chooses a unit of length and then names something in the room that measures close to the first player's number in the chosen unit of length.

3. Both players measure to check.

4. If the number of units is within 20% of the first player's number, the second player wins the round. If not, the first player wins the round.

Sample Game

Round 1:   Melanie picked 500.
                Umberto chose millimeters. He said that the side of the desk was 500 millimeters long. They measured the side of the desk. It was 452 millimeters long. Since 20% of 500 is 100, any number between 400 and 600 would win. 452 is between 400 and 600. Umberto won this round.

Round 2:   Umberto picked 1.
                Melanie chose meters. She said that the door was 1 meter wide. They measured the width of the door. It was 0.9 meters wide. Since 0.9 is within 20% of 1, Melanie won this round.

Round 3:   Melanie picked 15.
                Umberto chose centimeters. He said that his new pencil was 15 centimeters long. They measured and found that the pencil was 17 centimeters long. Since 17 is within 20% of 15, Umberto won this round.

Round 4:   Umberto picked 5.
                Melanie chose centimeters. She said that the blackboard eraser was 5 centimeters long. They found that the eraser was 12 centimeters long. Since 12 is not within 20% of 5, Umberto won this round.

Umberto is ahead 3 rounds to 1.

In a *proper fraction* the numerator is smaller than the denominator. In an *improper fraction* the numerator is greater than the denominator. A *mixed number* is a whole number followed by a proper fraction.

These are proper fractions:

$$\frac{1}{2} \quad \frac{3}{5} \quad \frac{7}{11}$$

These are improper fractions:

$$\frac{7}{3} \quad \frac{11}{2} \quad \frac{80}{7}$$

These are mixed numbers:

$$2\frac{1}{3} \quad 5\frac{1}{2} \quad 11\frac{3}{7}$$

In order to combine traditional measurements and for some other purposes, you must be able to do arithmetic with mixed numbers and with improper fractions. We are going to review this arithmetic in this lesson.

To add or subtract mixed numbers, do the arithmetic with the fractions first—regrouping with the whole-number part (if necessary)—and then do the whole-number arithmetic.

Example: $4\frac{1}{3} + 2\frac{3}{4}$

$4\frac{1}{3}$
$+\ 2\frac{3}{4}$

Add the fraction parts. To do this we first have to find a common denominator.

$4\frac{1}{3} = 4\frac{4}{12}$; $2\frac{3}{4} = 2\frac{9}{12}$. So 12 is a common denominator.

$4\frac{4}{12}$
$+\ 2\frac{9}{12}$
$\overline{\frac{13}{12}}$

Now we can add the fraction parts.

$^{1}4\frac{4}{12}$
$+\ 2\frac{9}{12}$
$\overline{\frac{\cancel{13}}{12}\ \frac{1}{12}}$

We can change $\frac{13}{12}$ to $1\frac{1}{12}$. We write $\frac{1}{12}$ and add 1 to the whole numbers.

$^{1}4\frac{4}{12}$
$+\ 2\frac{9}{12}$
$\overline{7\ \frac{\cancel{13}}{\cancel{12}}\ \frac{1}{12}}$

Add the whole numbers.

The answer is $7\frac{1}{12}$.

Check: Does the answer make sense?

$4 + 2 = 6$ $\frac{1}{3} + \frac{3}{4}$ is about 1. $6 + 1 = 7$

The answer is about 7. So it makes sense.

Example: $4\frac{1}{3} - 2\frac{3}{4}$

$4\frac{1}{3}$

$-\ 2\frac{3}{4}$
_____

Subtract the fraction parts. To do this we have to find a common denominator.

$4\frac{1}{3} = 4\frac{4}{12}; 2\frac{3}{4} = 2\frac{9}{12}$. So 12 is a common denominator.

$4\frac{4}{12} \rightarrow 3\frac{16}{12}$

$-\ 2\frac{9}{12} \quad\ -\ 2\frac{9}{12}$
_____

Subtract the fraction parts. Since we can't take 9 from 4, we rewrite $4\frac{4}{12}$ as $3\frac{16}{12}$, using 1 whole to make $\frac{12}{12}$.

$3\frac{16}{12}$

$-\ 2\frac{9}{12}$
_____
$\frac{7}{12}$

Now we can subtract the fraction parts.

$3\frac{16}{12}$

$-\ 2\frac{9}{12}$
_____
$1\frac{7}{12}$

Subtract the whole numbers.

The answer is $1\frac{7}{12}$.

Check: Does the answer make sense?
Round $4\frac{1}{3}$ to 4. Round $2\frac{3}{4}$ to 3.
$4 - 3 = 1$ The answer should be about 1.
$1\frac{7}{12}$ is about 1. So the answer makes sense.

Here's how to convert $4\frac{1}{3}$ to an improper fraction:

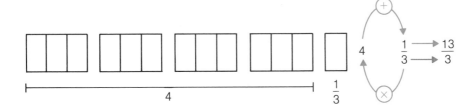

To find the numerator of the improper fraction, you multiply the denominator of the fraction in the mixed number times the whole number and then add the numerator of the fraction. The denominator of the improper fraction is the denominator of the fraction in the mixed number.

Instead of using the procedures on pages 251 and 252, you may convert the mixed numbers to improper fractions before you do the arithmetic.

Examples: $4\frac{1}{3} + 2\frac{3}{4} = 4\frac{4}{12} + 2\frac{9}{12} = \frac{52}{12} + \frac{33}{12} = \frac{85}{12} = 7\frac{1}{12}$

$4\frac{1}{3} - 2\frac{3}{4} = 4\frac{4}{12} - 2\frac{9}{12} = \frac{52}{12} - \frac{33}{12} = \frac{19}{12} = 1\frac{7}{12}$

Add or subtract. Leave your answers as mixed numbers, whole numbers, or proper fractions. Reduce fractions where possible.

1. $2\frac{2}{3} + 3\frac{2}{3}$

2. $2\frac{2}{3} + 4\frac{5}{6}$

3. $4\frac{5}{6} - 2\frac{2}{3}$

4. $2\frac{3}{10} + 4\frac{4}{5}$

5. $4\frac{4}{5} - 2\frac{3}{10}$

6. $1\frac{4}{5} - 1\frac{2}{5}$

7. $1\frac{4}{5} + 1\frac{2}{5}$

8. $1\frac{3}{5} + 1\frac{3}{5}$

9. $1\frac{3}{5} - 1\frac{3}{5}$

10. $3\frac{1}{5} + 4\frac{4}{5}$

11. $4\frac{4}{5} - 3\frac{1}{5}$

12. $3\frac{3}{4} - 2\frac{1}{8}$

13. $3\frac{3}{4} + 2\frac{1}{8}$

14. $2\frac{3}{8} + 3\frac{1}{6}$

15. $2\frac{3}{8} - 1\frac{1}{6}$

Convert each of the following mixed numbers to an improper fraction.

1. $5\frac{1}{2} = \frac{}{2}$

3. $2\frac{3}{8} = \frac{}{8}$

2. $3\frac{2}{3} = \frac{}{3}$

4. $1\frac{1}{4} = \frac{}{4}$

5. $1\frac{3}{5}$ **6.** $5\frac{1}{7}$ **7.** $2\frac{1}{3}$ **8.** $5\frac{3}{4}$ **9.** $2\frac{7}{10}$ **10.** $1\frac{1}{8}$

Add. Use any procedure you like. Reduce answers when possible.

11. $1\frac{1}{3} + 2\frac{1}{3}$ **16.** $3\frac{1}{6} + 2\frac{1}{3}$ **21.** $3\frac{2}{3} + 5\frac{1}{2}$

12. $2\frac{1}{6} + 3\frac{1}{6}$ **17.** $1\frac{1}{7} + 1\frac{1}{5}$ **22.** $1\frac{3}{4} + 3\frac{4}{7}$

13. $2\frac{1}{3} + 3\frac{1}{4}$ **18.** $1\frac{3}{7} + 1\frac{3}{5}$ **23.** $4\frac{1}{8} + 1\frac{9}{10}$

14. $2\frac{2}{3} + 3\frac{3}{4}$ **19.** $2 + 4\frac{1}{3}$ **24.** $2\frac{3}{5} + 5\frac{7}{10}$

15. $2\frac{5}{12} + 3\frac{1}{4}$ **20.** $1\frac{3}{7} + 8$ **25.** $1\frac{5}{12} + 2\frac{7}{12}$

Subtract. Use any procedure you like. Reduce answers when possible.

26. $2\frac{1}{3} - 1\frac{1}{3}$ **31.** $3\frac{1}{6} - 2\frac{1}{3}$ **36.** $5\frac{1}{2} - 3\frac{2}{3}$

27. $3\frac{5}{6} - 2\frac{1}{6}$ **32.** $1\frac{1}{5} - 1\frac{1}{7}$ **37.** $3\frac{4}{7} - 1\frac{3}{4}$

28. $3\frac{1}{4} - 2\frac{1}{3}$ **33.** $1\frac{3}{5} - 1\frac{3}{7}$ **38.** $4\frac{1}{8} - 1\frac{9}{10}$

29. $3\frac{3}{4} - 2\frac{2}{3}$ **34.** $4\frac{1}{3} - 2$ **39.** $5\frac{7}{10} - 2\frac{3}{5}$

30. $3\frac{3}{4} - 2\frac{5}{12}$ **35.** $8 - 1\frac{3}{7}$ **40.** $2\frac{7}{12} - 1\frac{5}{12}$

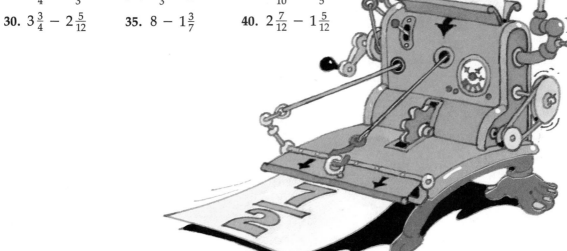

Using Mixed Numbers and Improper Fractions: Applications

1. A recipe calls for $4\frac{1}{2}$ cups of flour. You misread the instructions and put in $2\frac{1}{4}$ cups of flour. How can you fix it?

2. One scruple equals 20 grains. There are 5 grains in an ordinary aspirin tablet. How many scruples are there in 2 aspirins?

3. A sheet of paper is $8\frac{1}{2}$ inches wide. If you tape 2 of these sheets together side by side, how wide a sheet will they make?

4. Pat wants to put in a new mailbox post. The hole for the post must be at least $3\frac{1}{2}$ feet deep so the frost won't push it up in the winter. The mailbox should be about $4\frac{1}{4}$ feet above the ground. How long a post does he need to buy?

5. Without consulting a mathematician, a man left $\frac{1}{2}$ of his estate to his oldest daughter, $\frac{1}{3}$ to his next oldest daughter, $\frac{1}{4}$ to his third daughter, and the rest to his favorite charity. How much was left for the charity?

6. In Scottstown, $\frac{1}{2}$ of the town's budget is spent on schools and $\frac{1}{3}$ is spent on police and fire protection. How much is left for other town expenditures?

7. A woman left $\frac{1}{3}$ of her estate to her youngest son, $\frac{1}{4}$ to the next older son, $\frac{1}{5}$ to her oldest son, and the rest to her daughter.
   a. Who received a greater share, the daughter or the oldest son?
   b. How much more?

8. The weight limit for a suitcase on Bumble Bee Airlines is 60 pounds. Hannah's empty suitcase weighs $10\frac{1}{2}$ pounds. She has already put out $33\frac{3}{4}$ pounds of things she must take with her.
   a. When she gets those things packed, how much will the suitcase and her things weigh?
   b. How much more can she pack and still stay under the 60-pound limit?

To multiply or divide mixed numbers, first convert them to improper fractions and then proceed as with fractions less than 1.

Example: $4\frac{1}{3} \times 2\frac{3}{4} = \frac{13}{3} \times \frac{11}{4} = \frac{143}{12} = 11\frac{11}{12}$

Check: Does the answer make sense?

The answer will be more than 4×2, or 8.

The answer will be less than 5×3, or 15.

So the answer should be between 8 and 15.

It is. So the answer makes sense.

You can also check this by rounding $4\frac{1}{3}$ to 4 and rounding $2\frac{3}{4}$ to 3.

$4 \times 3 = 12$. So the answer should be about 12.

$11\frac{11}{12}$ is close to 12. So the answer makes sense.

Example: $4\frac{1}{3} \div 2\frac{3}{4} = \frac{13}{3} \div \frac{11}{4} = \frac{13}{3} \times \frac{4}{11} = \frac{52}{33} = 1\frac{19}{33}$

Check: Does the answer make sense?

If you round both numbers to the nearest whole number, you get $4 \div 3$, or $1\frac{1}{3}$. $1\frac{19}{33}$ is close to $1\frac{1}{3}$. So the answer makes sense.

You should make a habit of approximating answers to problems like these to be sure you have an answer that is reasonable.

Multiply. Reduce your answers and change them back to mixed numbers.

1. $2\frac{1}{3} \times 3\frac{1}{5}$ **6.** $4\frac{1}{2} \times 2\frac{1}{3}$ **11.** $1\frac{7}{8} \times 3\frac{1}{3}$

2. $8\frac{1}{3} \times 2\frac{2}{5}$ **7.** $1\frac{1}{6} \times \frac{4}{7}$ **12.** $2\frac{3}{5} \times 1\frac{4}{7}$

3. $\frac{1}{6} \times 5\frac{1}{4}$ **8.** $7\frac{1}{2} \times 3\frac{3}{5}$ **13.** $3\frac{1}{6} \times 2\frac{1}{8}$

4. $1\frac{3}{7} \times 2\frac{1}{10}$ **9.** $1\frac{1}{4} \times 1\frac{1}{5}$ **14.** $4\frac{1}{3} \times 1\frac{1}{3}$

5. $4\frac{2}{3} \times 1\frac{2}{7}$ **10.** $2\frac{1}{4} \times 2\frac{2}{3}$ **15.** $1\frac{1}{2} \times 1\frac{1}{3}$

Divide. Reduce your answers and change them back to mixed numbers.

16. $1\frac{1}{4} \div \frac{1}{4}$ **21.** $5\frac{1}{2} \div 1\frac{1}{3}$ **26.** $1\frac{2}{3} \div 4\frac{1}{6}$

17. $1\frac{1}{4} \div \frac{1}{2}$ **22.** $4\frac{2}{3} \div 1\frac{1}{6}$ **27.** $1\frac{1}{2} \div 3\frac{3}{4}$

18. $1\frac{1}{4} \div \frac{3}{4}$ **23.** $2\frac{1}{2} \div 7\frac{1}{2}$ **28.** $2\frac{1}{3} \div 1\frac{1}{7}$

19. $3\frac{1}{2} \div 1\frac{3}{4}$ **24.** $1\frac{4}{7} \div 3\frac{2}{3}$ **29.** $4\frac{3}{8} \div 2\frac{1}{3}$

20. $6\frac{1}{8} \div 1\frac{3}{4}$ **25.** $4\frac{1}{5} \div 3\frac{1}{2}$ **30.** $\frac{1}{6} \div 2\frac{1}{4}$

31. Steve is going to tile a porch floor with square tiles that are $\frac{3}{4}$ of a foot on a side. The porch is $15\frac{3}{4}$ feet wide and $22\frac{1}{2}$ feet long.

   a. How many tiles will he need to make 1 row the width of the porch?

   b. How many tiles will he need to make 1 row the length of the porch?

32. Victoria measured the height of a step in her apartment building. It was $8\frac{1}{2}$ inches. She climbs 65 steps to get to her apartment.

   a. How many inches is that?

   b. How many feet is it?

Multiply or divide. Leave your answers as mixed numbers, whole numbers, or proper fractions. Reduce fractions where possible.

1. $2\frac{4}{5} \div 1\frac{3}{5}$ 6. $2\frac{4}{7} \times 2\frac{1}{3}$ 11. $1\frac{2}{3} \times \frac{3}{5}$

2. $2\frac{4}{5} \times 1\frac{3}{5}$ 7. $2\frac{4}{7} \div 2\frac{1}{3}$ 12. $1\frac{2}{3} \div \frac{5}{3}$

3. $1\frac{3}{5} \times 2\frac{4}{5}$ 8. $2\frac{1}{3} \times 2\frac{4}{7}$ 13. $\frac{3}{5} \div 1\frac{2}{3}$

4. $1\frac{3}{5} \div 2\frac{4}{5}$ 9. $2\frac{1}{3} \div 2\frac{4}{7}$ 14. $\frac{5}{3} \times 1\frac{2}{3}$

5. $2\frac{3}{5} \times 1\frac{4}{5}$ 10. $1\frac{4}{7} \times 2\frac{1}{3}$ 15. $1\frac{2}{3} \div \frac{3}{5}$

Leave your answers as mixed numbers, whole numbers, or proper fractions. Reduce fractions where possible.

16. $2\frac{4}{5} + 1\frac{3}{5}$ 26. $6\frac{3}{4} + 3\frac{1}{9}$ 36. $2\frac{1}{2} \times \frac{3}{4}$

17. $3\frac{2}{7} - 1\frac{4}{7}$ 27. $6\frac{3}{4} - 3\frac{1}{9}$ 37. $2\frac{1}{2} \div \frac{3}{4}$

18. $5\frac{1}{2} + 2\frac{3}{4}$ 28. $6\frac{3}{4} \times 3\frac{1}{9}$ 38. $\frac{2}{5} + 1\frac{3}{4}$

19. $5\frac{1}{2} - 2\frac{3}{4}$ 29. $6\frac{3}{4} \div 3\frac{1}{9}$ 39. $1\frac{5}{8} - \frac{3}{4}$

20. $5\frac{1}{2} \times 2\frac{3}{4}$ 30. $5\frac{4}{7} + 3\frac{3}{7}$ 40. $\frac{2}{5} \times 1\frac{3}{4}$

21. $5\frac{1}{2} \div 2\frac{3}{4}$ 31. $5\frac{4}{7} - 3\frac{3}{7}$ 41. $\frac{2}{5} \div 1\frac{3}{4}$

22. $5\frac{3}{4} + 2\frac{1}{3}$ 32. $5\frac{4}{7} \times 3\frac{3}{7}$ 42. $7\frac{1}{2} - 1\frac{7}{8}$

23. $5\frac{3}{4} - 2\frac{1}{3}$ 33. $5\frac{4}{7} \div 3\frac{3}{7}$ 43. $7\frac{1}{2} + 1\frac{7}{8}$

24. $5\frac{3}{4} \times 2\frac{1}{3}$ 34. $2\frac{1}{2} + \frac{3}{4}$ 44. $7\frac{1}{2} \div 1\frac{7}{8}$

25. $5\frac{3}{4} \div 2\frac{1}{3}$ 35. $2\frac{1}{2} - \frac{3}{4}$ 45. $7\frac{1}{2} \times 1\frac{7}{8}$

ROLL A PROBLEM FRACTION GAME

Players: 2 or more
Materials: Two 0–5 cubes, two 5–10 cubes
Object: To make a problem with an answer closest to the goal

Rules

1. Pick a goal between 0 and 10 (such as 0, 1, $3\frac{1}{4}$, or 10).

2. Take turns rolling all 4 cubes.

3. Make 2 fractions and add, subtract, multiply, or divide them.

4. The player with the answer closest to the goal wins.

Sample Games

Ursula and Esther chose 10 as the goal.

Ursula rolled: 9 5 4 3   Esther rolled: 7 5 3 3

She made: $\frac{9}{4} \times \frac{5}{3} = \frac{45}{12} = 3\frac{9}{12} = 3\frac{3}{4}$ She made: $\frac{7}{3} \times \frac{5}{3} = \frac{35}{9} = 3\frac{8}{9}$

Esther won.

Paul and Delfun chose $2\frac{1}{2}$ as the goal.

Paul rolled: 10 6 4 2   Delfun rolled: 9 8 5 3

He made: $\frac{4}{2} + \frac{6}{10} = 2\frac{3}{5}$ He made: $\frac{9}{3} - \frac{5}{8} = 2\frac{3}{8}$

Paul won.

Another Way to Play This Game

Add this rule: In 4 games each player must use each operation
exactly once.

There are some situations in which numbers less than 0 are useful and make sense. In other situations, numbers less than 0 make no sense at all.

If 0°C is the temperature at which water freezes, then the temperature can fall below 0.

If 0 is the time at which a rocket is going to be fired, then the time before the firing can be described with numbers less than 0 and the time after by numbers greater than 0.

If 0 is what your bank statement reads when you have no money in your bank account, then a loan from the bank to you, or an overdraft that the bank accepts, could be described with numbers less than 0.

The word *negative* is used to designate numbers less than 0. The word *positive* is used for numbers greater than 0. Negative numbers are usually written with a minus sign in front of them: −5, −20. Positive numbers are sometimes written with a plus sign in front of them: +5, +20. When a number is written without a sign, it is assumed to be positive.

To avoid confusion with the negative sign and the sign for subtraction, some people use a raised minus sign to indicate negative. For example, ⁻3 is negative 3. We will use parentheses whenever there might be doubt: (−3).

If we are going to do arithmetic with these numbers, we would like the results to be useful in the sense of corresponding with real situations. Thinking about the following situations should help.

[1] For each of the following, the temperature is 3°C.

   a. If it goes down 2°C, what will the temperature be?
      $3 - 2 = ?$

   b. If it goes down 3°C, what will it be?
      $3 - 3 = ?$

   c. If it goes down 4°C, what will it be?
      $3 - 4 = ?$

   d. If it goes down 5°C, what will it be?
      $3 - 5 = ?$

[2] For each of the following, the temperature is −4°C.

    a. If it goes down 2°C, what will it be? $-4 - 2 = ?$

    b. If it goes up 3°C, what will it be?
       $-4 + 3 = ?$

    c. If it goes up 4°C, what will it be?
       $-4 + 4 = ?$

    d. If it goes up 5°C, what will it be?
       $-4 + 5 = ?$

[3] Wei-ming's bank account has $20 in it.

    a. If she withdraws $10, what will the balance be? $20 - 10 = ?$

    b. If she withdraws $20, what will the balance be?
       $20 - 20 = ?$

    c. If she withdraws $30, what will the balance be?
       $20 - 30 = ?$

[4] Warren's bank statement says he owes the bank $20 (−20).

    a. If he withdraws $10, what will his balance be? $-20 - 10 = ?$

    b. If he deposits (adds) $10, what will his balance be?
       $-20 + 10 = ?$

    c. If he deposits (adds) $20, what will his balance be?
       $-20 + 20 = ?$

    d. If he deposits (adds) $50, what will his balance be?
       $-20 + 50 = ?$

[5] Mr. Medlock's bank statement said his balance was $50. He saw that the bank charged him for a withdrawal of $20 that he didn't make. So the bank took away the $20 withdrawal.

    a. Now how much is his balance? $50 - (-20) = ?$ (Take away a withdrawal of $20.) Notice that taking away negative 20 has the same effect as adding positive 20, so $50 - (-20) = 50 + 20$.

    b. Suppose the original statement said his balance was $30.
       $30 - (-20) = ?$

    c. Suppose the original statement said he had $20. $20 - (-20) = ?$

    d. Suppose the original statement said he had $0. $0 - (-20) = ?$

    e. Suppose the original statement said he owed the bank $50.
       $-50 - (-20) = ?$

    f. Suppose it said he owed the bank $20. $-20 - (-20) = ?$

    g. Suppose it said he owed the bank $10. $-10 - (-20) = ?$

Absolute Value of a Number

We can summarize the discussion on pages 260 and 261 with 2 simple rules. These rules are on page 263. It is important, however, that you understand the models so that you remember and use the rules well.

The concept of absolute value helps us state these rules.

The *absolute value* of a number is the distance the number is from 0 on the number line. This distance is always measured by a positive number. So the absolute value of 3 is 3, of −4 is 4, of 0 is 0, of −18 is 18, of 12 is 12, and so on.

The symbol $|x|$ means the absolute value of x. So $|+4| = 4$ and $|-3| = 3$.

Solve the following for x. Caution: Equations such as $|x| = 3$ have 2 solutions (3 and −3). And remember, $-(-x) = x$.

1. $|+7| = x$
2. $|-7| = x$
3. $|x| = 7$
4. $|0| = x$
5. $|x| = 0$
6. $|-8| = x$
7. $x = |+4|$
8. $|x| = +4$
9. $|x| = -2$
10. $|-2| = x$

11. $|x| = 2$
12. $73 = |x|$
13. $|-x| = 3$
14. $|4| = -x$
15. $|4| = x$
16. $|x| = 3$
17. $|-5| = -x$
18. $|-9| = x$
19. $|7| = -x$
20. $|-73| = x$

These are the rules that you can use when you add and subtract signed numbers.

Rule 1

To add 2 signed numbers:

A. If their signs are the same, add their absolute values and use their common sign.
B. If their signs are different, subtract the smaller absolute value from the larger and use the sign of the one with the larger absolute value.

Rule 2

To subtract 2 signed numbers, change the sign of the second (subtrahend) and add as in rule 1.

Add. Use rule 1.

1. $(+8) + (+7) = n$
2. $(+8) + (-7) = n$
3. $(-8) + (+7) = n$
4. $(-8) + (-7) = n$
5. $n = (-5) + (-3)$

6. $n = (-4) + (+9)$
7. $n = (-9) + (+4)$
8. $n = (-4) + (-5) + (-6)$
9. $(-9) + (+3) + (+6) = n$
10. $n = (+4) + (-4) + (+2)$

Subtract. Use rule 2.

11. $(+8) - (+7) = n$
12. $(+8) - (-7) = n$
13. $(-8) - (+7) = n$
14. $(-8) - (-7) = n$
15. $n = (-5) - (-3)$

16. $n = (-4) - (+9)$
17. $n = (-9) - (+4)$
18. $n = [(-4) - (-5)] - (-6)$
19. $n = -4 - [(-5) - (-6)]$
20. $n = [(-4) - (-4)] - (-4)$

To save ourselves work, we usually leave the plus sign off positive numbers. For example, instead of "(+8) + (+7)," we say and write "8 + 7." Instead of "(−8) − (+7)" we say and write "−8 − 7" or "(−8) − 7."

Compute.

21. $10 - 4 = n$
22. $10 - 14 = n$
23. $8 + 16 = n$
24. $-10 - 4 = n$
25. $-10 - 14 = n$
26. $-8 + 16 = n$
27. $10 - (-4) = n$
28. $10 - (-14) = n$
29. $8 + (-16) = n$
30. $-10 - (-4) = n$

31. $-10 - (-14) = n$
32. $-8 + (-16) = n$
33. $8 - 12 = n$
34. $8 - (-12) = n$
35. $8 + 12 = n$
36. $-8 - 12 = n$
37. $-8 - (-12) = n$
38. $-8 + 12 = n$
39. $-8 + (-12) = n$
40. $0 - 18 = n$

41. $0 + 18 = n$
42. $0 - (-18) = n$
43. $0 + (-18) = n$
44. $7 + 0 = n$
45. $-7 + 0 = n$
46. $-7 - 0 = n$
47. $7 - 0 = n$
48. $4 - (-5) = n$
49. $8 - (-6) = n$
50. $-3 - (-2) = n$

51. $-3 + (-2) = n$
52. $-3 + 2 = n$
53. $-3 - (+2) = n$
54. $428 - 134 = n$
55. $428 + 134 = n$
56. $428 - (-134) = n$
57. $428 + (-134) = n$
58. $-428 - (-134) = n$
59. $-428 - 134 = n$
60. $-428 + (-134) = n$

61. Ms. Thurber, the English teacher, gives grades based on test averages, but she subtracts 5 points from that average for every homework paper not turned in.

   a. After deductions for missing homework, Bill has a grade of 74. If he turns in the 3 homework papers he owes and gets credit for them, what will his average be?

   b. Kayla has a grade of 83. She has failed to hand in 2 homework papers. What would her average be if she turned them in?

c. Franklin has a grade of 91. He turned in all of his homework. What would his grade be if he had not turned in 3 homework papers?

d. Joyce got perfect grades of 100 on all 5 tests but failed to turn in any of the 6 homework papers. What is her grade?

20-gallon mark

The workers at a dairy try to fill the 20-gallon milk cans to the line that shows there is exactly 20 gallons of milk in the can. Sometimes they put a bit too much in, and sometimes they put too little in. A customer has claimed that the dairy is regularly giving too little milk. You have been asked to decide if this is true.

For each of the following samples of 10 containers, you measured the height of the milk in centimeters above or below the 20-gallon mark. For each sample, give

a. The total number of centimeters you measured above or below the mark.

b. The average number of centimeters above or below the mark.

c. Your decision whether the customer is being seriously short-changed on that sample.

62. 2, −3, 0, 1, 1, −4, 2, 1, −1, 0
63. 1, 1, 2, 1, 3, 0, 2, −4, 0, 1
64. −3, −2, −4, 0, −1, 3, −4, −2, 1, −1
65. 1, 4, −3, 1, 0, 0, 0, 1, −1, 1
66. −2, −3, −2, −4, 0, 1, −2, −1, 1, −3
67. 1, 1, 0, 0, −4, 0, −4, −3, 0, −3
68. −2, −3, −3, −4, −2, −1, −3, −4, −2, −2
69. 1, 1, 1, 2, 0, 1, 2, 1, 0, 2
70. 0, 0, 0, 1, 0, −1, 0, 1, 1, −1
71. −1, −1, −2, 0, −1, 4, −1, 0, −1, 3

Multiplication with Signed Numbers

When you look at something through a magnifying lens, it usually has a bigger image. Some magnifying lenses can also invert the image. That means that the magnifying lens turns the image upside down.

Suppose we have 4 different magnifying lenses: one that magnifies twice, one that magnifies 3 times, one that magnifies twice and inverts, and one that magnifies 3 times and inverts. We'll call them (2), (3), (−2), and (−3).

Think about the following situations. What will the size and position of the images be? The pictures will help you.

Imagine looking at a small △ through the (2) and (3) lenses.

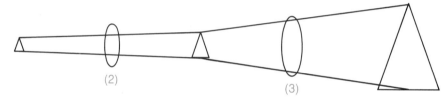

Imagine looking at the △ through the (2) and (−3) lenses.

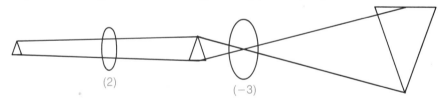

Imagine looking at the △ through the (−2) and (3) lenses.

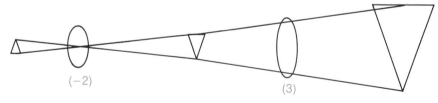

Imagine looking at the △ through the (−2) and (−3) lenses.

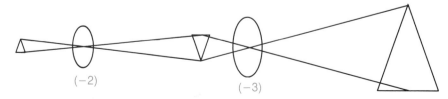

You could think about these situations as multiplication problems. They should help you understand the following rule for multiplying any 2 numbers.

Remember

If both factors have the same sign, their product is positive. If their signs are different, their product is negative.

Solve for n. Use the rule.

1. $3 \times 5 = n$
2. $3 \times (-5) = n$
3. $(-3) \times 5 = n$
4. $(-3) \times (-5) = n$
5. $n = 4 \times (-7)$
6. $n = 8 \times 7$
7. $n = (-7) \times (-8)$
8. $n = (-9) \times 7$
9. $n = 7 \times (-9)$
10. $4 \times (-8) = n$

11. $(-8) \times (-7) = n$
12. $(-9) \times (-7) = n$
13. $(-4) \times (-8) = n$
14. $5 \times 0 = n$
15. $(-5) \times 0 = n$
16. $7 - 3 = n$
17. $3 - 7 = n$
18. $-3 + 7 = n$
19. $-3 - 7 = n$
20. $3 - (-7) = n$

21. $7 - (-3) = n$
22. $-3 - (-7) = n$
23. $3 \times 7 = n$
24. $(-3) \times 7 = n$
25. $3 \times (-7) = n$
26. $(-3) \times (-7) = n$
27. $3 \times n = 21$
28. $3 \times n = -21$
29. $-3 \times n = -21$
30. $-3 \times n = 21$

[1] **Look at problems 27–30. Can you give a rule for division of signed numbers?**

[2] **Is it essentially the same as the rule for multiplication?**

Remember

If divisor and dividend have the same sign, the quotient is positive. If their signs are different, the quotient is negative.

Solve for n.

31. $20 \div 4 = n$
32. $20 \div (-4) = n$

33. $32 \div (-8) = n$
34. $-32 \div 8 = n$

35. $-20 \div (-5) = n$
36. $20 \div (-5) = n$

SIGNED MATHNESS

Players: 2 or more
Materials: One 0–5 cube, one 5–10 cube, pencil, paper
Object: To get an answer as close to zero as possible

Rules

1. The first player rolls both cubes 5 times. On each roll, write the number on the 5–10 cube. Give the number a sign determined by the 0–5 cube: + for even numbers (0, 2, and 4) and − for odd numbers (1, 3, and 5).

2. Add any 2 of the numbers.

3. Subtract another of the numbers from the sum in step 2.

4. Multiply the difference in step 3 by 1 of the 2 unused numbers.

5. Divide the product in step 4 by the remaining number.

6. The other players repeat steps 1–5.

7. The player whose final answer is closest to zero wins.

Sample Game

Ilene rolled `2` `9`, `5` `5`, `1` `9`, `3` `10`, and `0` `5`. She wrote 9, −5, −9, −10, 5. She added 9 and −5 to get 4. Then she subtracted 5 to get −1, multiplied by −9 to get 9, and divided by −10 to get $-\frac{9}{10}$.

Bryan rolled `3` `5`, `5` `9`, `0` `6`, `4` `5`, and `3` `5`. He wrote −5, −9, 6, 5, −5. He added −9 and 5 to get −4. Then he subtracted −5 to get 1, multiplied by −5 to get −5, and divided by 6 to get $-\frac{5}{6}$.

Cora rolled `5` `6`, `2` `7`, `3` `6`, `5` `9`, and `2` `5`. She wrote −6, 7, −6, −9, 5. She added −9 and 5 to get −4. Then she subtracted −6 to get 2, multiplied by −6 to get −12, and divided by 7 to get $-1\frac{5}{7}$.

Bryan won because $-\frac{5}{6}$ is closer to zero than $-\frac{9}{10}$ or $-1\frac{5}{7}$.

Practice with Signed Numbers

Solve for n.

1. $5 + 10 = n$	**11.** $-5 \times 10 = n$	**21.** $10 + (-5) = n$
2. $5 - 10 = n$	**12.** $-5 \div 10 = n$	**22.** $10 - (-5) = n$
3. $5 \times 10 = n$	**13.** $-5 + (-10) = n$	**23.** $10 \times (-5) = n$
4. $5 \div 10 = n$	**14.** $-5 - (-10) = n$	**24.** $10 \div (-5) = n$
5. $5 + (-10) = n$	**15.** $-5 \times (-10) = n$	**25.** $-10 + (-5) = n$
6. $5 - (-10) = n$	**16.** $-5 \div (-10) = n$	**26.** $-10 - (-5) = n$
7. $5 \times (-10) = n$	**17.** $10 + 5 = n$	**27.** $-10 \times (-5) = n$
8. $5 \div (-10) = n$	**18.** $10 - 5 = n$	**28.** $-10 \div (-5) = n$
9. $-5 + 10 = n$	**19.** $10 \times 5 = n$	**29.** $-10 + 5 = n$
10. $-5 - 10 = n$	**20.** $10 \div 5 = n$	**30.** $-10 - 5 = n$

Suppose you are playing Signed Mathness. You get these sets of 5 numbers. What's the best score you can get in each case?

31. $5, -8, -10, 5, 9$
32. $-5, -8, -10, -5, 9$
33. $8, -6, 6, -6, 7$
34. $9, 5, 10, 7, -9$

35. How can you get a perfect score of zero in Signed Mathness?

In each problem, 4 of the answers are unreasonable and 1 is reasonable. Choose the reasonable answer.

1. Lou Ann is proud that she ran 12 ___ today. (in, cm, yd, km, g)

2. She ran that far in only 57 ___. (sec, ml, min, A, hr)

3. When she finished running, Lou Ann weighed herself again and discovered that she had lost 2 ___. (lb, g, tsp, t, yd³)

4. She was very thirsty and drank a whole ___ of water. (yd³, L, fl oz, A, cm)

5. After that she spent 5 hours mowing a lawn that has an area of about $\frac{1}{2}$ ___. (m, mi², ha, cm², kg)

6. Lou Ann weighs ___ kilograms. (3, 10, 50, 110, 240)

7. Lou Ann is ___ centimeters tall. (0.1, 1.5, 8, 64, 165)

Choose the correct answer.

8. There are ___ centimeters in a meter. (12, 36, 80, 100, 5280)

9. There are ___ inches in a mile. (36; 512; 10,000; 43,880; 63,360)

10. There are ___ millimeters in a kilometer. (100; 5280; 68,540; 244,880; 1,000,000)

11. There are ___ inches in a foot. (10, 12, 22, 50, 75)

Compute. Leave your answers as mixed numbers, whole numbers, or proper fractions. Reduce fractions where possible.

12. $3\frac{4}{5} + 2\frac{3}{5}$
13. $4\frac{1}{7} - 2\frac{4}{7}$
14. $2\frac{1}{4} + 3\frac{2}{5}$
15. $5\frac{1}{3} - 3\frac{1}{2}$
16. $1\frac{1}{3} \times 2\frac{2}{3}$
17. $6\frac{3}{4} \div 2\frac{1}{4}$
18. $5\frac{1}{3} \times 2\frac{1}{4}$
19. $2\frac{1}{2} \div 3\frac{1}{3}$

Solve for n. Watch the signs.

20. $3 + 7 = n$

21. $3 - 7 = n$

22. $3 + (-7) = n$

23. $(-3) + 7 = n$

24. $(-3) - 7 = n$

25. $(-3) \times 7 = n$

26. $(-3) \times (-7) = n$

27. $3 - (-7) = n$

28. $(-3) - (-7) = n$

29. $(-7) + (-3) = n$

30. $(-7) - (-3) = n$

31. $3 \times (-7) = n$

32. $3 \div 6 = n$

33. $3 \div (-6) = n$

34. $(-3) \div 6 = n$

35. $(-3) \div (-6) = n$

36. $(-7) - 3 = n$

37. $(-6) \div 3 = n$

38. $6 \div (-3) = n$

39. $7 + (-7) = n$

40. $(-7) - (-7) = n$

Enrichment

Humans in prehistoric times lived from day to day and from season to season with little concern for the passing time. They began to watch the movements of the sun, the moon, and the stars. They used these regular, natural events to keep track of time.

These natural events still govern the way we keep track of time. Our calendar year is based on the time required for the earth to make a full trip around the sun.

Do some research on time. See what you can find out about calendars, clocks, and other ways to measure time.

Even though people use different systems for measuring other quantities, nearly everyone uses the same system for time. Why do you think this is so?

Work in small groups. Try to develop a "metric" system for measuring time. Think about the units we now use. Which would have to stay the same, and which could be changed?

In each problem, 4 of the answers are unreasonable and 1 is reasonable. Choose the reasonable answer.

1. Martin woke up refreshed after sleeping 8 ___.
   (hr, min, sec, yr, kg)

2. He picked up his 3-month-old sister, Bridget, who weighs 6 ___. (mg, c, tsp, tons, kg)

3. Bridget drank 6 ___ of orange juice.   (fl oz, mm³, lb, ft, L)

4. Martin walked 600 ___ to school.   (mi, in, min, m, mg)

5. It took him 8 ___ to get to school.   (hr, da, min, ft, yd)

6. The area of his classroom is about 1200 ___.
   (yd³, yd², ft², km², A)

7. The height of the ceiling in the classroom is about 15 ___.
   (ft, in, mm, cm, kg)

Choose the correct answer.

8. There are ___ millimeters in a meter.   (1, 10, 50, 100, 1000)

9. There are ___ square feet in a square yard.   (1, 3, 6, 9, 25)

10. There are ___ grams in a kilogram.   (100; 220; 1000; 22,000; 100,000)

11. There are ___ feet in a mile.   (36, 640, 1000, 5280, 7500)

Compute. Leave your answers as mixed numbers, whole numbers, or proper fractions. Reduce fractions where possible.

12. $2\frac{3}{4} + 3\frac{3}{4}$

13. $3\frac{1}{5} - 1\frac{2}{5}$

14. $3\frac{1}{3} + 4\frac{2}{5}$

15. $4\frac{1}{4} - 1\frac{2}{3}$

16. $1\frac{1}{2} \times 2\frac{2}{4}$

17. $6\frac{2}{3} \div 2\frac{1}{3}$

18. $3\frac{1}{3} \times 4\frac{2}{5}$

19. $3\frac{1}{2} \div 2\frac{1}{3}$

Solve for n. Watch the signs.

20. $2 + 8 = n$ **27.** $2 - (-8) = n$ **34.** $(-4) \div 8 = n$

21. $2 - 8 = n$ **28.** $(-2) - (-8) = n$ **35.** $(-4) \div (-8) = n$

22. $2 + (-8) = n$ **29.** $(-8) + (-2) = n$ **36.** $(-8) - 2 = n$

23. $(-2) + 8 = n$ **30.** $(-8) - (-2) = n$ **37.** $(-8) \div 4 = n$

24. $(-2) - 8 = n$ **31.** $2 \times (-8) = n$ **38.** $8 \div (-4) = n$

25. $(-2) \times 8 = n$ **32.** $4 \div 8 = n$ **39.** $8 + (-8) = n$

26. $(-2) \times (-8) = n$ **33.** $4 \div (-8) = n$ **40.** $(-8) - (-8) = n$

Enrichment

The minute hand is directly over the hour hand several times during a day.

1. How many times during a day does this happen?

2. How long is it between the times that this happens?

CHAPTER 7
STATISTICS
RATIOS

This is the title page of a book that was published by John Graunt.

Natural and *Political*

OBSERVATIONS

Mentioned in a following INDEX,

and made upon the

Bills of Mortality.

By *JOHN GRAUNT*,

Citizen of

LONDON.

With reference to the *Government*, *Religion*, *Trade*,
Growth, *Ayre*, *Diseases*, and the several Changes of the
said CITY.

——— *Non, me ut miretur Turba, laboro.*
Contentus paucis Lectoribus ———

LONDON,
Printed by *Tho: Roycroft*, for *John Martin*, *James Allestry*,
and *Tho: Dicas*, at the Sign of the *Bell* in St. Paul's
Church-yard, MDCLXII.

---

[1] **How much of the title page can you understand?**

[2] **In what year was the book published?**

Graunt's book contained studies of records of births and deaths in the various parishes of London from 1604 to 1661. The causes of death ranged from "Affrighted" to "Worms" and from "Teeth" to "Grief." In 1632 the 17th most common of 63 causes of death was "Suddenly."

Graunt described and evaluated the way the material was collected and gave his opinion about what various data meant. One of the things Graunt showed was that the percentage of deaths due to causes such as accidents or certain diseases seemed to remain about the same from one locality to another and from one year to another.

The idea that there is a regularity in large numbers of apparently unrelated individual events is the basis of the science of statistics. Statistics allows us to predict what will tend to happen in large groups but does not allow us to say for sure what will happen in individual cases.

For example, one of the things Graunt noticed was that consistently more boys were born than girls. This has proved to be true for large groups of births studied since then. But such a statistical trend does not tell us whether a couple that is considering having a baby next year *will* have a boy or a girl.

After collecting a large number of data, we usually try to organize them or describe them simply so that others can easily understand their significance.

For example, Pia measured the heights, in centimeters, of the students in her class. She made this list:

153, 157, 158, 159, 149, 150, 147, 152, 155, 164, 154,
153, 153, 156, 144, 158, 156, 160, 151, 168, 161, 152,
155, 164, 158, 151, 159, 162, 149, 156, 161, 158, 159

How might she describe or organize these data in a way that could be more convenient or more understandable?

Here are some of the things she might do:

A. She could put the data in order, from smallest to largest. Then she would have this list:

144, 147, 149, 149, 150, 151, 151, 152, 152, 153, 153,
153, 154, 155, 155, 156, 156, 156, 157, 158, 158, 158,
158, 159, 159, 159, 160, 161, 161, 162, 164, 164, 168

B. She could use a calculator to find the *mean,* or *average,* of the data. Here the mean is about 155.8. It is found by dividing the sum of the heights (5142) by the number of students (33).

C. She could report the *median* datum. The median is the middle one, starting from the bottom and counting up in order of size. Here the median is 156, since the 17th item is the middle item of 33.

D. She could tell what the *mode* of the data was. The mode is the most common value in a set of data. Here the mode is 158.

E. She could show the *range* of the data. The range of a set of data is the difference between the largest and smallest values. Here the range is 24.

F. She could make a *bar graph* or *histogram* of the data. It would look like this:

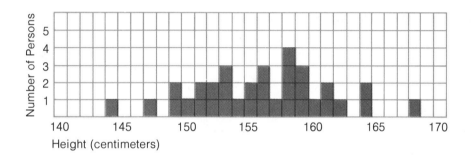

There are many other ways she could describe or organize these data for clarity. We will discuss some of them in this chapter.

CUBE AVERAGING GAME

Players: 2
Materials: One 5–10 cube
Object: To get the higher average

Rules

1. The first player rolls the cube no more than 5 times and writes down each number as it is rolled.

2. The second player may tell the first player to stop after 3 or 4 rolls or may allow the first player to roll 5 times.

3. The first player calculates the average of the numbers rolled (for 3, 4, or 5 rolls).

4. The players reverse roles.

5. For each round, the player with the higher average is the winner.

6. The loser becomes the first player in the next round.

Sample Game

Candice rolled: 7 6 7 5
Klaus told her to stop.
Candice calculated her average:

7 + 6 + 7 + 5 = 25
25 ÷ 4 = 6.25

Klaus rolled: 7 6 5
Candice told him to stop.
Klaus could see that his average was 6, because 5 is 1 less than 6 and 7 is 1 more than 6.

Candice won the round because her average (6.25) was greater than Klaus's (6).

Computing the Mean

To compute the mean of several numbers, you divide the sum of the numbers by the number of numbers. Note that the mean is often called the average.

Example

What is the average of 8, 5, 5, 9, and 7?
Mean = (8 + 5 + 5 + 9 + 7) ÷ 5 = 34 ÷ 5 = 6.8

Another way to find the mean involves estimating the answer first. Then you average the deviations from the estimate and add the average deviation to the estimated answer. We'll do the problem above this way, as an example. 7 seems to be about in the middle of the numbers.

Example

Numbers: 8, 5, 5, 9, 7
Deviations from 7: 1, −2, −2, 2, 0
Total deviation: 1 + (−2) + (−2) + 2 + 0 = −1
Average deviation: −1 ÷ 5 = −0.2
Mean: 7 + (−0.2) = 6.8

The second method is complicated to describe. But it will often save work when the numbers are about the same, are organized in a regular way, or are very large.

Find the average of each set of numbers.

1. 5, 6, 7, 8, 9
2. 105, 106, 107, 108, 109
3. 2436, 2436, 2436, 2436, 2436
4. 83, 81, 79, 77
5. 0, 3, 8, 1, 5
6. 10, 20
7. 1, 2, 3, 4, 5, 6, 7, 8, 9
8. 71, 72, 73, 74, 75, 76, 77, 78, 79

9. 3, 5, 7, 9, 11
10. 173, 173, 173, 173, 173, 173
11. 10, 10, 10, 10, 15
12. 10, 10, 10, 10, 11
13. 10, 10, 10, 10, 9
14. 4, 7, 3, 6, 5
15. 8, 11, 1, 9, 7
16. 4, 8, 6, 6, 10, 2

Is the average of a set of whole numbers always a whole number?

Averages: Applications

1. María kept a record of her scores on 5 spelling tests.

Spelling Tests	
Date	Score
12-20	100
1-6	89
1-10	93
1-13	90
1-17	18

What is the average of those 5 scores?

[1] Do you think that her average really describes how well she did on the 5 tests?

2. Carolyn kept a record of her scores on the same 5 tests.

Spelling Tests	
Date	Score
12-20	85
1-6	88
1-10	90
1-13	92
1-17	95

What is the average of her 5 spelling scores?

[2] Do you think her average really describes how well she did on the 5 tests?

3. Dot and Dan had a contest to see who was the better jumper.
   a. Dot jumped 5 times. Her jumps were measured as 220 centimeters, 215 centimeters, 224 centimeters, 216 centimeters, and 225 centimeters. What is the average length of her jumps?
   b. Dan's 5 jumps were measured as 250 centimeters, 270 centimeters, 190 centimeters, 240 centimeters, and 175 centimeters. What is the average length of his jumps?
   c. Whose average jump was longer?
   d. Dot and Dan usually jump the way they did in the contest. If they both jump over a 2-meter stream, who is more likely to get wet?

Remember

To find the average number of kilometers a car goes on a liter of gasoline, divide the number of kilometers traveled by the number of liters used.

4. When the odometer on Mr. Watt's car read 26,532.8 kilometers, he filled his gas tank by putting in 43.2 liters. When the odometer reading was 26,912.4, he filled the tank again, adding 32.7 liters of gas. What was the average number of kilometers per liter for his car?

   (Hint: One of the numbers provided in the problem is not needed. Which one? Why?)

5. In February Mr. Watt kept this record of odometer readings and amount of gas added each time he filled the tank:

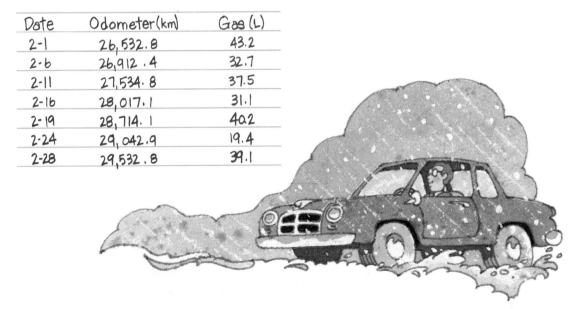

Date	Odometer (km)	Gas (L)
2-1	26,532.8	43.2
2-6	26,912.4	32.7
2-11	27,534.8	37.5
2-16	28,017.1	31.1
2-19	28,714.1	40.2
2-24	29,042.9	19.4
2-28	29,532.8	39.1

   What was the average number of kilometers per liter for February?

   Play the Cube Averaging Game. Use medians or modes instead of means.

The number that is most commonly called the average of a set of numbers is the mean. The mean is found by dividing the sum of the numbers by the number of numbers.

Other numbers are sometimes used instead of the mean. 2 of these are the median and the mode.

The median of a set of numbers is the number in the middle when they are all arranged in order from smallest to largest. If there are an even number of data, the number halfway between the 2 middle numbers is usually called the median.

The mode of a set of data is the datum that occurs most often. Sometimes there are 2 or more modes. For example, in the set of data 1, 1, 1, 2, 3, 3, 3, 4, 4, 5, 5, 5, there are 3 modes: 1, 3, and 5.

The Compact Compass Company has 10 employees. They are paid the following weekly salaries:

$375, $375, $375, $375, $380, $380, $390, $400, $600, $950

1. What is the average salary of these employees?
2. How many of the employees make more than the average?
3. How many of the employees make less than the average?
4. Does the average salary seem like a good description of the salaries paid by the company?

Let's find the mean, median, and mode of the Compact Compass Company salaries.

The mean $= \frac{4600}{10} = 460$
The median $= 380$ (halfway between the two 380s)
The mode $= 375$

[1] **If you were a union representative for the workers at the Compact Compass Company and wanted to convince people that the workers were underpaid, which figure would you report: the mean, the median, or the mode?**

[2] **If you owned the Compact Compass Company and wanted to show how generous salaries were, would you report the mean, the median, or the mode?**

5. Copy and complete this chart:

Set	Data	Mean	Median	Mode
A	5, 5, 5, 5, 6, 7, 7, 7, 16	▨	▨	▨
B	5, 5, 5, 6, 7, 7, 7, 7, 16	▨	▨	▨

a. Do the sets of data seem quite different from each other or quite similar?
b. Which changed most between sets A and B: the mean, the median, or the mode?
c. Which of the 3 figures changed the least?

6. Jill rolled a 5–10 cube 15 times. She recorded the numbers rolled: 7, 7, 5, 10, 6, 8, 9, 7, 5, 10, 10, 10, 9, 7, 10.

a. What is the mean for this set of numbers?
b. What is the median?
c. What is the mode?

(Hint: To find the mode and median, you may wish to arrange the numbers from smallest to largest: 5, 5, 6, 7, 7, 7, 7, 8, 9, 9, 10, 10, 10, 10, 10. Count to be sure you copied all 15.)

7. Jill repeated this activity 10 times. She made a table showing the mean, median, and mode(s) for each set of numbers.

Trial	Mean	Median	Mode(s)
1	8	8	10
2	7.33	7	7
3	7.47	8	9
4	7.47	7	7
5	6.8	6	5
6	7.2	7	5
7	7	7	6,8
8	7.47	8	6
9	7.47	8	9
10	7.2	7	9

a. Which varied most in Jill's experiments: mean, median, or mode?
b. Which varied least?
c. If the cube were perfect, you would expect the mean of the means to be about 7.5. Is it?

[3] **Do you think the cube is biased in favor of small numbers?**

8. Repeat Jill's activity with 10 trials of 15 rolls of a 5–10 cube. Make a chart of your results. Compare your results with hers.

Often large numbers of data are summarized with 1 simple phrase or statistic. This can lead to misunderstanding, especially if the data are oversimplified. Occasionally it seems that such oversimplification is used in order to be confusing.

Consider each of the following situations. Discuss them with other people. Answer the questions as you think they should be answered. (Many of the questions have more than 1 correct answer.)

A. In a labor dispute, the union representative announced that the average salary was $8000 a year, the management representative said the average salary was $14,000 a year, and the mediator said the average salary was $10,000 a year. Assume that there were 9 employees and that all 3 reports were truthful (as each observer saw the situation). Write out a list of salaries that might produce these 3 reports.

[1] Which average do you think is the fair one to report?

[2] Why?

B. A certain advertisement claims that 4 out of 5 dentists responding to a survey recommend sugarless gum for those patients who chew gum.

[3] How many questionnaires do you think were sent out?

[4] How many dentists do you think responded to the survey?

[5] Is there any way to guess how many were asked but refused to respond?

[6] How many dentists do you think recommended chewing gum at all?

[7] What do you suppose the other 1 out of 5 dentists said?

C. Some researchers were trying to find a cure for chicken pox in chickens. They reportedly announced these results for a certain medicine: "$33\frac{1}{3}$% were cured, $33\frac{1}{3}$% died, and the other one got away."

[8] How many chickens were involved in the experiment?

[9] Why do you think these results were reported this way?

[10] Do you think the story is true?

D. An advertisement says that $7\frac{1}{2}$ out of every 10 people surveyed preferred the product of the advertiser.

[11] How many people do you think were surveyed? Why?

E. Willard Jones announced that he had a 50% increase in sales during his second week as a car salesman.

[12] How many cars might he have sold his first and second weeks?

F. Suppose Willard Jones had a 50% decrease in sales his third week.

[13] How many cars might he have sold in each of the first 3 weeks?

[14] Since he had a 50% increase and then a 50% decrease, did he sell the same number in the first and third weeks?

G. Carrie Moore sold 2 cars during her first week on the job and had a 100% increase her second week.

[15] How many cars did she sell the second week?

In her third week, she had a 150% increase in sales.

[16] How many cars did she sell the third week? (Be careful—if she'd had a 100% increase, how many would she have sold? Is a 150% increase more than a 100% increase?)

She had a 50% decrease the fourth week.

[17] How many did she sell the fourth week?

She had a 100% decrease the fifth week.

[18] How many did she sell then?

[19] Could she have had a 150% decrease in any week? Why?

LETTER ARITHMETIC ACTIVITY

You can do this activity alone, in small groups, or with the whole class. We've given you some variations, but there are many more that you will think of.

Rules

1. Assign the following numerical values to each letter of the alphabet.

A	B	C	D	E	F	G	H	I	J	K	L	M	N	O	P	Q	R	S	T	U	V	W	X	Y	Z
1	2	3	4	5	6	7	8	9	10	11	12	13	14	15	16	17	18	19	20	21	22	23	24	25	26

2. Find a word that has 30 as the sum of its letter values. Find words for 10, 40, and 22. Choose other sums and find words for them.

Variations

1. Find words with letter products of 100, 1000, and so on. For example, *DAY* ($4 \times 1 \times 25 = 100$).

2. Choose a word with 4 letters. Use the rules of Cubo to make a score of 21. For example, *MARK* (13, 1, 18, 11) makes $18 + 13 - 11 + 1 = 21$.

3. Whose name in your class has a sum that is prime?

4. Write a simple message to a friend. At first, try a sentence with 3 or 4 words. Give the sum of the numbers for each word. This is hard and clues may be necessary. Here's an example:

$$19 \quad 61 \quad 36?$$

Give clues like these one at a time:

a. The first word has 2 letters.
b. The second word has 3 letters.
c. The third word has 5 letters.
d. The first word begins with *D*.
e. The third word has 2 *E*s.
f. The third word has a *G*.
g. The third word begins with *A*.

Add or subtract. Reduce answers completely.

1. $\frac{2}{3} - \frac{1}{6}$ 4. $\frac{7}{8} - \frac{3}{4}$ 7. $\frac{2}{5} - \frac{2}{7}$

2. $\frac{2}{3} + \frac{1}{6}$ 5. $\frac{7}{9} + \frac{2}{3}$ 8. $\frac{2}{5} + \frac{2}{7}$

3. $\frac{7}{8} + \frac{3}{4}$ 6. $\frac{7}{9} - \frac{2}{3}$ 9. $\frac{1}{7} + \frac{1}{3}$

Multiply or divide. Reduce answers completely.

10. $\frac{2}{3} \times \frac{1}{6}$ 13. $\frac{7}{8} \times \frac{2}{7}$ 16. $\frac{2}{5} \div \frac{2}{7}$

11. $\frac{2}{3} \div \frac{1}{6}$ 14. $\frac{5}{9} \times \frac{2}{15}$ 17. $\frac{2}{5} \times \frac{2}{7}$

12. $\frac{7}{8} \div \frac{3}{4}$ 15. $\frac{5}{9} \div \frac{2}{3}$ 18. $\frac{1}{7} \times \frac{1}{3}$

Solve for n. Reduce answers completely.

19. $\frac{3}{7} + \frac{1}{3} = n$ 25. $\frac{2}{3} + \frac{1}{9} = n$

20. $\frac{3}{7} - \frac{1}{3} = n$ 26. $\frac{2}{3} \div \frac{1}{9} = n$

21. $\frac{3}{7} \times \frac{1}{3} = n$ 27. $\frac{5}{8} + \frac{3}{5} = n$

22. $\frac{3}{7} \div \frac{1}{3} = n$ 28. $\frac{5}{8} - \frac{3}{5} = n$

23. $\frac{2}{3} - \frac{1}{9} = n$ 29. $\frac{5}{8} \div \frac{3}{5} = n$

24. $\frac{2}{3} \times \frac{1}{9} = n$ 30. $\frac{5}{8} \times \frac{3}{5} = n$

Halley and the First Life Insurance Tables

Edmund Halley (1656–1742) was an outstanding scientist and scholar who contributed much to the fields of astronomy, physics, and mathematics. He was interested in astronomy from a very young age. When he was at college in Oxford, he had his own instruments for studying the stars, including a 24-foot telescope.

The contribution for which he is most famous is his study of the orbit of the comet that is now named for him. Most people in Halley's time thought that comets traveled randomly through space. Halley studied the orbits of comets that had appeared in the past. He decided that comets were part of the solar system and had regular paths around the sun. His studies showed that the comets of 1531, 1607, and 1682 had orbits that were very much alike. He decided that they must be orbits of the same comet and predicted that the comet would return in 1758. It did, and the comet is now known as Halley's Comet.

[1] When was Halley's Comet last seen?

[2] When will it reappear? (Assume the comet reappears about every 76 years.)

In 1693, Halley published the first life insurance tables. He used data from the monthly tables of births and deaths from the city of Breslau for the 5 years from 1687 through 1691.

Breslau is a city on the Oder River. When Halley was alive, Breslau was in a part of Germany known as Schlesien. Today Breslau is in Poland and is called Wroclaw.

Halley was sure that very few people moved into or out of Breslau and that the numbers of births and deaths remained fairly constant from year to year. In that 5-year period there were 6193 births.

[3] About how many births is that per year?

From his tables, he established that an average of 348 children usually died before reaching their first birthdays.

[4] About how many children celebrated their first birthdays each year?

He also found that an average of 198 children from the ages of 1 to 6 died each year.

[5] About how many 6-year-old children were there in Breslau in any given year?

In this way, Halley was able to estimate the number of people of any given age who were living in Breslau at that time. He concluded that there were then a total of about 34,000 people of all ages living in Breslau.

He used this information to construct a table showing how many persons would be alive at each given age from among 1000 persons who were alive at age 1. A copy of this table is on the next page. According to this table, if there were 1000 1-year-old children, 855 of them would live to become 2 years old, and so on.

Remember that the numbers in this table apply only to persons living in the late 1600s.

[6] Why would a similar table for people today look quite different?

Using a Mortality Table

The table below shows for each age the number of persons who would be alive out of every 1000 persons alive at age 1.

The First Life Insurance Table as Constructed by Edmund Halley in 1693.

Age	Persons	Age	Persons	Age	Persons	Age	Persons
1	1000	22	586	43	417	64	202
2	855	23	579	44	407	65	192
3	798	24	573	45	397	66	182
4	760	25	567	46	387	67	172
5	732	26	560	47	377	68	162
6	710	27	553	48	367	69	152
7	692	28	546	49	357	70	142
8	680	29	539	50	346	71	131
9	670	30	531	51	335	72	120
10	661	31	523	52	324	73	109
11	653	32	515	53	313	74	98
12	646	33	507	54	302	75	88
13	640	34	499	55	292	76	78
14	634	35	490	56	282	77	68
15	628	36	481	57	272	78	58
16	622	37	472	58	262	79	49
17	616	38	463	59	252	80	41
18	610	39	454	60	242	81	34
19	604	40	445	61	232	82	28
20	598	41	436	62	222	83	23
21	592	42	427	63	212	84	20

You can use the table to work out answers to various questions of interest. Here are some examples.

A. What was the probability of a 1-year-old living to age 2?

Of 1000 1-year-olds, the table shows that 855 would become 2-year-olds (and 145 would die). So the probability is about $\frac{855}{1000}$ or 0.855.

B. What was the probability of a 10-year-old living to be 20?

Of 661 10-year-olds, 598 would live to the age of 20. So the probability is $\frac{598}{661} = 0.90$. (If a calculator is available, you will find it useful for such calculations.)

C. What were the odds that a 1-year-old would live another year?

The chances of living to be 2 were 855 out of 1000, and the chances of dying before becoming 2 were $1000 - 855$, or 145. So the odds in favor of living to be 2 were 855 to 145 (or about 5.9 to 1).

D. To what age did a 10-year-old have an even chance of living?

There were 661 10-year-olds. The table shows half that many people between the ages 51 and 52. So the answer is that a 10-year-old had an even chance (or a probability of $\frac{1}{2}$) of living to between 51 and 52 years of age.

Remember

The odds in favor of something occurring are the ratio of the number of favorable cases to the number of unfavorable cases.

Use the table on page 292 to answer the following questions.

1. What was the probability of a 1-year-old child living to age
    a. 5?   c. 20?   e. 50?   g. 80?
    b. 10?   d. 34?   f. 60?   h. 84?

2. What was the probability of a 10-year-old living to age
    a. 10?   c. 20?   e. 50?   g. 80?
    b. 11?   d. 34?   f. 60?   h. 84?

3. What was the probability of a 1-year-old living another
    a. 4 years?   c. 20 years?
    b. 10 years?   d. 60 years?

4. What was the probability of a 10-year-old living another
    a. 4 years?   c. 20 years?
    b. 10 years?   d. 60 years?

5. What was the probability of a 20-year-old living another
    a. 4 years?   c. 20 years?
    b. 10 years?   d. 60 years?

6. What were the odds that a 1-year-old would live to be
    a. 5?   c. 20?   e. 60?
    b. 10?   d. 50?   f. 80?

7. What were the odds that a 10-year-old would live to be
    a. 10?   c. 40?   e. 60?
    b. 20?   d. 50?   f. 80?

8. To what age did a 7-year-old have an even chance of living?

9. To what age did a 9-year-old have an even chance of living?

10. To what age did a 19-year-old have an even chance of living?

Pretend you are living in Breslau in the late 1600s. Use the table on page 292 to answer these questions.

11. How old would you have to be to have an even chance of reaching age 81?

12. How old would you have to be to have an even chance of reaching age 79?

13. How old would you have to be to have an even chance of reaching age 71?

14. How old would you have to be to have an even chance of reaching age 70? Give your answer to the nearest year.

15. How old would you have to be to have an even chance of reaching age 60? Give your answer to the nearest year.

16. How old (to the nearest year) would you have to be to have an even chance of reaching age

    a. 50?   b. 40?   c. 34?   d. 33?

17. For each of the following ages, decide how many more years you have an even chance of living. Give answers to the nearest year. (For example, at age 7 you have an even chance of reaching age 50. So you have an even chance of living another 43 years.)

    a. 1   c. 3   e. 5   g. 7   i. 9   k. 11   m. 20
    b. 2   d. 4   f. 6   h. 8   j. 10   l. 12   n. 30

18. Make up 3 problems of your own based on the table. Make them different from problems in this book. Choose something that people in 17th-century Breslau might have found interesting. Share your problems with others.

You know that a ratio is a way of comparing 2 numbers. If you look at the table on page 292, you can see that the ratio of the number of persons alive at age 3 to the number of persons alive at age 1 is $\frac{798}{1000}$. Sometimes we read this as "798 to 1000" or just "0.798."

When you find a ratio, you get a rational number that is written either as a fraction or as a decimal. Since we are interested only in approximate ratios, we can always use a decimal approximation, such as 0.333 for $\frac{1}{3}$.

Go back to the table on page 292 (and in time and place to 17th-century Breslau). Use the table to answer these questions.

1. What is the ratio of the number of persons alive at age 34 to the number of persons alive at age 1?

2. What is the ratio of the number of persons alive at age 59 to the number of persons alive at age 34?

3. What is the ratio of the number of persons alive at age 59 to the number of persons alive at age 80?

4. What is the ratio of the number of persons alive at age 84 to the number of persons alive at age 80?

Ratios and Gears

Ratios have many uses. One use is to do calculations with gears.
Look at these gears:

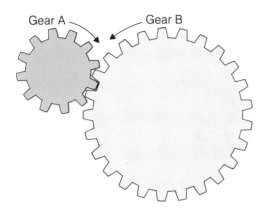

Gear A   Gear B

[1] **How many teeth are there on the small gear?**

[2] **How many teeth are there on the large gear?**

[3] **If the large gear made 1 complete revolution (or turn), how far would the small gear turn? (More than 1 complete turn? More than 2 complete turns?)**

[4] **If the large gear made 12 complete turns, how many complete turns would the small gear make?**

[5] **Is it true that the ratio of the number of turns of gear *A* to the number of turns of gear *B* equals the ratio of the number of teeth on gear *B* to the number of teeth on gear *A*?**

1. If gear *A* turns 300 times, how many times will gear *B* turn?

2. If gear *B* turns 300 times, how many times will gear *A* turn?

Gear *C* has 16 teeth. Gear *D* has 28 teeth. The teeth mesh (come together) as in the drawing of gears *A* and *B*.

3. What is the ratio of the number of teeth on gear *C* to the number of teeth on gear *D*?

4. What is the ratio of the number of turns of gear *C* to the number of turns of gear *D*?

5. If gear *C* turns 112 times, how many times will gear *D* turn?

6. If gear *D* turns 112 times, how many times will gear *C* turn?

Find or construct at least 5 squares of different sizes. Use these squares to do problems 1, 2, and 3.

1. Measure the length of a side of the square and the length of a diagonal to the nearest tenth of a centimeter. For each square, find the ratio of the length of the diagonal to the length of the side. We'll use this square as an example:

 Diagonal: about 2.8 centimeters
Side: about 2.0 centimeters
Ratio of diagonal to side: about $\frac{2.8}{2}$, or 1.4

   a. Are all the ratios about the same?
   b. If so, about what is the ratio?
   c. If you drew a square with a 1-meter side, about how long do you think the diagonal would be?

2. Find the perimeter of (distance around) each square. What is the ratio of the perimeter of each square to the length of its side?

3. Find the area (number of square units) of each square. For each square, find the ratio of the area in square units to the length of the side. Does this ratio seem to be about the same for all the squares?

Find or construct at least 5 circles of different sizes.

4. Measure the diameter of and circumference of (distance around) the circles. (Use a tape measure or a string to measure the circumference.) For each circle, find the ratio of the circumference to the diameter. Does this ratio seem to be the same for all the circles?

Ratios in Maps and Blueprints

Ratios are also used in maps and blueprints.

Milan made a map of his living room. He used a scale of 1 centimeter on the map to 50 centimeters in the real room. This could be written 1 to 50 or 1 cm to 0.5 m or 1 cm:0.5 m or 2 cm:1 m.

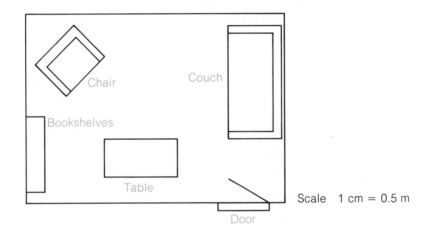

Scale   1 cm = 0.5 m

1. About how long is Milan's living room?
2. About how wide is Milan's living room?
3. About how wide is the door to Milan's living room?
4. About how long is the couch?
5. About how wide is the couch?
6. About how long is the table?
7. About how wide is the table?
8. About how tall is the table?
9. About how long is the chair?
10. About how wide is the chair?
11. About how long are the bookshelves?
12. About how wide are the bookshelves?
13. Make a map of some room in your house. Choose whatever scale (ratio of length on the map to real length) you want to use, but report it on your map.

Ratios are often used in interpreting data. We usually assume that ratios for certain measurements will remain about the same even if the measurements are made at different times. For example, we assume that the ratio of heads to the total number of tosses of a coin will be about 1 to 2, or $\frac{1}{2}$, if the coin is tossed often enough.

You can use this kind of assumption to estimate how many fish are in a pond. Try the following experiment, which shows how this can be done.

Get a large container (a bucket, a wastebasket, a box) and lots (more than 100) of small, identical objects (such as corks, counters, or pieces of paper) that can be easily marked. The large container will represent a pond, and the small objects will represent the fish.

We'll use a box and pieces of paper. First we'll put more than 100 but fewer than 500 pieces of paper in the box.

You could estimate how many are in the box as follows:

A. Draw out 20 pieces of paper and mark each one with an X. (Think of this as netting 20 fish in a pond.)

B. Put the marked pieces of paper back and mix thoroughly. (Think of this as tagging the 20 fish and putting them back in the pond.)

C. Draw out 20 pieces of paper. Count how many are marked with an X. (Think of this as netting another 20 fish in the same pond.)

In step C, it isn't necessary to draw out the same number as in step A. You could have drawn out 23, 30, or almost any number.

Let's say that 3 of the pieces of paper you draw out in step C have Xs.

[1] **What is the ratio of the number of marked pieces of paper to the number of pieces you drew out?**

[2] **Does it seem reasonable that the ratio of the number of marked pieces of paper in the box to the number of all pieces of paper in the box is also about $\frac{3}{20}$?**

[3] **How many marked pieces of paper are there altogether?**

Then we can let x be the total number of pieces of paper in the box. And so we can write an equation showing that the 2 ratios are equal.

$$\frac{3}{20} = \frac{20}{x}$$

[4] Can you determine what x is?
Hint: By what can you multiply 3 to get 20?

So if you multiply the other 20 by $6\frac{2}{3}$, you get x. Apparently there were about 133 pieces of paper in the box.

Solve these problems.

1. Last week Ranger Gorman caught 50 fish, tagged them, and threw them back. Today he caught 50 fish from the same lake. 8 are tagged. About how many fish are there in the lake?

2. Ranger Wharton caught 100 fish 3 weeks ago. She tagged them and threw them back. Today she caught 60 fish from the same lake. 20 are tagged. About how many fish are there in the lake?

3. Last week the 7 rangers at the Three Hundred Lakes Forest Preserve each caught, tagged, and threw back 100 fish at a different lake. Today they went back and caught 60 more. Copy and complete the head ranger's table for this project.

Project: Fish Count

Ranger	Lake	Tagged Fish Caught	Fish Count
Sipe	Two Falls	10	
Paz	Musket	5	
Koch	Chickadee	4	
Paterson	Irwin	3	
Swimmer	Grass	2	
Kessler	Melon	1	
Rayner	Cricket	0	

Compute. Show answers as decimals where necessary.

1. $15 + (-10)$
2. $-10 + (-15)$
3. $-15 \times (-10)$
4. $15 \div 10$
5. $-15 \div (-10)$

6. $15 - (-10)$
7. $-15 - (-10)$
8. $15 \times (-10)$
9. $-15 + (-10)$
10. $-15 - 10$

11. $-60 + (-15)$
12. $60 - (-15)$
13. $60 \times (-15)$
14. $-60 \div (-15)$
15. $-60 \div 15$

16. $-60 \times (-15)$
17. $60 \div (-15)$
18. $-60 + 15$
19. -60×15
20. $60 \div 15$

21. $15 - 30$
22. $-15 - (-30)$
23. $-15 \div 30$
24. $15 \times (-30)$
25. $-15 \div (-30)$

26. 30×15
27. $30 \times (-15)$
28. $30 \div (-15)$
29. $-30 \div (-15)$
30. $30 - 15$

31. $16 \div (-20)$
32. $16 \times (-20)$
33. $-16 + (-20)$
34. $16 - 20$
35. $16 - (-20)$

36. $20 - (-16)$
37. -20×16
38. $-20 \times (-16)$
39. $20 + (-16)$
40. $-20 + (-16)$

41. $25 - (-20)$
42. $25 \times (-20)$
43. $-25 \times (-20)$
44. $25 + (-20)$
45. $-25 - 20$

46. $20 \div (-25)$
47. $-20 \div (25)$
48. $-20 \div (-25)$
49. $-20 \times (-25)$
50. $20 - 25$

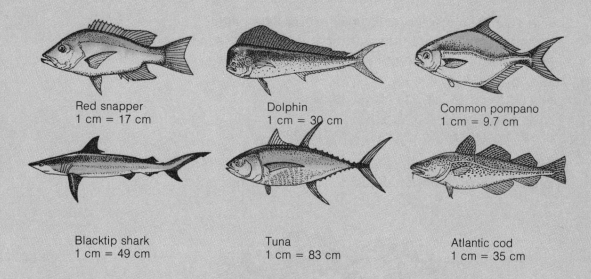

Red snapper
1 cm = 17 cm

Dolphin
1 cm = 30 cm

Common pompano
1 cm = 9.7 cm

Blacktip shark
1 cm = 49 cm

Tuna
1 cm = 83 cm

Atlantic cod
1 cm = 35 cm

1. Can you tell without checking the scales which of these fish is the longest?

2. Compare the scales and decide which fish is the longest.

3. Use the scales to determine the length of each fish.

4. List the fish in order from shortest to longest.

5. Would these fish be in the same order if you arranged them according to weight?

Fish	Weight (kilograms)
Red snapper	16
Atlantic cod	95
Blacktip shark	136
Dolphin	34
Tuna	455
Common pompano	4

6. The table above gives the weight of each of these fish. Is the ratio of weight to length (kilograms per centimeter) the same for all these fish?

1. Calculate the mean (average), median (middle), mode (most common), and range (difference between smallest and largest) for each of the following sets of data.

    a. 1, 2, 2, 3, 3, 3, 4, 4, 5
    b. 11, 12, 12, 13, 13, 13, 14, 14, 15
    c. 1, 1, 1, 1, 2, 2, 2, 3, 3, 4, 13
    d. 11, 11, 11, 11, 12, 12, 12, 13, 13, 14, 23

2. Seth drove 750 kilometers and used 60 liters of gas. What is his average (mean) number of kilometers per liter for the trip?

3. Marina rode her bicycle 750 kilometers in 60 hours. What was the average number of kilometers per hour for the trip?

4. Ms. Takuda owns a small store. On Monday she sold $50 worth of merchandise. On Tuesday there was a 50% increase in sales over Monday. On Wednesday there was a 100% increase in sales over Tuesday.

    a. How much money did Ms. Takuda take in on Tuesday?
    b. How much money did she take in on Wednesday?

5. For the whole week, Ms. Takuda sold $500 worth of merchandise, not counting sales tax. She has to charge 5% sales tax on everything sold. How much sales tax did she collect?

6. A ranger caught 100 fish, tagged them, and put them back in the lake. 2 weeks later he caught 100 fish. 25 of them were tagged. About how many fish do you think were in the lake?

7. Suppose only 4 of the 100 fish he caught the second time were tagged. About how many fish would you guess were in the lake?

For problems 8–13, use these parts of Halley's mortality table.

Age	Persons	Age	Persons	Age	Persons
10	661	16	622	50	346
11	653	17	616	51	335
12	646	18	610	52	324
13	640	19	604	53	313
14	634	20	598	54	302
15	628	21	592	55	292

8. What was the probability that a 13-year-old would live to be

   a. 18?   **b.** 50?   **c.** 55?

   (Give answers as decimals correct to 2 places.)

9. What were the odds that a 13-year-old would live to be

   a. 19?   **b.** 54?

   (Leave answers as ratios of whole numbers.)

10. What were the odds that a 19-year-old would live to be 54?

11. To what age did a 19-year-old have an even chance of living?

12. To what age did a 12-year-old have an even chance of living?

13. What was the ratio of the number of persons alive at age 54 to the number of persons alive at age 17?

14. In this scale drawing of a living room, 1 centimeter in the drawing represents 1.5 meters. What are the length and width of the room? (The rectangle has a length of 4 centimeters and a width of 3 centimeters.)

Living room

Scale   1 cm : 1.5 m

1. Calculate the mean (average), median (middle), mode (most common), and range (difference between smallest and largest) for each of the following sets of data.

   a. 5, 6, 6, 7, 7, 7, 8, 8, 9
   b. 21, 22, 22, 23, 23, 23, 24, 24, 25
   c. 11, 11, 11, 11, 12, 12, 12, 13, 13, 14, 23
   d. 22, 22, 22, 22, 24, 24, 24, 26, 26, 28, 46

2. Janice drove 500 kilometers and used 40 liters of gas. What is her average (mean) number of kilometers per liter for the trip?

3. Max rode his bicycle 500 kilometers in 40 hours. What was the average number of kilometers per hour for the trip?

4. Mr. Major owns a sandwich shop. On Monday he sold $80 worth of sandwiches. On Tuesday there was a 50% increase in sales over Monday. On Wednesday there was a 100% increase in sales over Tuesday.

   a. How much money did Mr. Major take in on Tuesday?
   b. How much money did he take in on Wednesday?

5. For the whole week, Mr. Major sold $800 worth of sandwiches, not counting sales tax. He has to charge 6% sales tax on his sandwiches. How much sales tax did he collect?

6. A ranger caught 80 fish, tagged them, and put them back in the lake. 2 weeks later he caught 80 fish. 20 of them were tagged. About how many fish do you think were in the lake?

7. Suppose only 2 of the 80 fish he caught the second time were tagged. About how many fish would you guess were in the lake?

For problems 8–13, use these parts of Halley's mortality table.

Age	Persons	Age	Persons	Age	Persons
10	661	16	622	50	346
11	653	17	616	51	335
12	646	18	610	52	324
13	640	19	604	53	313
14	634	20	598	54	302
15	628	21	592	55	292

8. What was the probability that a 14-year-old would live to be

   a. 20?   **b.** 51?   **c.** 55?

   (Give answers as decimals correct to 2 places.)

9. What were the odds that a 15-year-old would live to be

   a. 21?   **b.** 53?

   (Leave answers as ratios of whole numbers.)

10. What were the odds that a 17-year-old would live to be 51?

11. To what age did a 17-year-old have an even chance of living?

12. To what age did a 15-year-old have an even chance of living?

13. What was the ratio of the number of persons alive at age 55 to the number of persons alive at age 21?

14. In this scale drawing of a cafeteria, 1 centimeter in the drawing represents 7.5 meters. What are the length and width of the room? (The rectangle has a length of 4 centimeters and a width of 3 centimeters.)

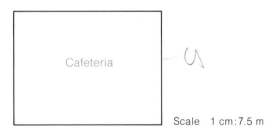

Cafeteria

Scale   1 cm : 7.5 m

Ratios are rational numbers. So you can do arithmetic with them just as with other numbers. However, some real situations that seem to suggest doing addition really require quite a different operation.

For example, suppose the Blue Hornets win 3 out of the first 4 games and 2 out of the next 4 games. Fractions representing these records are $\frac{3}{4}$ and $\frac{2}{4}$. The situation suggests that we should add to get the overall record: $\frac{3}{4} + \frac{2}{4} = \frac{5}{4}$. This tells us that the Blue Hornets won 5 out of 4 games. But we know that's impossible.

In fact, to solve this problem, you would add the numerators of these fractions ($3 + 2 = 5$) and the denominators of these fractions ($4 + 4 = 8$). Then you would say that the team won 5 out of 8 games.

This is a very different kind of "addition" from the kind you usually use. Notice that if you had reduced $\frac{2}{4}$ to $\frac{1}{2}$, you would have gotten $\frac{4}{6}$ as an answer, which is also incorrect. This form of "addition" applies only to the symbols in their original form. Don't think of this as the usual addition of rational numbers.

Solve these problems. Use this new "addition" when needed.

1. In February the Bouncers won 5 of the 6 basketball games they played, and the Dribblers won 8 of the 10 games they played. Which team had the better record in February?

2. In March the Bouncers won 6 of their 14 games, and the Dribblers won 4 of their 10 games. Which team had the better record in March?

3. What is the Bouncers' record for their 20 games in February and March?

4. What is the Dribblers' record for their 20 games in February and March?

5. Which team has the better overall record?

6. How can that happen? Try to find other numbers that give this kind of result.

Solve these problems. Then discuss them with others.

1. Gail has a pile of baseball cards. If she tries to make 2 equal piles, 1 card is left over. If she tries to make 3 or 4 piles, 1 card is left also. However, she can make 5 equal piles.

   a. Could Gail have 322 cards? 323 cards? 324 cards? 325 cards? 326 cards? 327 cards?
   b. What is the smallest number of cards Gail could have?

2. Two buses were going in opposite directions. One, going from Philadelphia to New York City, left at 4:30 P.M. The other, going from New York City to Philadelphia, left at 5:00 P.M. When the buses meet, which one will be farther from Philadelphia?

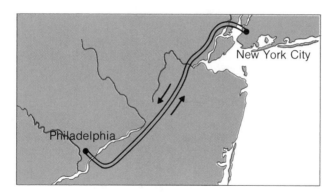

3. "I have 79¢ in my purse," said Angela. "If you can guess exactly what coins they are, I'll give you one of them. You can have 5 guesses."

   a. What are your 5 guesses?
   b. Can you be sure that 1 of these guesses is right?

4. Jordan is hauling sand up from the beach to fill a sandbox for his little children. He has a large bucket and a small bucket. If he uses the large bucket he can carry 56 pounds at one time, but it takes him 35 minutes to make the round trip to and from the beach. If he uses the smaller bucket he can carry only 22 pounds, but it takes him only 15 minutes to make the round trip. Which is the faster way to carry the sand?

CHAPTER 8

2- AND 3-DIMENSIONAL GEOMETRY

The word *geometry* comes from 2 Greek words meaning "earth measure." The earliest known use of geometry was in ancient Egypt. Geometric methods were used to measure land to determine the amount of taxes that farmers owed. Each time the Nile River flooded, the amount of land owned by individual farmers increased or decreased. So landholdings had to be recalculated often.

How could you report the area (or approximate area) of a piece of land? One way would be to tell how many equilateral triangles of a certain size fit into it.

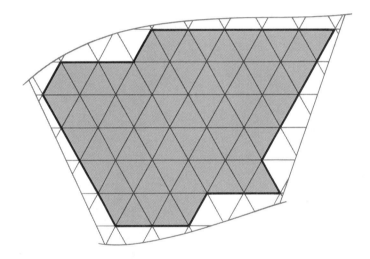

In this piece of land, for example, there appear to be about 63 whole equilateral triangles this size: ⟨triangle⟩ You could go on to estimate that there are about 19 other triangles of the same size if you put the little pieces together. Of course, this is a rough estimate, and you would probably want more reliable methods to arrive at an answer. In any case, if you decided there were about 82 equilateral triangles with sides of 1 centimeter in the figure, you might say the figure has an area of 82 triangular centimeters.

Instead of using equilateral triangles to fill the area, you might use regular hexagons, squares, rhombuses, or other figures. However, you would have to choose figures that left no open spaces when packed together tightly. Regular pentagons, for example, have angles of 108°. When they are packed together, they leave small spaces. So regular pentagons don't work well for this purpose.

Now let's use squares that are 1 centimeter on a side to estimate the area of the figure on page 312.

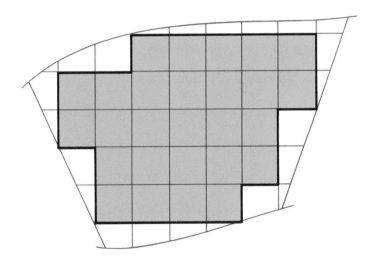

This time you can count about 27 full squares and see that you could make about 11 other squares by putting the little pieces together. So you would say there are about 38 square centimeters in the figure.

The ordinary way to measure area is in square units. We will measure area that way.

We can only estimate the number of square units in the area of many figures. For others, we can calculate the areas if we know the exact measures of certain lengths.

Suppose rectangle *ABCD* is 7 centimeters long and 4 centimeters wide. What is its area in square centimeters?

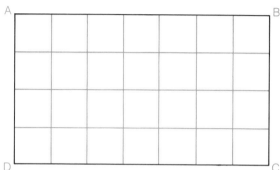

You can simply draw 7 square centimeters along the base *DC* of the rectangle, 7 more above those, and so on, and then count the squares. So the area of rectangle *ABCD* is 28 square centimeters, or 28 cm².

[1] Is there a quicker way than counting to find out how many square centimeters are in rectangle *ABCD*?

[2] What is it?

The area of a rectangle is the product of the number of units in the length and the number of units in the width. This could be written: $A = l \times w$ (area equals length times width), but the $\times$ sign is usually left out to avoid confusing it with the variable x. So we usually write the formula for the area of a rectangle this way:

$$A = lw$$

where

A is the number of square units in the area,
l is the number of units in the length, and
w is the number of units in the width.

The numbers of units in the lengths of the sides of a rectangle need not be whole numbers.

Calculate the area of each of the following figures. Be sure to include the units (cm², ft², in², m², and so on) in your answer.

1. Rectangle *ABCD*

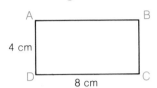

2. Rectangle *EFGH*

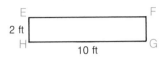

3. Rectangle *IJKL*

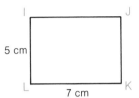

4. Rectangle *MNOP*

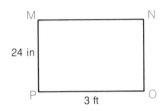

5. Rectangle *QRST*

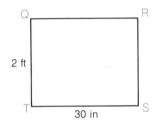

6. Rectangle *UVWX*

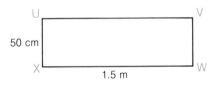

(Hint: Be careful with units.)

7. Triangle *ABC*

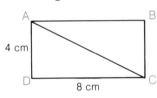

8. Triangle *EGH*

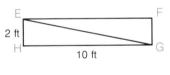

9. Square *ZYQU*

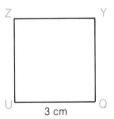

(Hint: Is $\triangle ABC \cong \triangle CDA$?
Do they have the same area?)

Remember

This is a square centimeter: 1 cm

Some symbols for units of square area are:

cm² (square centimeter)   in² (square inch)
m² (square meter)   ft² (square foot)

Area of a Parallelogram

The little symbol ⌐ in angle PQC indicates that PQ is perpendicular to DC.

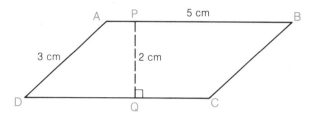

Suppose you wanted to find the area of parallelogram $ABCD$.

On wax paper or tracing paper, copy $ABCD$ and cut it out. Fold the figure along a line that goes through A so that D is on QC. (This will form a line AX that is perpendicular to DC.) Cut along AX. You will form a triangle. Let's call this triangle $A'X'D$. Slide triangle $A'DX'$ to the other end of the figure so that $A'D$ lies along BC.

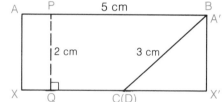

[1] **Does *A'D* fit exactly on *BC*?**

[2] **How long is *AB*?**

[3] **How long is *XX'*?**

[4] **How long is *AX*?**

[5] **How long is *A'X'*?**

[6] **What kind of figure is *ABX'X*?**

[7] **What is the area of *ABX'X*?**

[8] **Could you calculate that area from the measurements of parallelogram *ABCD*?**

[9] **How?**

[10] **Does the length of *AD* enter your calculation?**

[11] **Can you suggest a formula for calculating the area of a parallelogram?**

The area of a parallelogram is found by multiplying the height (the perpendicular distance between the bases) times the length of the base.

$$A = hb, \text{ or } A = bh.$$

Calculate the area of each of the following figures. Be sure to include units in your answers.

1. Rectangle *ABCD*

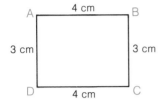

2. Rhombus *ABCD*

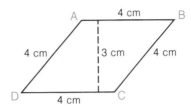

3. Parallelogram *ABCD*

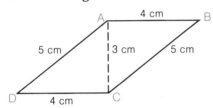

4. Parallelogram *ABCD*

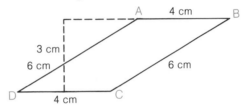

5. Parallelogram *ABCD*

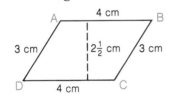

6. Parallelogram *ABCD*

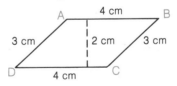

7. Parallelogram *ABCD*

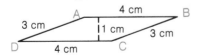

8. Parallelogram *ABCD*

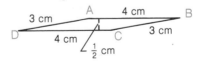

[12] **The lengths of the bases and the sides of the parallelograms in problems 5–8 are the same.**

   a. **Are the areas the same?**

   b. **Why is this so?**

ABCD is a parallelogram. Its height is 3 centimeters and its base is 4 centimeters.

[1] What is the area of *ABCD*?

Consider triangles *ADC* and *CBA*.

[2] Is *AD* equal to *BC*?

[3] Is *DC* equal to *BA*?

[4] Is *AC* equal to *CA*?

[5] Do you think △*ADC* is congruent to △*CBA*?

[6] Trace △*ADC* on wax paper. Turn your tracing around. Try to make it fit on △*CBA*. Does it?

[7] What do you think the area of △*ADC* is?

You can take any triangle and make a parallelogram that has the base of the triangle as its base and has the height of the triangle as its height.

Start with △*ABC*. Draw any triangle you like.

Trace △*ABC* on wax paper. Turn the tracing around so that *C* is on *A* and *A* is on *C*. Push the 2 triangles together to form a parallelogram. The area of this parallelogram is twice the area of △*ABC*.

To find the area of the parallelogram, you would need to know the height (*AD*). Sometimes it would be necessary to extend the base (*BC*) in order to find *AD*. Notice that *AD* is also the height of △*ABC*.

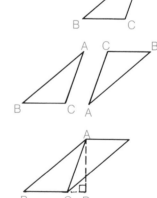

The area of the parallelogram is found by multiplying base (*BC*) times height (*AD*).

[8] What is the area of △*ABC*?

The area of a triangle is one-half the base times the height.

$$A = \tfrac{1}{2}bh$$

Calculating Areas

For problems 1–6, find the area of each figure. Remember to use square centimeters in your answers. Round answers to the nearest tenth.

1.

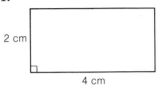

2 cm

4 cm

2.

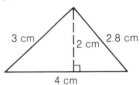

3 cm   2 cm

4 cm

3.

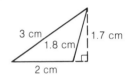

3 cm   2 cm   2.8 cm

4 cm

4.

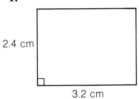

2.4 cm

3.2 cm

5.

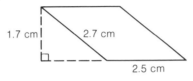

1.7 cm   2.7 cm

2.5 cm

6.

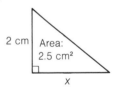

3 cm   1.7 cm
1.8 cm

2 cm

For problems 7–9, the area of each figure is given in square centimeters. Find the value of x (to the nearest tenth of a centimeter). (Hint: It may be helpful to turn the page for some problems so that you see the figure in a more familiar position.)

7.

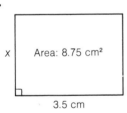

x Area: 8.75 cm²

3.5 cm

8.

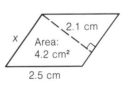

2.1 cm

x Area:
4.2 cm²

2.5 cm

9.

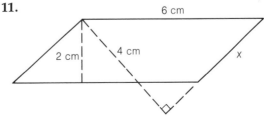

2 cm   Area:
2.5 cm²

x

For problems 10 and 11, find the value of x (to the nearest tenth of a centimeter). (Hint: Finding the area of the figure may help.)

10.

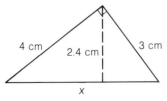

4 cm   2.4 cm   3 cm

x

11.

6 cm

2 cm   4 cm x

Finding Areas

You will need a centimeter ruler for pages 320, 321, and 323. If one is not available, make one by holding a strip of paper or cardboard next to the scale along the side of this page and copying the scale onto your strip.

Measure to the nearest tenth of a centimeter the distance you need to find the area of each figure. Then calculate each area to the nearest tenth of a centimeter.

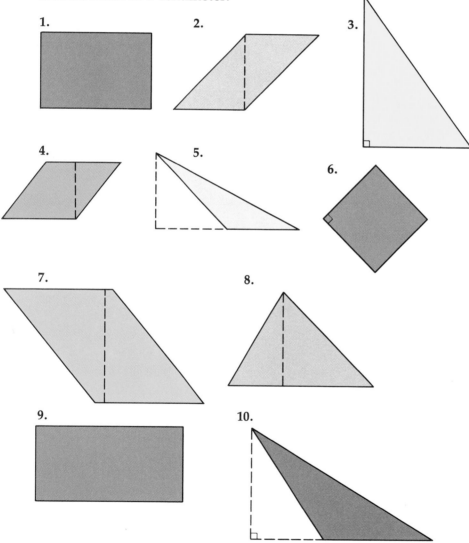

1.

2.

3.

4.

5.

6.

7.

8.

9.

10.

A measurement is just an estimate of what the true measure of something is. So when you measure parts of a figure and then calculate area or perimeter, the area or perimeter you find is also just an estimate. When we ask you to *find* the area or perimeter of figures by measuring them, we are really asking you to make an *estimate*. When you do make this kind of estimate, be sure that you round your answers to the number of decimal places in the least precise measurement.

Find the area and perimeter of each figure. Measure lengths to the nearest tenth of a centimeter.

11.   **12.**

13.

14.   **15.**

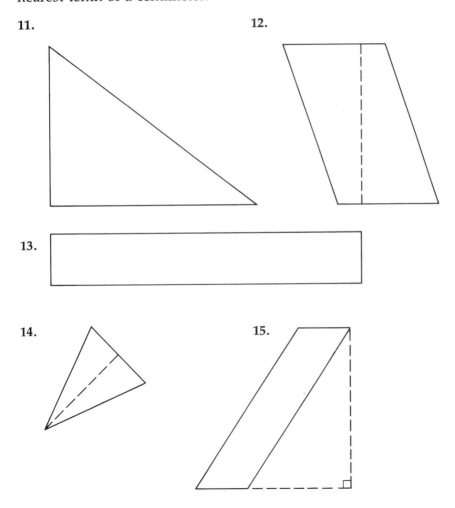

Finding Areas of Unusually Shaped Figures

Sometimes you may want to find the area of a region that is not bounded by a triangle, rectangle, parallelogram, or other figure for which you already know an area formula. In such a case, you can divide the figure into these familiar shapes by drawing in some lines. Then you can add the areas of the different parts to find the area of the figure. Usually, there will be more than one possible way to divide a figure into familiar shapes. One way to divide this figure is shown. The lengths have been measured to the nearest tenth of a centimeter.

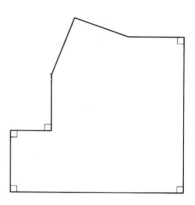

So the areas of the rectangles, starting from the bottom, are approximately

$$4.7 \times 1.6 = 7.5 \text{ cm}^2$$
$$3.6 \times 1.5 = 5.4 \text{ cm}^2$$
$$3.2 \times 1.0 = 3.2 \text{ cm}^2.$$

The areas of the triangles are approximately

$$\frac{1}{2} \times 0.5 \times 1.7 = 0.4 \text{ cm}^2$$
$$\frac{1}{2} \times 1.0 \times 0.5 = 0.3 \text{ cm}^2.$$

And the total area is about 16.8 cm², or 17 cm².

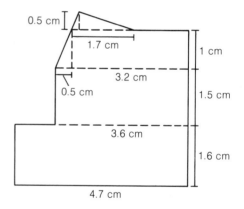

Very small errors in measurement may make large errors in the estimated area. For example, if we had measured the height of the bottom rectangle as 1.7 centimeters instead of 1.6 centimeters and the width as 4.8 centimeters, we would have found the area to be 8.2 square centimeters instead of 7.5 square centimeters, and the area of the entire figure would have been 17.5 square centimeters. So the sum that is the final estimate of the area should probably be rounded to the nearest square centimeter, as shown.

Find the area and perimeter of each figure. Draw lines to separate
the figure into smaller regions if necessary. Measure distances to
the nearest tenth of a centimeter.

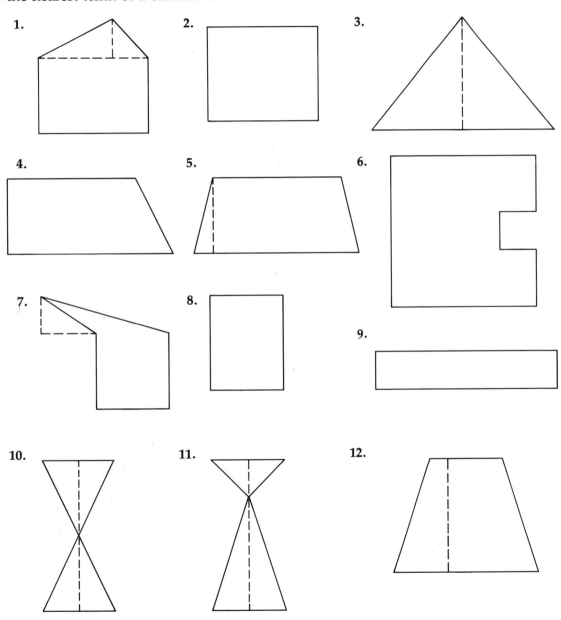

Can 2 figures have the same area but different perimeters?

Area of Trapezoids

Remember, a trapezoid is a quadrilateral with just 1 pair of sides parallel.

ABCD is a trapezoid. Its bases (*AB* and *CD*) are 3 centimeters and 5 centimeters long, respectively, and its height is 2 centimeters. How can we determine its area?

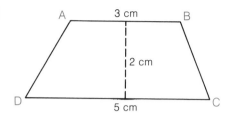

If you drew lines through *A* and *B* perpendicular to *CD*, you could divide the figure into a rectangle and 2 small triangles. The 2 triangles could be put together to form 1 big triangle with base 2 centimeters and height 2 centimeters.

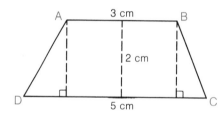

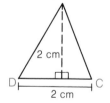

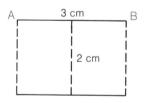

The area of the big triangle would be $\frac{1}{2} \times 2 \times 2$, or 2, square centimeters. The area of the rectangle would be 2×3, or 6, square centimeters. The area of the trapezoid would be $6 + 2$, or 8, square centimeters.

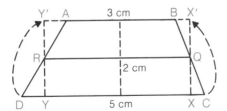

Another way to determine the area of *ABCD* is to draw $QR \parallel$ to *AB* and *CD* and halfway between them, and to draw $QX \perp DC$. Then imagine cutting off triangle *QXC* and turning it around *Q* so that *C* moves up and touches *B* (*X* goes to *X'*). Think the same way about triangle *RYD* on the left of the trapezoid. Since *XX'* is perpendicular to the 2 bases and goes through the midpoint (*Q*) of *BC*, and since *YY'* is perpendicular to the 2 bases and goes through the midpoint (*R*) of *AD*, then *Y'X'XY* will be a rectangle with the same height as trapezoid *ABCD* and with a width that is the average of the lengths of the bases of the trapezoid.

[1] What is the length of *RQ*? Of *XY*? Of *Y'X'*?

[2] What is the area of *Y'X'XY*?

[3] What is the area of trapezoid *ABCD*?

If *b* is the length of one base of a trapezoid and *B* is the length of the other base, and if *h* is the height, then the area of the trapezoid is

$$h\frac{(B + b)}{2}, \text{ or } \frac{1}{2}h(B + b).$$

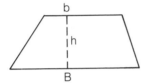

Finding Areas of Figures

Find the area of each figure. Give answers to the nearest tenth of a square centimeter.

1.

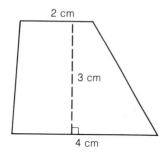

2 cm

3 cm

4 cm

2.

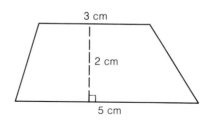

3 cm

2 cm

5 cm

3.

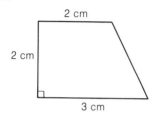

2 cm

2 cm

3 cm

4.

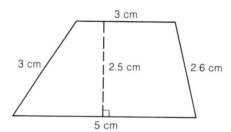

3 cm

3 cm   2.5 cm   2.6 cm

5 cm

5.

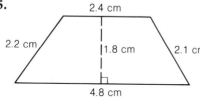

2.4 cm

2.2 cm   1.8 cm   2.1 cm

4.8 cm

6.

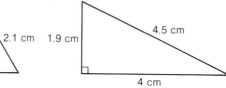

4.5 cm

1.9 cm

4 cm

For problems 7–12, measure (to the nearest tenth of a centimeter) the distances you need to find the area of each figure. Calculate areas and give answers to the nearest square centimeter.

7.

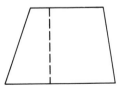

8.

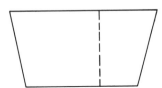

9.

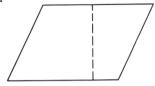

10.

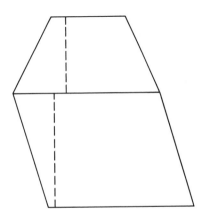

11.

12.

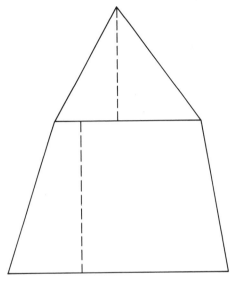

Volume of Rectangular Boxes

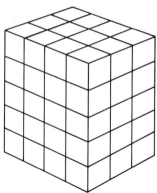

[1] If you stacked cubes until you had a pile that was 5 cubes high, 4 cubes long, and 3 cubes wide, how many cubes would there be in the entire pile?

We measure volume in cubic units. Remember that a cube with a 1-centimeter edge has a volume of 1 cubic centimeter (cm³), a cube with a 1-meter edge has a volume of 1 cubic meter (m³), and so on.

[2] If a rectangular box is 5 centimeters high, 4 centimeters long, and 3 centimeters wide, what is the volume of the box in cubic centimeters? (All angles in a rectangular box are right angles.)

[3] How many faces does a box have? (A *face* is the geometric term for a side of a solid figure.)

[4] What is the total area of the 6 faces of a box that is 5 centimeters by 4 centimeters by 3 centimeters? (This area is called the *surface area* of the box.)

[5] Think of a cube that is $\frac{1}{2}$ centimeter on each edge. How many such cubes would fit in a cube 1 centimeter on an edge? Would there be 4 in the bottom layer and 4 in the top layer?

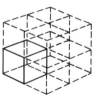

A cube that is $\frac{1}{2}$ centimeter on each edge has a volume of $\frac{1}{8}$ cubic centimeter.

[6] What is the surface area of a cube $\frac{1}{2}$ centimeter on each edge?

In general, the volume of a rectangular box is found by multiplying its length times its width times its height:

$$V = lwh$$

where

V = number of cubic units of volume,
l = number of units in length,
w = number of units in width,
h = number of units in height.

This works even if l, w, and h are not whole numbers, just as for area.

Find the volume in cubic meters (m³) and the surface area in square meters (m²) of these boxes.

1. $l = 4$ m, $w = 7$ m, $h = 2$ m
2. $l = 3$ m, $w = 4$ m, $h = 5$ m
3. $l = 2$ m, $w = 4$ m, $h = 8$ m
4. $l = 4$ m, $w = 4$ m, $h = 4$ m
5. $l = \frac{1}{2}$ m, $w = \frac{1}{2}$m, $h = 256$ m

6. $l = 8$ m, $w = 8$ m, $h = 1$ m
7. $l = 16$ m, $w = 16$ m, $h = \frac{1}{4}$ m
8. $l = 7$ m, $w = 3.4$ m, $h = 4.1$ m
9. $l = 1.2$ m, $w = 2.4$ m, $h = 3.6$ m
10. $l = 2$ m, $w = 3$ m, $h = 5$ m

11. In order to reduce heat loss, engineers often design boxes that have as much volume as possible but as little surface area as possible. What do you think are the dimensions (length, width, and height) of a box that has a volume of 64 cubic meters and as small a surface area as possible? Try some examples. Discuss your answer with others.

12. Sometimes the goal is to have as great a surface area as possible for a given volume. What do you think are the dimensions of a box that has a volume of 64 cubic meters and as great a surface area as possible? Try some examples. Discuss your answer with others.

13. Try to determine dimensions of a box that has a surface area of 96 square meters and the greatest possible volume. Try examples and discuss your answers with others.

14. Try to determine dimensions of a box that has a surface area of 96 square meters and the smallest possible volume.

Here are 3 pieces of ice. *A* is a cube. *B* and *C* are long blocks.

A.

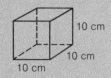

B.

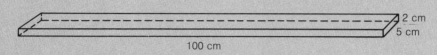

C.

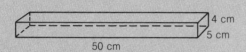

[1] What is the volume of each piece of ice?

[2] What is the surface area of each piece of ice?

[3] What is the ratio of surface area to volume for each piece of ice?

[4] Suppose you placed each piece of ice in a separate, very large container of water at the same temperature. In what order would the pieces of ice melt completely?

[5] Under what conditions will a piece of ice with a high ratio of surface area to volume melt more slowly than a piece with the same volume but with a very low ratio?

Here are 2 containers full of hot water.

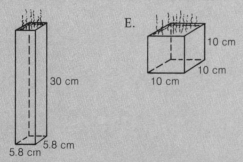

[6] Which container has the greater ratio of surface area to volume?

[7] If both are filled at the same time with exactly 1 liter of water at 80°C, which will cool to room temperature more quickly?

Work in small groups on this activity. Make pieces of ice of different shapes from equal volumes of water. Use plastic or waxed cardboard containers or open dishes. Closed glass containers will crack if completely filled with water and frozen.

Estimate the surface area of each piece of ice. Then predict how long it will take to melt if kept at classroom temperature.

Margaret, Spencer, and Debbie did this experiment and put their results in this chart.

General Shape of Ice	Approximate Volume (cm^3)	Approximate Surface Area (cm)^2	Ratio of Surface Area to Volume	Time to Melt at Room Temperature (minutes)	
				Predict	Actual
Long block	612	603	0.99	180	285
Cylinder	603	553	0.92	240	345
Block	600	460	0.77	300	435

Use your results to make a chart like this one. Work individually or in teams for the contest.

The Great Ice-Melting Contest

The object of this contest is to see who can keep a piece of ice from melting for the longest time. The rules are simple.

A. Each piece of ice must have the same volume.
B. The ice must stay in the classroom and cannot be put in a freezer or a refrigerator.

Volume of Prisms

Some boxes do not have rectangular bases. A box that has ends that are congruent polygons with parallel edges connecting corresponding vertices is called a *prism*. If the parallel edges are perpendicular to the 2 ends, the prism is called a *right prism*.

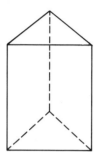 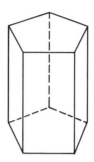 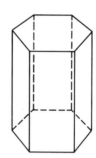

You may have noticed that we use *height* in 2 ways. We use it to mean the perpendicular distance between the top and base in triangles and quadrilaterals. And we use it to mean the vertical distance in 3-dimensional figures.

Another word for the perpendicular distance between top and base in plane figures is *altitude*. So from now on, whenever it may be confusing, we'll use *altitude* to refer to the height of a plane figure and *height* for the height of a 3-dimensional figure.

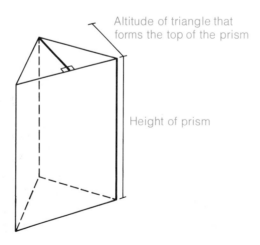

Altitude of triangle that forms the top of the prism

Height of prism

To find the volume of a box, we multiplied the length times the width times the height. But the length times the width is just the area of the bottom (or top) of the box. When we find the volume of a box, we are really multiplying the area of the bottom (or top) by the height of the box.

This is a right triangular prism.

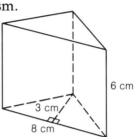

[1] Can you think of a way to find its volume?

[2] What is the area of the bottom (or top) of the prism?

[3] What is the height of the prism?

[4] What is the volume of the prism?

The volume of a right prism can be found by multiplying the area of the bottom (or top) by the height. This can be written:

$$V = Bh$$

where

V = number of cubic units in the right prism,
B = area in square units of bottom (or top),
h = number of units in the height.

[5] If the bottom of a right prism is a rectangle 4 centimeters long and 3 centimeters wide, what is the area of the bottom?

[6] If the height of that prism is 5 centimeters, what is its volume?

[7] How does this answer compare with the answer you get using formula $V = lwh$?

1. What is the volume of a right prism that is 5 centimeters tall and has right triangles as ends? The altitude of the right triangle is 1.5 centimeters and the base of the right triangle is 2 centimeters.

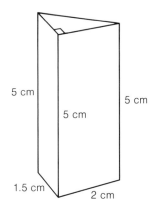

2. The ends of this right prism are trapezoids with the given measurements. Its height is 5 centimeters. What is its volume?

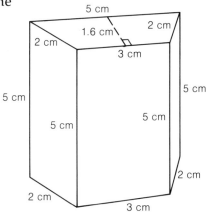

3. The ends of this right prism are parallelograms. What is its volume?

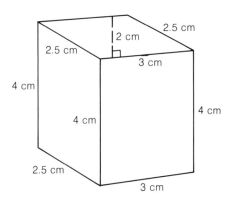

4. Look at the figures that appear on this page. Each is a rectangular box.

  a. Which seems to have the greatest volume?
  b. Which seems to have the smallest volume?
  c. List what you think the order of volumes is, from greatest to smallest.
  d. Their measurements are given. Calculate their volumes.
  e. Put them in order from greatest to smallest. Compare this list with your list for problem 4c above.

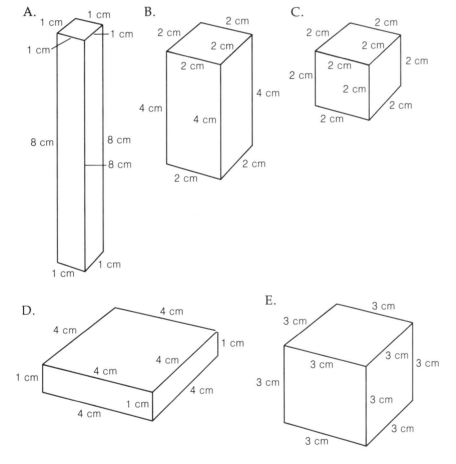

5. Figure *E* is how many times as big as figure *C*?

6. Which figure has the smallest surface area? Is there another figure that has the same volume? If so, which one?

AREA GAME

Players: 2 or more
Materials: Two 0–5 cubes, two 5–10 cubes, paper, pencil
Object: To make 5 different figures with the greatest possible area

Rules

1. Each game has 5 rounds. You may play all 5 at once or take turns doing 1 polygon at a time.

2. Roll all 4 cubes. Choose a polygon from the table below and use 1, 2, or 3 of the numbers rolled as the dimensions. You may choose a polygon only once in each game.

Polygon	Dimensions
Square	side
Rectangle	base, height
Parallelogram	base, side, height (Note: side must be greater than or equal to height.)
Trapezoid	top base, bottom base, height
Triangle	base, height

3. Calculate the area of each polygon. Find the sum of all 5 areas.

4. The player with the greatest total area wins.

Sample Game

Round	Duncan's Roll	Polygon	Dimensions	Area
1	9 6 4 3	square	side 9	81
2	10 5 5 2	parallelogram	base 10, height 5, side 5	50
3	8 8 4 3	rectangle	base 8, height 8	64
4	6 5 5 0	trapezoid	bases 6, 5; height 5	27.5
5	5 5 5 4	triangle	base 5, height 5	12.5
			Total Area	235

Round	Cathy's Roll	Polygon	Dimensions	Area
1	9 6 2 0	triangle	base 9, height 6	27
2	9 8 5 3	trapezoid	bases 5, 8; height 9	58.5
3	7 5 5 1	parallelogram	base 7, side 5, height 5	35
4	9 6 3 2	square	side 9	81
5	9 8 4 2	rectangle	base 9, height 8	72
			Total Area	273.5

Cathy is the winner.

Suppose you know that the area of a square is 16 cm² and you want to know the length of its side. You must find a number that can be multiplied by itself to give 16.

[1] Do you know such a number?

16 cm²

16 is called the *square* of 4. Using exponents, we write $4^2 = 16$. We read it, "4 squared equals 16."

4 is called the *square root* of 16.

Suppose you wanted to find the length of a side of a square that has an area of 10 square centimeters.

[2] Do you know a number whose square is 10?

[3] Is 3 too small?

[4] Is 4 too large?

[5] Which is closer to 10, 3^2 or 4^2?

Can we get closer? 3.2 might be a reasonable next guess.

$$(3.2)^2 = 10.24$$

That's too big. Try 3.1 next.

$$(3.1)^2 = 9.61$$

That's too small. Which is closer to 10, $(3.1)^2$ or $(3.2)^2$? Try 3.17 now.

$$(3.17)^2 = 10.0489 \quad \text{(too big)}$$
$$(3.16)^2 = 9.9856 \quad \text{(too small)}$$

If you continue this way, you will get better and better approximations of the square root of 10, but you will never get a number that you can square to get exactly 10. It is easier to do this with a calculator than with pencil and paper.

If you have a cube with volume 27, what is the length of its side? 27 is the *cube* of 3 ($3^3 = 27$), and 3 is the *cube root* of 27.

1. Without using a calculator, find the square root of each of the following.

   a. 4   c. 81   e. 144   g. 625   i. 10,000
   b. 25   d. 100   f. 196   h. 56.25   j. 1

2. Without using a calculator, find the cube root of each of the following.

   a. 8   c. 64   e. 216   g. 1000   i. 1.331
   b. 125   d. 343   f. 3.375   h. 1,000,000   j. 1

3. Use a calculator to approximate the square root of each of the following correct to 4 or more places.

   a. 5   b. 10   c. 2   d. 1000   e. 200

4. The symbol for the square root of 5 is $\sqrt{5}$. Some calculators have a ▨ key. If yours does, push ⑤ and then ▨ .

   a. Does your answer match the answer for problem 3a?
   b. Is it almost the same? Slight differences may occur because the calculator does not round to the nearest possible number. It simply drops the digits it can't handle. If your calculator has a ▨ button, compare its answers to those you got for problems 3b–3e.

5. Use a calculator to help you find the cube root of each of the following correct to 4 or more places.

   a. 2   b. 7   c. 15   d. 100   e. 500

You can make 3-dimensional figures by folding paper or cardboard. In chapter 4, you learned some ways to do this. You can make 3-dimensional figures without as much planning and tucking if you put the polygons for the faces together in a pattern and add tabs to them that can be glued to other faces. For example, to make a tetrahedron (a regular triangular pyramid), you can draw equilateral triangles on one strip of cardboard.

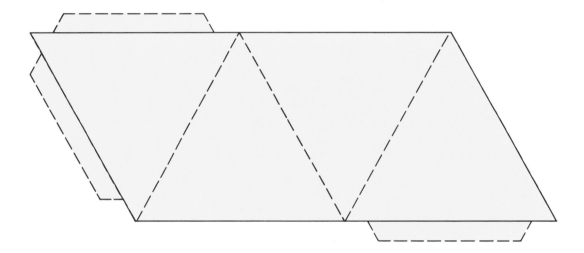

Use a knife, razor blade, or a scissors point to score on what will be the outside of your tetrahedron, the edges, and the lines between the faces and the flaps. When you fold the cardboard, each flap should be glued inside or outside another face that does not have a flap.

1. Draw the pattern of 4 triangles shown above. Arrange the flaps differently, but be sure that each can still be glued to a face without a flap.

2. How many different ways can you arrange the flaps on this pattern for a tetrahedron?

3. Suppose you wanted to make a cube.

   a. What shape would the faces be?

   b. How many faces would you need?

4. Draw a pattern for 6 faces that can be folded into a cube. Decide where the flaps should go.

5. How many different patterns can you make (with all the squares connected) that would fold to make a cube? (Forget about the flaps for this question.)

6. Make a tetrahedron and a cube.

In the word *polyhedron, poly* means "many" and *hedron* means "seat"—a face on which the figure can rest. Either *polyhedra* or *polyhedrons* can be used for the plural of *polyhedron*.

A cube and a regular tetrahedron are called regular polyhedra because all their faces are congruent regular polygons and the angles between these are all equal.

[1] Do you think there are other regular polyhedra?

[2] How many different kinds of regular polyhedra is it possible to make?

In order to make a regular polyhedron, at least 3 faces must meet at a vertex (or corner). In this pattern for a tetrahedron,

the shaded faces will all meet at vertex *V* when folded. In this pattern for a cube,

the shaded faces will all meet at vertex *V*. Now let's look at the regular polyhedra that can be formed with equilateral triangles. We know that in the pattern for a tetrahedron, 3 equilateral triangles meet at a vertex.

[3] Could you arrange a pattern in which 4 equilateral triangles meet at 1 vertex?

[4] Might part of the pattern look something like this figure?

[5] Could you fold this pattern so that faces *A, B, C,* and *D* meet at vertex *V*?

[6] Could you make a polyhedron with 4 equilateral triangles meeting at every vertex?

[7] Make a pattern like the one above but with 5 equilateral triangles meeting at a point.

[8] Can you fold the pattern so that it looks like the corner of a polyhedron?

[9] Could you make a polyhedron with 5 equilateral triangles meeting at every vertex?

[10] Try to make a pattern with 6 equilateral triangles that all meet at the same vertex. Can you fold it to look like the corner of a regular polyhedron? Why not? Try to explain in terms of the measures of the angles.

A cube is a regular polyhedron in which 3 squares meet at each vertex.

[11] Try to make a pattern in which 4 squares all meet at the same vertex. Can you make the pattern? Can you fold it to look like the corner of a regular polyhedron? Why or why not? Explain.

A regular pentagon has 5 equal sides and 5 equal angles.

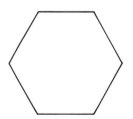

[12] What is the measure of each angle of a regular pentagon? (Hint: What is the sum of the angles of a triangle? How many triangles in the pentagon? How many degrees in the sum of the angles of the regular pentagon?)

[13] Try to make a pattern in which 3 regular pentagons meet at the same vertex. Can you? Can you fold it?

A regular hexagon has 6 equal sides and 6 equal angles.

[14] What is the measure of each of its angles?

[15] Can you make a regular polyhedron with hexagons as faces?

[16] Can you make a regular polyhedron with heptagons or octagons or regular polygons with more than eight sides?

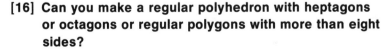

[17] If only 1 kind of regular polyhedron can be made with a given number of faces at a vertex, how many different kinds of regular polyhedra is it possible to make?

Regular polyhedra can be made with 4 faces (regular tetrahedron), 6 faces (regular hexahedron or cube), 8 faces (regular octahedron), 12 faces (dodecahedron), and 20 faces (icosahedron). Here are patterns for the latter 3:

Regular icosahedron (20-hedron)

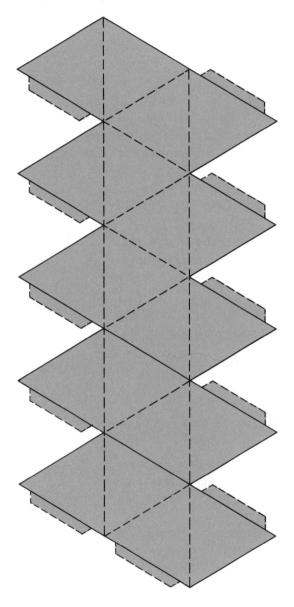

Regular octahedron (8-hedron)

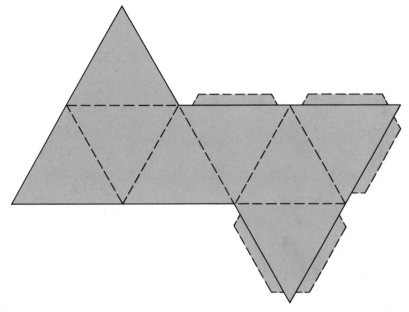

Regular dodecahedron (12-hedron)

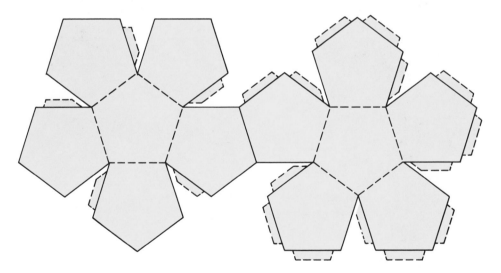

Make an octahedron, a dodecahedron, and an icosahedron.

Warm-blooded living things (called homeotherms) maintain a constant body temperature, even though the temperature of their environment varies.

Cold-blooded living things (called poikilotherms) maintain the approximate temperature of their environment, even though the temperature of their environment changes.

Warm-blooded living things   Cold-blooded living things

[1] Look at these illustrations. Can you make a list of other warm-blooded living things and a list of other cold-blooded living things?

Normal human body temperature is 37°C. Our bodies normally maintain that temperature unless the environmental temperature becomes very cold or very warm. When we are sick, our body temperature may vary from 37°C. When we do something very strenuous, our body temperature may rise slightly for a short time. But normally our temperature remains 37°C.

To understand how a constant body temperature is maintained, we can think of the following 7 points as a model:

A. Most of an animal's heat is produced when food is used by the body.

B. As a rule, the more food an animal uses, the more heat it produces.

C. The more heat an animal produces, the greater the increase in body temperature.

D. Most of the heat an animal loses escapes through the surface (skin).

E. The lower the environmental temperature, the more heat an animal loses.

F. The greater the animal's surface (skin) area, the more heat it loses.

G. The more heat it loses, the greater the decrease in body temperature.

Many other factors are involved in regulating an animal's temperature. (You may want to study these as a class project.) Nevertheless, this simple 7-point model can help you understand certain types of animal behavior.

[2] What position does a cat usually assume when it sleeps? Can you think of how that position might help the cat maintain its body temperature?

[3] Can you think of other types of behavior that tend to help an animal maintain a constant temperature?

The normal body temperatures of some warm-blooded animals are given in this chart. Notice that most of the animals maintain a body temperature near or above the upper limit of the temperature range of the environment.

Homeotherm	Body Temperature (°C)	Temperature Range of Environment (°C)	Mass (kg)
Mountain goat	39.9	−28–15	65
Domestic rabbit	38.5	0–32	1.75
Northern fur seal	37.7	0–15	500
Polar bear	37.3	−34–15	700
African elephant	36.4	15–32	7500
Blue whale	35.5	−2–27	100,000
Three-toed sloth	33.2	27–38	4.25
Spiny anteater	23.3	15–32	3.6
Rubythroat hummingbird	40.1	21–27	0.015
Ostrich	39.2	15–32	156
Emperor penguin	37.7	−55–3	35

Make up questions based on the information in the chart. Discuss the questions and answers in small groups. Here are some questions to get you started.

1. Which of the animals listed needs to maintain the greatest temperature difference between body temperature and environmental temperature?

2. Suppose all of the animals were about the same size and equally active. Which ones would need the largest food supply? Which would need the smallest food supply? (You can see that the animals are not the same size.)

Hummingbirds are the smallest homeothermic animals.

1 cm = 4 cm

Blue whales are the largest homeothermic animals.

1 cm = 2 m

3. Work in groups to make the following estimates.

   a. Estimate the body volume of a hummingbird in cubic centimeters.

   b. Estimate the surface area of a hummingbird in square centimeters.

   (Hints: What are the dimensions of the smallest box with straight sides that a hummingbird can fit into? What is the volume of that box? Can the volume of the hummingbird be greater than the volume of the box? About what fraction of that volume is not used? What is the surface area of that box? If you shape the surface to fit the bird as snugly as a glove, would you need more surface, less surface, or about the same surface?)

   c. Estimate the body volume of a blue whale in cubic meters.

   d. Estimate the surface area of a blue whale in square meters.

4. Use your estimates to find the ratio of surface area to volume for hummingbirds and whales.

[4] Do you think larger animals tend to have lower surface-volume ratios than smaller animals? Find the ratios for a few animals. Are your expectations about correct?

Now think about this experiment.

5. Suppose you were heating 2 identical containers of water on 2 identical burners. That is, both containers were receiving the same amount of heat energy. But suppose one container contained 500 milliliters of water and the other 250 milliliters.

   a. If the initial temperature of the water in both containers is 25°C, which container will reach 50°C first?

   b. If the water in the 500-milliliter container would take about 2 minutes to reach 50°C, about how many minutes would it take the 250-milliliter container to reach the same temperature?

Josephine and Harrison did the experiment described above and put the results in the following graph:

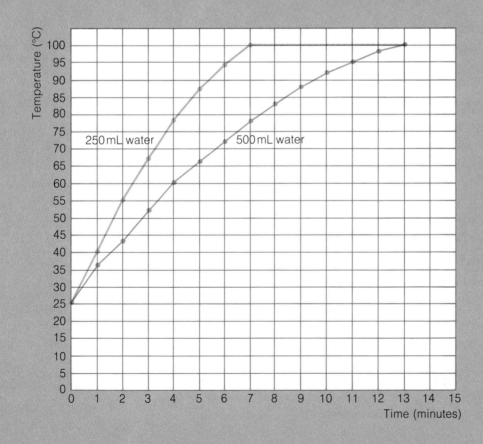

Study the graph. Then work in small groups to discuss these questions.

[5] **If heat energy is supplied at the same rate to 2 identical containers containing the same amount of water, will the temperature change at the same rate in both containers? If one container has more water than the other, will the temperature change at the same rate in both containers?**

[6] **Try to describe in your own words the relationship between heat energy and temperature.**

[7] **If a whale and a hummingbird converted the same amount of food energy to heat energy, would the whale's body temperature increase more than the hummingbird's, less than the hummingbird's, or about the same as the hummingbird's?**

The amount of heat energy a living thing contains at any given temperature is roughly proportional to the volume of the living thing. That is, if 2 living things are at the same temperature, the larger one contains more heat energy. If the larger one has twice the volume of the smaller one, it contains about twice as much heat energy.

If 2 living things have the same body temperature and are in the same cold environment, the rate at which they lose heat energy will be about proportional to their surface areas—that is, the larger the surface area, the higher the rate of heat energy loss.

A polar bear and an emperor penguin both have body temperatures of about 35°C. Both live in environments of about the same temperature.

[8] **Which animal will lose heat to the environment more quickly?**

[9] **Which animal's body temperature will fall more rapidly?**

[10] **Which animal will have to consume more food to maintain body temperature?**

[11] **Which animal needs to consume more food per unit of body volume?**

For problems 1–9, calculate the area of each of the following figures. The symbol ⌐ indicates a right angle. Round answers to the nearest tenth of a square centimeter.

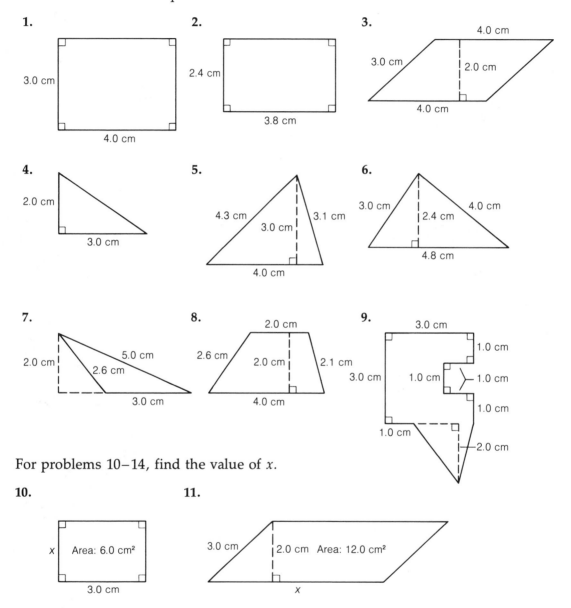

1.

3.0 cm
4.0 cm

2.

2.4 cm
3.8 cm

3.

4.0 cm
3.0 cm
2.0 cm
4.0 cm

4.

2.0 cm
3.0 cm

5.

4.3 cm
3.1 cm
3.0 cm
4.0 cm

6.

3.0 cm
4.0 cm
2.4 cm
4.8 cm

7.

2.0 cm
5.0 cm
2.6 cm
3.0 cm

8.

2.0 cm
2.6 cm
2.0 cm
2.1 cm
4.0 cm

9.

3.0 cm
1.0 cm
3.0 cm
1.0 cm
1.0 cm
1.0 cm
1.0 cm
2.0 cm

For problems 10–14, find the value of x.

10.

x
Area: 6.0 cm²
3.0 cm

11.

3.0 cm
2.0 cm
Area: 12.0 cm²
x

12.

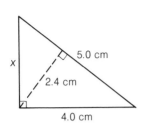

x

5.0 cm

2.4 cm

4.0 cm

13.

Square

Area: 9.0 cm²

x

14.

Cube, volume 8 cm³

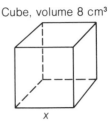

x

15. What is the volume of a rectangular box that is 5 centimeters long, 5 centimeters wide, and 4 centimeters high?

16. What is the surface area of the box in problem 15?

17. Draw a pattern that could be folded into an octahedron. Draw in flaps, and show by arrows where they would attach.

18. Without a calculator, find the square root of 30 to the nearest hundredth.

19. Without a calculator, find the cube root of 30 to the nearest hundredth.

20. Suppose you roll a regular 8-sided die (with from 1 to 8 dots on each face). What is the probability of rolling a 7?

21. What is the probability of rolling an 8 if you roll a regular 8-sided die?

22. If you roll 2 regular 8-sided dice, what is the probability that the total number of dots up will be 2?

23. If you roll 2 regular 8-sided dice, what is the probability of rolling a total of 16?

24. If you roll 2 regular 8-sided dice, what is the probability of rolling a total of 9?

25. Cixto made a big cube out of 64 small cubes (4 cubes on an edge) and painted the outside of the big cube blue. Then he took the big cube apart. How many little cubes had paint on

   a. 4 sides?   **d.** 1 side?
   b. 3 sides?   **e.** 0 sides?
   c. 2 sides?

For problems 1–9, calculate the area of each of the following figures. The symbol ⌐ indicates a right angle. Round answers to the nearest tenth of a square centimeter.

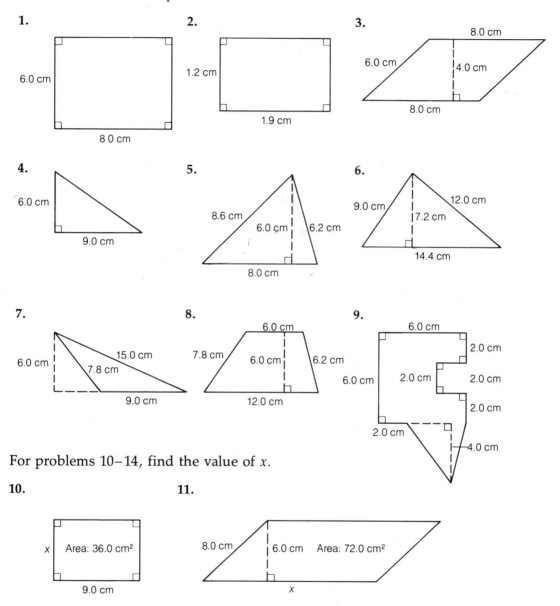

1.

6.0 cm

8 0 cm

2.

1.2 cm

1.9 cm

3.

8.0 cm

6.0 cm

4.0 cm

8.0 cm

4.

6.0 cm

9.0 cm

5.

8.6 cm

6.0 cm

6.2 cm

8.0 cm

6.

9.0 cm

12.0 cm

7.2 cm

14.4 cm

7.

6.0 cm

15.0 cm

7.8 cm

9.0 cm

8.

6.0 cm

7.8 cm

6.0 cm

6.2 cm

12.0 cm

9.

6.0 cm

2.0 cm

6.0 cm

2.0 cm

2.0 cm

2.0 cm

2.0 cm

2.0 cm

4.0 cm

For problems 10–14, find the value of x.

10.

x   Area: 36.0 cm²

9.0 cm

11.

8.0 cm   6.0 cm   Area: 72.0 cm²

x

12.

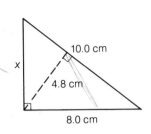

10.0 cm

x

4.8 cm

8.0 cm

13.

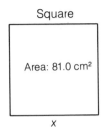

Square

Area: 81.0 cm²

x

14.

Cube, volume 27 cm³

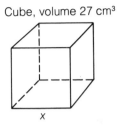

x

15. What is the volume of a rectangular box that is 4 centimeters long, 4 centimeters wide, and 5 centimeters high?

16. What is the surface area of the box in problem 15?

17. Draw a pattern that could be folded into a hexahedron. Draw in flaps, and show by arrows where they would attach.

18. Without a calculator, find the square root of 60 to the nearest hundredth.

19. Without a calculator, find the cube root of 60 to the nearest hundredth.

20. Suppose you roll a regular 4-sided die (with from 1 to 4 dots on each face). What is the probability of rolling a 2?

21. What is the probability of rolling a 3 if you roll a regular 4-sided die?

22. If you roll 2 regular 4-sided dice, what is the probability that the total number of dots up will be 2?

23. If you roll 2 regular 4-sided dice, what is the probability of rolling a total of 8?

24. If you roll 2 regular 4-sided dice, what is the probability of rolling a total of 5?

25. Zoe made a big cube out of 27 small cubes (3 cubes on an edge) and painted the outside of the big cube red. Then she took the big cube apart. How many little cubes had paint on

    a. 4 sides?   **d.** 1 side?

    b. 3 sides?   **e.** 0 sides?

    c. 2 sides?

Some popular games use dice in the shape of each of the 5 regular solids with different numbers of dots on each face. The tetrahedron has 1 dot on the first face, 2 dots on the second face, 3 dots on the third face, and 4 dots on the last face. The others are designed the same way, with 1 dot on the first face, 2 on the second, and so on.

Imagine that you have a set of these 5 dice.

1. On the hexahedron (cube), how many dots would the face with the most dots have?

2. On the octahedron, how many dots would the face with the most dots have?

3. On the dodecahedron, how many dots would the face with the most dots have?

4. On the icosahedron, how many dots would the face with the most dots have?

5. What is the probability of rolling a 3 (that is, the face with 3 dots up) on the cube?

6. What is the probability of rolling a 3 with the octahedron?

7. What is the probability of rolling a 3 with the dodecahedron?

8. What is the probability of rolling a 3 with the icosahedron?

9. Suppose you roll 2 cubical dice (regular hexahedrons). What is the probability that the total number of dots up is

a. 2?	d. 5?	g. 8?	j. 11?
b. 3?	e. 6?	h. 9?	k. 12?
c. 4?	f. 7?	i. 10?	

(Compare your answers with your answers to problem 10 on page 197 in chapter 5.)

10. Repeat problem 9 for pairs of tetrahedra, octahedra, dodecahedra, and icosahedra, using all the possible dot sums for each. (Note: Dice that are tetrahedra always have 3 faces equally *up*. So the face that is *down* is the one that is counted.)

TRIANGLE TANGLE

Players: 2
Materials: 2 different colored pencils, paper
(Something to draw circles would be helpful.)
Object: To make triangles whose sides are not all one color

Rules

1. Draw a circle.

2. Place 5 dots evenly around the circle.

3. Each player uses a different colored pencil.

4. Take turns connecting any 2 unconnected dots with a straight line.

5. The player who finishes the game without completing a triangle in his or her color is the winner. Check only the triangles with vertices on the dots.

Sample Game

Kim used a blue pencil. Ato used a red one. This is what their game looked like:

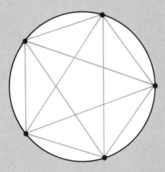

Ato won, because Kim made a triangle with her last blue line.

Variation

For rule 2, place 6, 7, or 8 dots evenly around the circle.

CHAPTER 9
ROOTS
ERROR ANALYSIS
π

Sir Isaac Newton

Isaac Newton was born on Christmas day in 1642 in the town of Woolsthorpe in Lincolnshire, England, and he died at the age of 85. This man is regarded as one of the world's greatest thinkers. His ideas are still stimulating mathematical and scientific thought today.

During his life, Newton made discoveries in physics, mathematics, and astronomy. He was also interested in alchemy. He was a professor of mathematics at Cambridge University, a member of Parliament, master of the Royal Mint, and president of the Royal Society. When he was young, science was a hobby for wealthy men. Largely because of his efforts, science became a profession in its own right.

After spending many years studying the way planets moved, Johannes Kepler worked out 3 experimental rules to explain their movements. Newton saw these rules and found that he could express them in 1 mathematical law. He then had the brilliant idea that this law governed not only the way planets moved but also the way everything in the universe moved and behaved. He set forth this discovery as the theory of universal gravitation and formulated what we know today as Newton's Three Laws of Motion.

While working with his ideas on motion, Newton found that he needed a new kind of mathematics to do certain kinds of calculations. He put together ideas in mathematics that came from early Greek thought and from the work of his time to develop calculus. Calculus today is an important part of mathematics and is a subject that you might study in high school or college. One of Newton's mathematical discoveries is the basis for a method of finding square roots that you will learn in this chapter.

[1] If you divide 1 by 3 on a calculator that displays 8 digits, what answer will the calculator show?

[2] If you multiply that answer by 3, what answer will the calculator show?

[3] Use a calculator. Divide 1 by 3 and then multiply by 3. What answer do you get?

[4] Do you believe that (1 ÷ 3) × 3 = 1? Why does the calculator give the answer that it does?

Use a calculator with a ▨ or ▨ key. Start with any number that is not a perfect square. Take the square root of the number (by pushing the ▨ key) and then square the number. (Push x^2 if the calculator has one; push ✕ , ▤ if not. If neither of these works, try putting the square root into the memory, or just write down the square root and then multiply it by itself.)

[5] Do you get the original number back?

Repeat the process of finding the square root and squaring it several times. Write your results after each step on a sheet of paper. What seems to be happening?

Olive tried this with her calculator, starting with 50. This is what she wrote:

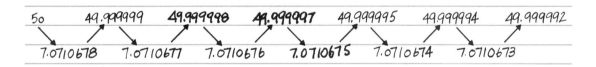

50   49.999999   49.999998   49.999997   49.999995   49.999994   49.999992

7.0710678   7.0710677   7.0710676   7.0710675   7.0710674   7.0710673

[6] Why do the numbers keep getting smaller?

Does your calculator round answers to the nearest number it can show, or does it just drop the digits it can't show? Compare your results with those on a different kind of calculator.

Some calculators don't have a square root key. If you are using a calculator that doesn't have a , you can still find square roots by guessing and multiplying, as we suggested in the last chapter. (See page 338.) But there are some efficient ways to guess. Here's a good way:

Problem: Find $\sqrt{10}$ without using a ▨ key.

First guess: 3

Divide 10 by 3 and look at the result: 3.3333333

Think:

If 3 is $\sqrt{10}$, then $10 \div 3$ should be 3.
If 3 is greater than $\sqrt{10}$, then $10 \div 3$ should be less than $\sqrt{10}$.
If 3 is less than $\sqrt{10}$, then $10 \div 3$ should be greater than $\sqrt{10}$.

Since we know 3 is less than $\sqrt{10}$, we can see that $\sqrt{10}$ is between 3 and $10 \div 3$, or 3.3333333. So for the next guess, we take the average of these 2 numbers.

We can do the entire process this way on a calculator:

Push ⬛ ⬛ , ⬛ , ⬛ , ⬛ . Look at your answer.

Then push ⬛ , ⬛ , ⬛ , ⬛ , ⬛ . The display will show ▨ 3.1666666

Second guess: 3.1666666

So again we divide 10 by our guess, compare the quotient with our guess, and decide whether we want to make another guess, which will be the average of the quotient and this guess.

On the calculator we do this:

$$10 \div 3.1666666 = 3.1578948$$
$$(3.1578948 + 3.1666666) \div 2 = 3.1622807$$

Third guess: 3.1622807

Go through the procedure again on the calculator:

$$10 \div 3.1622807 = 3.1622746$$
$$3.1622746 + 3.1622807 = 6.3245553$$
$$6.3245553 \div 2 = 3.1622776$$

If you do this again with 3.1622776 as your guess, you should get 3.1622776 again. Now you have reached the best approximation of $\sqrt{10}$ that you can get on your calculator. Each time you repeat this process, you will usually double the number of correct digits in your guess (depending on the limits of your calculator).

We will call this the guess-and-average method for finding square roots. It is based on Newton's method for finding the solutions to quadratic equations. Quadratic equations have terms like x^2 in them.

Comparing Methods for Finding Square Roots

If you enter 10 into your calculator and then push the square root key, you will probably get 3.1622776. Some calculators may give 3.162277, but most calculators will show that the square root of 10 is 3.1622776.

Remember that squaring a number just means multiplying the number by itself.

Enter and square these numbers on your calculator:

$$3.1622776$$
$$3.1622777$$
$$3.1622778$$
$$3.1622779$$

In each case, what is the answer?

Try to explain these results.

In displaying an answer, most calculators simply drop the digits they can't show. For example, the square root of 10 is 3.16227766017 to the nearest hundred billionth (11 places to the right of the point). But the calculator will show it as 3.1622776. Also 3.1622778^2 is 10.00000088437284 to the nearest ten trillionth, but the calculator will show it as 10 (10.000000).

Some calculators do round answers just as you would. They keep in memory the digits that don't show on the display and use them in doing continuing calculations. On one of these calculators, if you enter 10, press $\sqrt{x}$ to get the square root, and then press x^2 to square the square root, you'll get 10 back.

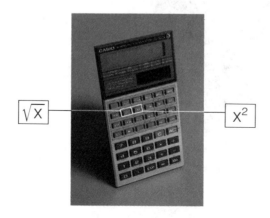

Let's look at some of the differences:

Operation	Result with Calculator That Drops Digits	Result with Calculator That Rounds
Enter 10.	10	10
Use the guess-and-average method for square root.	3.1622776	3.1622777
Use $\sqrt{x}$	3.1622776	3.1622776
Use x^2 or multiply number by itself.	9.9999996	10
Enter and square 3.1622776.	9.9999996	9.9999996
Enter and square 3.1622777.	10	10
Enter and square 3.1622778.	10	10.000001
Enter and square 3.1622779.	10.000001	10.000002

So finding the closest approximation to the square root of 10 will depend on both the method you choose to use and the kind of calculator you have.

Use your calculators. For each of these numbers, find

a. the square root by the guess-and-average method.
b. the square root using $\sqrt{}$.
c. a number that multiplied by itself gives a result closest to the original number.

1. $\sqrt{10}$ 3. $\sqrt{50}$ 5. $\sqrt{2}$ 7. $\sqrt{100}$ 9. $\sqrt{1000}$
2. $\sqrt{5}$ 4. $\sqrt{500}$ 6. $\sqrt{20}$ 8. $\sqrt{200}$

10. Compare your answers to problems 1, 7, and 9. See if you can explain the similarities between 2 of these answers. Does your explanation work for problems 2, 3, and 4? For problems 5, 6, and 8?

Cube Roots and Other Roots

The cube root of a number n is the number r that produces n when used as a factor 3 times ($r \times r \times r = n$, or $r^3 = n$). The cube root of 27 is 3, since $3 \times 3 \times 3 = 27$.

The symbol for the cube root of 27 is $\sqrt[3]{27}$.

The fourth root of a number n is the number r that produces n when used as a factor 4 times ($r \times r \times r \times r = n$, or $r^4 = n$).

If $\sqrt[4]{n} = r$, then $r^4 = n$.

$$\overbrace{r \times r \times \ldots \times r}^{m \text{ factors}}$$

In general, r is the mth root of n if $r \times r \times \ldots \times r = n$, or $r^m = n$. If $\sqrt[m]{n} = r$ then $r^m = n$.

Determine each of the following roots.

1. $\sqrt{16}$
2. $\sqrt[3]{8}$
3. $\sqrt[4]{81}$
4. $\sqrt[3]{1000}$
5. $\sqrt[4]{16}$
6. $\sqrt[3]{125}$
7. $\sqrt[3]{216}$
8. $\sqrt{64}$
9. $\sqrt[5]{32}$
10. $\sqrt[3]{64}$
11. $\sqrt{100}$
12. $\sqrt[6]{64}$

Finding approximations for cube roots, fourth roots, and so on is possible many different ways. For example, to find $\sqrt[3]{10}$, pick a number—say, 2. Cube it: $2^3 = 8$. That's too small. Try 2.3.

$$2.3^3 = 12.167 \text{ (too large)}$$
$$2.2^3 = 10.648 \text{ (too large)}$$
$$2.1^3 = 9.261 \text{ (too small)}$$
$$2.15^3 = 9.938375 \text{ (too small)}$$
$$2.155^3 = 10.007873 \text{ (too large)}$$
$$2.154^3 = 9.9939482 \text{ (too small)}$$

So $\sqrt[3]{10} \approx 2.154$. (The symbol $\approx$ means "is approximately.")

Find approximations for the following roots correct to the nearest thousandth.

13. $\sqrt[3]{5}$
14. $\sqrt[5]{3}$
15. $\sqrt[4]{10}$
16. $\sqrt[3]{20}$

A procedure that requires repeating the same steps over and over is called an *iterative* procedure. The guess-and-average method for finding approximations of square roots is an iterative procedure. (Look back at pages 362 and 363 if you don't remember the procedure.)

See if you can develop an iterative procedure for finding an approximation for the cube root of a number. Compare your procedure with procedures other people develop. Use these questions as you make the comparisons.

A. Does the procedure end with a good approximation? (The approximation cubed should be close to the original number.)

B. If you start with the same first guess, how many steps are required to arrive at the best approximation the calculator can make?

C. Is the process easy to perform on your calculator? (Do you have to write some numbers with pencil and paper and then repunch them into the calculator?)

17. Use your procedure to approximate $\sqrt[3]{83}$. Compare your procedure with those of other people using questions A, B, and C above. To be fair, everybody should start with 4 as the first guess.

18. Approximate each of the following cube roots to 4 or more decimal places.

    a. $\sqrt[3]{10}$
    b. $\sqrt[3]{100}$
    c. $\sqrt[3]{1000}$
    d. $\sqrt[3]{10,000}$
    e. $\sqrt[3]{100,000}$
    f. $\sqrt[3]{300}$
    g. $\sqrt[3]{171}$

A formula that is sometimes used to estimate the distance it takes a car to stop after the driver steps on the brake is:

$$210d = v^2$$

where d is the distance in meters and v is the speed (or velocity) of the car in kilometers per hour. The following examples show how this formula can be used.

Example 1: If a car is traveling at 70 kilometers per hour, about how many meters will the car travel after the driver steps on the brake?

Here $v = 70$. We put that into the equation.

$$210d = (70)^2$$
$$210d = 4900$$
$$d = \frac{4900}{210}$$
$$d = 23\tfrac{1}{3}$$

So the car will travel about 23 meters before it stops.

Example 2: A car was brought to a stop 40 meters from the point where the driver's foot hit the brake. How fast was the car traveling before the driver stepped on the brake?

Here $d = 40$. We put that into the equation.

$$210 \times 40 = v^2$$
$$v^2 = 8400$$
$$v = \sqrt{8400}$$
$$v \approx 91.7$$

So the car was traveling about 92 kilometers per hour.

Solve.

1. Copy and complete this chart.

A Car Traveling	Will Stop in This Distance
88 km/h	
66 km/h	
44 km/h	
22 km/h	
11 km/h	

2. A police officer examined the scene of an automobile accident. The driver said he was traveling at the speed limit of 50 kilometers per hour. The officer measured the black tracks made by the tires while the car was stopping. They were 45 meters long.

   a. Do you believe the driver?
   b. Explain your answer to part a.

3. At another accident scene, the driver said she was going 80 kilometers per hour. The track left on the road by the braking tires was 25 meters long.

   a. Do you think the driver was telling the truth?
   b. Explain your answer to part a.

4. At 80 kilometers per hour, about how long a distance is required to stop a car after the driver's foot reaches the brake?

   a. Does this mean that a driver should stay more than 30 meters behind the car in front when traveling 80 kilometers per hour?
   b. Explain your answer to part a.

Square and Cube Roots: Applications

1. The area of a square is approximately 50 square meters. What is the length of a side of the square?

2. The volume of a cube is approximately 50 cubic meters. What is the length of a side of the cube?

3. The surface area of a cube is 600 square centimeters.
   a. What is the area of 1 face of the cube?
   b. What is the length of a side of the cube?
   c. What is the volume of the cube?

4. The volume of a cube is 1000 cubic centimeters. What is the surface area of the cube?

5. The surface area of a cube is 216 square centimeters. What is the volume of the cube?

6. The volume of a cube is 1728 cubic decimeters. What is the surface area of the cube?

7. Sam is going to cover a box with plastic sheeting. Does he need to find the volume, the surface area, or the width?

8. Claudia is going to make some concrete stepping stones by filling a round form with concrete. Does she need to find the volume, the surface area, or the perimeter?

9. Jesse has a plastic cube that is 20 centimeters on a side. It is made of very thin but strong plastic, and 1 face opens so that he can put things inside.
   a. Suppose he wants to paper the cube. How much paper will he need?
   b. Suppose he wants to fill the cube with sheets of paper. How much paper will he need?

10. Cheryl is going to fence a 4-acre field.
    a. How much fencing should she buy?
    b. If the field is square, how much fencing should she buy?
    c. If the field is 4 times as long as it is wide, how much fencing should she buy?

Copy and complete these function charts:

1. x —(+6)→ y

x	y
1	■
3	■
7	■
■	16
■	23

2. x —(÷7)→ y

x	y
14	■
35	■
49	■
■	2
■	5

3. x —(×7)→ y

x	y
■	14
■	35
■	49
2	■
5	■

4. x —(÷9)→ y

x	y
■	9
99	■
28	■
■	$2\frac{1}{9}$
72	■

5. x —(+3)→ n —(×2)→ y

x	y
1	■
2	■
3	■
■	16
■	22

6. x —(+10)→ n —(÷5)→ y

x	y
10	■
15	■
■	35
■	45
■	50

7. x —(×3)→ n —(−6)→ y

x	y
1	■
2	■
3	■
■	36
■	51

8. x —(−3)→ n —(÷2)→ y

x	y
7	■
11	■
■	$\frac{1}{2}$
■	10
■	7

9. x —(÷2)→ n —(+7)→ y

x	y
■	7
■	17
2	■
3	■
■	12

10. x —(−6)→ n —(×3)→ y

x	y
1	■
2	■
3	■
■	36
■	51

To make a right angle, fold a sheet of paper and crease it. Then fold again so that the crease falls on itself. The angle you make will be a right angle.

For the activities on these pages, use a piece of paper folded twice or use a protractor to draw right angles.

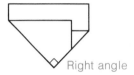

Right angle

Draw a right triangle in the middle of your paper. Then draw a square on each side of the right triangle. Make the necessary measurements and calculate the areas of the 3 squares. Yours doesn't have to be exactly like the one below.

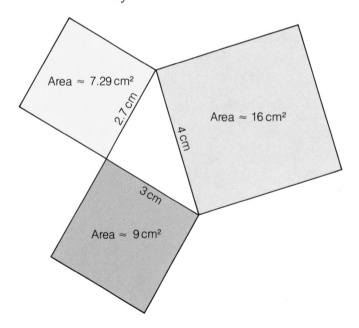

Area ≈ 7.29 cm²

2.7 cm

Area ≈ 16 cm²

4 cm

3 cm

Area ≈ 9 cm²

Draw several different right triangles and calculate the areas of the squares on each of the 3 sides. You don't need to draw the squares unless you want to. The work shown below was done without drawing the squares.

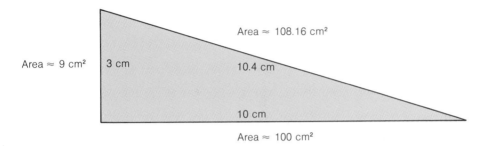

Make a table like this one of the areas of the squares on the sides of the right triangles.

Triangle	Area of Largest Square	Area of Second Largest Square	Area of Smallest Square
1	16.00 cm²	9.00 cm²	7.29 cm²
2	108.16 cm²	100.00 cm²	9.00 cm²
3	cm²	cm²	cm²
4	cm²	cm²	cm²

Look for a pattern in the areas. Do you see one? Try some more right triangles and see if the pattern seems to work for them. (Remember, your measurements will be only estimates. So the areas may be 1 or 2 square centimeters off.)

Discuss with a friend the pattern you found. Do other students' right triangles seem to produce the same pattern? Make a statement about the areas of the squares on the sides of a right triangle.

The Pythagorean Theorem

The ancient Egyptians apparently believed that the area of the square on the long side of a right triangle was equal to the sum of the areas of the squares on the other 2 sides. We don't know whether they believed this to be true of all right triangles or just of certain right triangles, but they appear to have used this fact in some of their work.

Pythagoras was a Greek mathematician and philosopher who lived about 584–495 B.C. He was the first to prove that the statement was true for all right triangles. The statement is known today as the Pythagorean Theorem and is often stated this way:

In a right triangle, the square on the hypotenuse is equal to the sum of the squares on the other two sides.

The *hypotenuse* of a right triangle is the side opposite the right angle. This side is always the longest side. When we say "the square" or "the squares," we mean the *areas* of the squares.

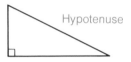

The Pythagorean Theorem can be used to estimate the length of a side of a right triangle that cannot be measured or is otherwise unknown.

Example: The hypotenuse of a right triangle is 9 centimeters long and one side is 3 centimeters long. Estimate the length (x) of the other side, in centimeters.

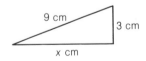

$$9^2 = 3^2 + x^2$$
So: $81 = 9 + x^2$
Think: What can you add to 9 to get 81?
So: $x^2 = 72$
Use your calculator: $x \approx 8.5$

So the other side is about 8.5 centimeters long.

Assume that the measurements given in problems 1–9 are exact.
Determine the value of x to the nearest tenth of a centimeter.

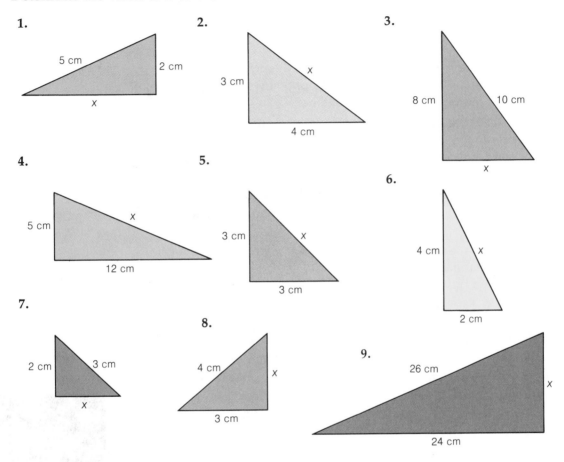

1.

5 cm   2 cm

x

2.

3 cm x

4 cm

3.

8 cm   10 cm

x

4.

5 cm x

12 cm

5.

3 cm x

3 cm

6.

4 cm x

2 cm

7.

2 cm   3 cm

x

8.

4 cm x

3 cm

9.

26 cm x

24 cm

10. Shelley wants to stretch a wire from the top of her apartment
building to a point 30 meters from the building. The building
is 21 meters tall. She needs at least an extra half meter at each
end to fasten the wire with, and she doesn't want more than
an extra meter at each end. She must buy a whole number of
meters of wire. How many meters of wire should she buy?

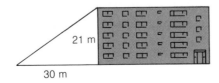

21 m

30 m

Errors in Measurement

Whenever you measure, you make small errors. You usually can guess about how big those errors are likely to be. What happens when you do arithmetic with measures? Does this make the errors more or less serious?

[1] **Suppose the true measures of each of 3 lengths are 7 centimeters, 4 centimeters, and 10 centimeters, and you were off on each measurement by 0.1 centimeter.**

  a. **What is the largest possible value you might report for the sum of the measurements?**

  b. **What is the smallest value you might report for the sum of the measurements?**

[2] **Suppose the true measures of each of 2 lengths are 12 centimeters and 5 centimeters, and your measurements had errors of 0.1 centimeter.**

  a. **What is the largest possible difference you might report for the measurements?**

  b. **What is the smallest possible difference you might report for the measurements?**

When you add or subtract measurements, the worst thing that can happen is that you add the errors. We often assume that about half of the measurements will be greater than the actual measure and that half will be less. Therefore the final error is less than the total of all the errors, and we say that there is an *averaging out* of the errors.

When you multiply measurements with errors, the results are complicated.

[3] **Suppose the true measures of the sides of a rectangle are 7 centimeters and 10 centimeters, and your measurements were off by 0.1 centimeter.**

  a. **What is the largest possible value you might report for the area?**

  b. **What is the smallest value you might report?**

  c. **How could you get errors of +1.71 square centimeters and −1.69 square centimeters when the error in measurement is only 0.1 centimeter?**

A rectangle with a base of b centimeters and height of h centimeters has an area of bh square centimeters.

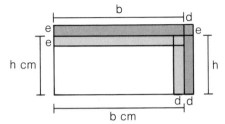

If the measured height is $h + e$ centimeters and the measured base is $b + d$ centimeters, then the area marked ▬ shows the error when the area is computed. The areas that produce the error are $be + hd + de$. So the area that is reported for these measurements would be $bh + be + hd + de$.

Note that the true lengths of the sides multiplied by the error in measurement are part of the total error in area.

Remember

You can also think about this using the distributive law.

$$A = (b + d)(h + e)$$
$$A = b(h + e) + d(h + e)$$
$$A = bh + be + dh + de$$

For negative errors in measurement, the measured height is $(h - e)$ centimeters and the measured base is $(b - d)$ centimeters. The area marked ▬ shows the error when the area is computed. In this case, the reported area would be $bh - be - dh + de$. We add de because we subtracted the small ▬ area twice—once with be (the top rectangle) and once with dh (the side rectangle).

Remember

Think about this using the distributive law.

$$A = (b - d)(h - e)$$
$$A = b(h - e) - d(h - e)$$
$$A = bh - be - dh + de$$

Upper and Lower Bounds

Remember that we never know the true measure when we make measurements. But we do know our measured estimate and what we think is the greatest possible error in that measurement. To find the possible error in practical situations, you can simply calculate the results 3 times. First, calculate assuming that your measurement is the same as the true measure. Next calculate assuming errors that will produce the largest positive error. We call this finding the *upper bound.* Then calculate assuming errors that will produce the negative error of greatest magnitude. We call this finding the *lower bound.* It isn't always necessary to make all 3 of these calculations. Sometimes only 1 or 2 will be enough to give you the information you need. Here are 3 examples:

A. Makoto measured the widths of 4 murals he planned to tape to the wall as 132 centimeters, 86 centimeters, 54 centimeters, and 107 centimeters. He thinks he may have made an error of as much as 1 centimeter in each measurement. If he is right, and if the murals are tight against each other, what are the greatest and least widths the murals might require?

The greatest width will be 133 + 87 + 55 + 108 = 383 centimeters. The least width will be 131 + 85 + 53 + 106 = 375 centimeters. Notice that these bounds are 4 centimeters greater and 4 centimeters less than the expected width.

B. Becky wants to cut a piece of string 800 centimeters long from a piece of string that is 1750 centimeters long. If each measurement may be off by 2 centimeters, what are the upper and lower bounds for the length of the remaining piece?

The upper bound is 1752 − 798 = 954 centimeters.
The lower bound is 1748 − 802 = 946 centimeters.
Notice that in finding bounds when subtracting, the minuend (first number) is large and the subtrahend is small for the upper bound. You'll reverse this for the lower bound.

C. Holly measured the length and width of a garden as 42 meters and 18 meters. The measurements may be off by $\frac{1}{2}$ meter. What are the upper and lower bounds for the area of the garden?

Upper: 42.5 × 18.5 = 786.25 m²
Lower: 41.5 × 17.5 = 726.25 m²

Solve. Use a calculator if you have one.

1. Carlota measured the length and width of a rectangular field. She found them to be 243 meters and 187 meters. She believed each measurement might have an error as great as 2 meters. Assume that she's right.
   a. What would she report as the perimeter of (distance around) the field?
   b. What is the upper bound for the perimeter?
   c. What is the lower bound for the perimeter?
   d. What would she report as the area of the field?
   e. What is the upper bound for the area?
   f. What is the lower bound for the area?
   g. What would she report as the difference between the length and the width?
   h. What is the upper bound for the difference?
      i. What is the lower bound for the difference?

2. When Ed measured the length and width of a rectangular field, his measurements were 87 meters and 43 meters. His measurement errors might each be as great as 2 meters.
   a. What would he report as the perimeter of the field?
   b. What is the upper bound for the perimeter?
   c. What is the lower bound for the perimeter?
   d. What would he report as the area of the field?
   e. What is the upper bound for the area?
   f. What is the lower bound for the area?
   g. What would he report as the difference between the length and the width?
   h. What is the upper bound for the difference?
   i. What is the lower bound for the difference?

Compare and comment on the possible errors in the perimeters, the differences between length and width, and the areas for problems 1 and 2.

Measuring Circular Objects

Carmen measured the distance around a circular wastebasket and then measured the distance directly across the basket. She made the same measurements on a circular lampshade, a circular bottle of glue, and a circle she drew on a piece of paper. She decided what the errors in these measurements were and then made the following table:

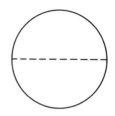

Circle	Circumference (C)			Diameter (d)		
	Upper Bound	C	Lower Bound	Upper Bound	d	Lower Bound
Basket	111	110	109	36	35	34
Lampshade	88	87.5	87	27.7	27.6	27.5
Bottle	17.1	17.0	16.9	5.5	5.4	5.3
Drawing	65.5	65	64.5	20.7	20.6	20.5

She used a calculator to find the sum, the difference, the product, and the quotient of each circumference and diameter. She also calculated the upper and lower bound for each one. Then she made a table of these calculations.

Circle	Sum			Difference		
	UB	C + d	LB	UB	C − d	LB
Basket	147	145	143	77	75	73
Lampshade	115.7	115.1	114.5	60.5	59.9	59.3
Bottle	22.6	22.4	22.2	11.8	11.6	11.4
Drawing	86.2	85.6	85.0	45.0	44.4	43.8

Circle	Product			Quotient		
	UB	C × d	LB	UB	C ÷ d	LB
Basket	3996	3850	3706	3.26	3.14	3.03
Lampshade	2437.6	2415	2392.5	3.2	3.17	3.14
Bottle	94.05	91.8	89.57	3.23	3.15	3.07
Drawing	1355.85	1339	1322.25	3.20	3.16	3.12

She looked at her table for interesting patterns. She was surprised to notice that 1 of the calculations always seemed to be the same number (within her bounds of error).

This table gives measurements with upper and lower bounds for the circumferences and diameters of 4 circles. Use a calculator to make a table of the sums, differences, products, and quotients with upper and lower bounds for each. Remember that to get the upper bound on a difference, use the largest possible minuend and the smallest possible subtrahend, and do the opposite for the lower bound. Similarly, find the upper bound for a quotient by using the greatest possible dividend and the smallest possible divisor, and do the opposite for the lower bound.

		Circumference			Diameter		
1.	Circle	UB	C	LB	UB	d	LB
	a.	152	150	148	47.8	47.7	47.6
	b.	98.1	97.9	97.7	31.2	31.1	31
	c.	40.9	40.8	40.7	13.1	13.0	12.9
	d.	6.7	6.6	6.5	2.2	2.1	2.0

2. Measure at least 4 circles yourself. Estimate the error in each measurement. Use a string or tape measure to measure circumferences. It is a good idea to make measurements several times or to have somebody else repeat your measurements. Make a table of your measurements with upper and lower bounds. Then use a calculator to make a table of the sums, differences, products, and quotients with their upper and lower bounds. Look for interesting patterns.

3. Do any of the results seem to come out the same no matter how big the circle? Which? Compare your answers with other students'.

The ratio of the circumference of a circle to the diameter of the circle is the same no matter how big or how small the circle is. Some people have used the number 3 for that ratio. Other numbers, such as $3\frac{1}{7}$ $\left(\text{or } \frac{22}{7}\right)$ and 3.14, are used as that ratio. For some purposes these numbers are close enough. For other purposes they are not close enough.

We use the Greek letter π (pronounced pī) to stand for the ratio of the circumference to the diameter of a circle. There are no 2 whole numbers whose ratio is equal to π, but there are many formulas that give approximations of π, and its value has been calculated to many thousands of places on computers.

Here is one formula that can be used to compute π:

$$\frac{\pi}{4} = 1 - \frac{1}{3} + \frac{1}{5} - \frac{1}{7} + \frac{1}{9} - \frac{1}{11} + \frac{1}{13} - \frac{1}{15} + \frac{1}{17} - \frac{1}{19} + \cdots$$

In using this formula, you may take as many terms as you please.

If you use just the first term $\left(\frac{\pi}{4} = 1\right)$, you'd approximate π to be 4.

If you use the first 2 terms $\left(\frac{\pi}{4} = 1 - \frac{1}{3}\right)$, you'd approximate π to be 2.6666666.

If you use the first 3 terms $\left(\frac{\pi}{4} = 1 - \frac{1}{3} + \frac{1}{5}\right)$, you'd approximate π to be 3.4666666.

The approximations will get closer together, but a lot of work is required, even with a calculator, to get them really close together.

After 19 terms, the approximation is 3.1941879. After 20 terms, it's 3.0916238. And after 21 terms, it's 3.1891848.

We call $1 - \frac{1}{3} + \frac{1}{5} - \frac{1}{7} + \cdots$ an *infinite series*. There are other infinite series with which π can be computed to the required accuracy much faster than with this one.

Correct to 8 places, $\pi \approx 3.1415927$, which is more than close enough for almost any practical purpose. For most purposes, either $3\frac{1}{7}$ or 3.14 is plenty close enough.

Using π

If you know that the diameter of a circle is about 4.21 centimeters, you can calculate its approximate circumference. Since $\frac{C}{d} = \pi$, $C = \pi d$. Using 3.14 as an approximation for π, $C \approx 3.14 \times 4.21$ = 13.2194. So the circumference is about 13.22 centimeters.

If you know the circumference of a circle, you can approximate its diameter. Suppose the circumference of a circle is 18.61 centimeters. Then $18.61 \approx 3.14 \times d$, and $d \approx \frac{18.61}{3.14} \approx 5.93$. So the diameter is about 5.93 centimeters.

Solve. Use 3.14 as your approximation of π. Use a calculator if you have one. Give answers to the nearest hundredth.

1. $C = 20$ cm, $d = $?

2. $C = 100$ cm, $d = $?

3. $C = $?, $d = 10$ cm

4. $C = $?, $d = 43$ cm

5. $C = 1$ m, $d = $?

6. $C = $?, $d = 1$ m

7. $C = 314$ m, $d = $?

8. $C = $?, $d = 3.14$ m

9. $C = 10$ m, $d = $?

10. $C = 1000$ m, $d = $?

11. $C = $?, $d = 100$ m

12. $C = $?, $d = 1000$ m

13. $C = $?, $d = 5$ m

14. $C = $?, $d = 500$ cm

15. $C = $?, $d = 5000$ mm

16. The measured circumference of a tree is about 4 meters. About what is its diameter?

17. The radius of the earth is about 3963.2 miles. About what is the distance around the earth in miles? (Remember: the radius is $\frac{1}{2}$ the diameter.)

18. The distance from the sun to the earth is about 92,900,000 miles. Assume that the earth travels in a circle around the sun once each year.

   a. How far does the earth travel each year?
   b. About how many miles per hour is that?

19. Which is closer to π, 3.14 or $3\frac{1}{7}$?

Suppose you wanted to find the area of a circle with a radius of 5 centimeters. You could try to put centimeter squares in the circle and estimate how many there are. Or you could cut the circle into lots of small segments like the ones shown here and then put the segments back together again, alternating the points: up, down, up, down, and so on.

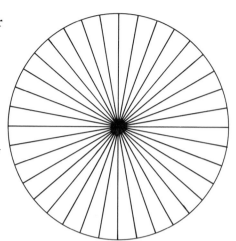

The figure you would make would be almost a parallelogram, but its top and bottom would be slightly wiggly.

[1] What would be the height of the "parallelogram"?

The circumference of the circle makes up both the top and bottom of the "parallelogram."

[2] What is the circumference of the circle?
[3] What is the length of the bottom of the "parallelogram"?
[4] Approximately what is the area of the "parallelogram"?

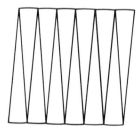

If you repeat this for any circle, the height of the "parallelogram" will be r units (the radius of the circle) and its base will be about πr units. So the area of a circle seems to be about $\pi r r$ square units, or πr^2.

It can be proved that the area of a circle is exactly πr^2. This is often written: $A = \pi r^2$.

Do problems 1–5. If you use a calculator, use 3.1415927 as your approximation for π. If not, use 3.14 for π. Round all answers to 2 decimal places.

1. Copy and complete this chart:

Circle	Radius	Area
a.	1 cm	
b.	7 cm	
c.	10 cm	
d.	37 cm	
e.	68 cm	
f.		30 cm²
g.		100 cm²

2. Dick wants to make a circle that will enclose a region with an area of about 100 m².
   a. How long should the radius of the circle be?
   b. How long should the circumference of the circle be?

3. Jan is going to make a circle whose circumference will be a rope that is about 100 meters long. About what will the area of the circle be?

4. The imaginary bibean needs 1000 square meters of land to survive. This bibean builds its nest in the center of a circle that encloses an area of 1000 square meters.
   a. How far is it between the 2 closest bibean nests?
   b. How far would a bibean walk to get around its entire territory?

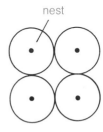

nest

5. A farmer has a square-shaped field that measures 100 meters on a side. The field is irrigated by a watering bar that sweeps a large circle. The bar is 50 meters long. The part of the field that is not watered is unproductive. What percent of the field is unproductive?

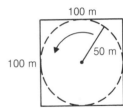

100 m

100 m

50 m

You know that the volume of a right prism is the length of its height times the area of its bottom or top base. The same relationship is true for a right cylinder. So, for a right circular cylinder (often just called a cylinder):

$$V = \pi r^2 h$$

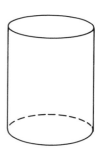

where V is the volume of the cylinder, r is the radius of 1 of its bases, and h is its height.

Do these problems.

1. Calculate the volumes of these cans.
   a. $h = 14$ cm, $r = 6$ cm
   b. $h = 7$ cm, $r = 12$ cm
   c. $h = 28$ cm, $r = 3$ cm

2. Draw pictures of the 3 cans in problem 1. Draw the pictures to scale (let 1 millimeter in your drawing stand for 1 centimeter, for example). In the pictures of the cans, do the volumes look as though they are about equal to each other, or do they look very different?

3. Draw pictures of 3 cans with heights and radii as given below. Calculate the volumes of the 3 cans.
   a. $h = 16$ cm, $r = 4$ cm
   b. $h = 8$ cm, $r = 8$ cm
   c. $h = 4$ cm, $r = 16$ cm

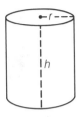

4. If the height of a closed cylinder (right circular cylinder) is h and its radius is r, try to figure out what its surface area is.

   a. What is the area of the top?
   b. What is the area of the bottom?
   c. Suppose you take off the top and bottom, cut the remaining piece along a line perpendicular to the bases, and then flatten out that piece. Would you get a rectangle? What is its height? Its area? Its base?
   d. So what is its surface area?

5. Using the formula from problem 4, calculate the surface area of cylinders with these heights and radii.

   a. $h = 17$ cm, $r = 6$ cm
   b. $h = 7$ cm, $r = 12$ cm
   c. $h = 28$ cm, $r = 3$ cm
   d. $h = 16$ cm, $r = 4$ cm
   e. $h = 8$ cm, $r = 8$ cm
   f. $h = 4$ cm, $r = 16$ cm

Mr. and Mrs. Ibrahim are trying to find ways to decrease the cost of heating their home. Their fuel bill for heating in a normal year is about $2000.

Discuss each of the situations described on the next page. For each situation, either decide what might be best for the Ibrahims to do or make a list of the additional information you would need to make the decision. Finally, supply that information and decide what the Ibrahims should do based on those assumptions.

1. They get an estimate for replacing the windows with storm windows at a cost of $100 per window. The house has 25 windows. The estimator estimates that this will save 10% of the heating costs. What should they do?

2. Mr. and Mrs. Ibrahim can switch fuels at a cost of $3000 for a new furnace. The new fuel is about 20% less expensive than the fuel they use now, but they are unsure whether the price difference will remain the same, widen, or narrow in future years. What should they do?

3. They can install a wood-burning stove in the den. The stove will cost about $800 and will look nice in the den. They estimate that the supplemental heat will save about 15% of the fuel bill.

   a. Suppose Mrs. Ibrahim enjoys splitting logs and wood is plentiful where they live. What should they do?

   b. Suppose neither Mr. nor Mrs. Ibrahim likes splitting logs, even though wood is plentiful. What should they do?

   c. Suppose they live in a city and wood is not plentiful. What should they do?

4. Consider situations 1, 2, and 3 again under each of the following conditions.

   a. They would have to borrow the money at 15% annual interest.

   b. They don't have to borrow money, but their savings are invested at 10%.

Do not use a calculator for the problems in this review. For problems 1–4, compute the values to the nearest tenth.

1. $\sqrt{64}$ **2.** $\sqrt[3]{64}$ **3.** $\sqrt{73}$ **4.** $\sqrt[3]{125}$

For problems 5 and 6, use the formula $210d = v^2$. In the formula, d is the number of meters required to stop a car after the driver's foot hits the brake and v is the speed of the car in kilometers per hour.

5. A car is traveling at 80 kilometers per hour. After the driver's foot hits the brake, how many meters (to the nearest meter) will the car travel before it stops?

6. A car left skid marks about 48 meters long. About how fast (to the nearest kilometer per hour) was the car apparently going?

7. The volume of a cube is 512 cubic centimeters. What is the surface area of the cube?

8. The surface area of a cube is 150 square centimeters. What is the volume of the cube?

For problems 9–11, determine x to the nearest tenth of a centimeter.

9.

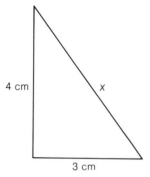

4 cm

x

3 cm

10.

2 cm

x

4 cm

11.

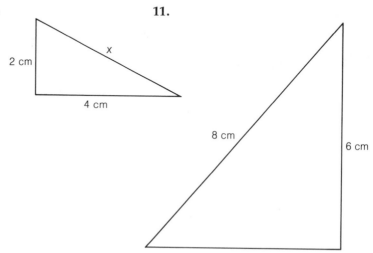

8 cm

6 cm

x

The length and width of a rectangle have been measured to be 6 meters and 4 meters respectively. It is possible that errors in these measurements could be as great as 0.05 meters (5 centimeters).

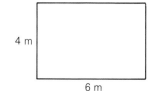

4 m

6 m

12. What would the reported area of the rectangle be?

13. What is the upper bound for the area of the rectangle?

14. What is the lower bound for the area of the rectangle?

15. What would the reported perimeter of the rectangle be?

16. What is the largest the perimeter could be?

17. What is the smallest the perimeter could be?

18. What would the reported difference between length and width be?

19. What is the largest that difference could be?

20. What is the smallest that difference could be?

For problems 21–29, use 3.14 for an approximation of π. C stands for the length in centimeters of the circumference, d for the length in centimeters of the diameter, r for the length in centimeters of the radius, and A for the area in square centimeters of a circle. Determine the missing values.

21. $d = 10$, $C = ?$ **24.** $r = 10$, $C = ?$ **27.** $C = 314$, $d = ?$

22. $C = 62.8$, $d = ?$ **25.** $C = 62.8$, $r = ?$ **28.** $C = 62.8$, $A = ?$

23. $r = 1$, $A = ?$ **26.** $r = 10$, $A = ?$ **29.** $A = 1256$, $r = ?$

30. What is the volume of a can that is 10 centimeters tall with a radius of 6 centimeters?

31. What is the volume of a can that is 5 centimeters tall with a radius of 12 centimeters?

Do not use a calculator for the problems in this test. For problems 1–4, compute the values to the nearest tenth.

1. $\sqrt{25}$ **2.** $\sqrt[3]{125}$ **3.** $\sqrt{51}$ **4.** $\sqrt[3]{216}$

For problems 5 and 6, use the formula $210d = v^2$. In the formula, d is the number of meters required to stop a car after the driver's foot hits the brake and v is the speed of the car in kilometers per hour.

5. A car is traveling at 60 kilometers per hour. After the driver's foot hits the brake, how many meters (to the nearest meter) will the car travel before it stops?

6. A car left skid marks about 36 meters long. About how fast (to the nearest kilometer per hour) was the car apparently going?

7. The volume of a cube is 729 cubic centimeters. What is the surface area of the cube?

8. The surface area of a cube is 216 square centimeters. What is the volume of the cube?

For problems 9–11, determine x to the nearest tenth of a centimeter.

9.

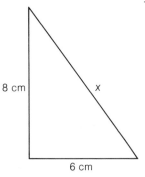

8 cm   x

6 cm

10.

4 cm   x

8 cm

11.

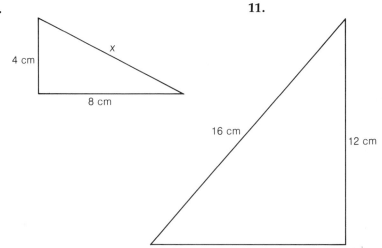

16 cm   12 cm

x

The length and width of a rectangle have been measured to be 12 meters and 8 meters respectively. It is possible that errors in these measurements could be as great as 0.1 meters (10 centimeters).

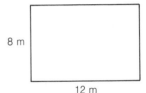

8 m

12 m

12. What would the reported area of the rectangle be?

13. What is the upper bound for the area of the rectangle?

14. What is the lower bound for the area of the rectangle?

15. What would the reported perimeter of the rectangle be?

16. What is the largest the perimeter could be?

17. What is the smallest the perimeter could be?

18. What would the reported difference between length and width be?

19. What is the largest that difference could be?

20. What is the smallest that difference could be?

For problems 21–29, use 3.14 for an approximation of π. C stands for the length in centimeters of the circumference, d for the length in centimeters of the diameter, r for the length in centimeters of the radius, and A for the area in square centimeters of a circle. Determine the missing values.

21. $d = 20$, $C = ?$ 24. $r = 20$, $C = ?$ 27. $C = 628$, $d = ?$

22. $C = 125.6$, $d = ?$ 25. $C = 125.6$, $r = ?$ 28. $C = 125.6$, $A = ?$

23. $r = 2$, $A = ?$ 26. $r = 20$, $A = ?$ 29. $A = 6280$, $r = ?$

30. What is the volume of a can that is 20 centimeters tall with a radius of 12 centimeters?

31. What is the volume of a can that is 10 centimeters tall with a radius of 24 centimeters?

CALCULATOR SQUARE ROOT GAME

Players: 1 or more
Materials: A calculator with 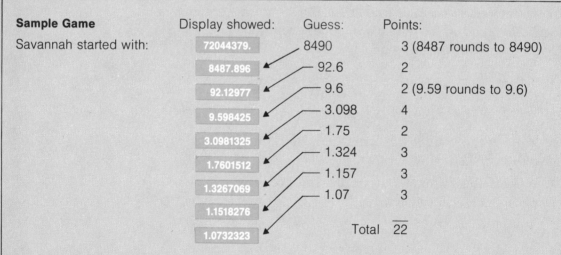 key, pencil, paper
Object: To guess as many digits of square roots as possible

Rules

1. Enter any 8-digit number on the calculator.

2. Guess the square root of the number.

3. Push the ▢. Compare your guess with the display.

4. Starting at the left, count all the digits of your guess that agree with the display. You may round the number on the display to get a point for the last place you count. Take that many points for that round.

5. Repeat steps 2, 3, and 4 seven more times. Keep score by recording your guesses and points.

6. If you correctly predict zeros at the right end of the square root, you get credit for them even though they do not show on the display. (So if you correctly predict when the display will show just ▮▮▮1.▮, you get 8 points.)

7. Your score is the sum of the points for the 8 steps.

Sample Game

Savannah started with:

Display showed:	Guess:	Points:
72044379.	8490	3 (8487 rounds to 8490)
8487.896	92.6	2
92.12977	9.6	2 (9.59 rounds to 9.6)
9.598425	3.098	4
3.0981325	1.75	2
1.7601512	1.324	3
1.3267069	1.157	3
1.1518276	1.07	3
1.0732323	Total	22

The last time Savannah played, she made 16 points. So this time she is playing better.

A different way to play this game is to repeat steps 2, 3, and 4 until the display shows ▓▓▓▓▓▓ 1.

Try playing the Calculator Square Root Game this way several times. Then try to answer these questions.

1. Savannah continued her game past the first 8 steps. Here is part of the rest of her score sheet:

Display showed:	Guess:	Points:
1.0732323	1.036	4 (1.0359 rounds to 1.036)
1.0359692	1.0178	5
1.0178257	1.00891	5 (1.00887 rounds to 1.0089)
1.0088734	1.004434	6 (1.004426 rounds to 1.00443)
1.0044269	1.002212	6
1.002211	1.0011050	7 (1.0011048 rounds to 1.001105)
1.0011048	1.0005523	7
1.0005522	1.0002760	8 (even though 0 isn't shown)
1.000276	1.0001379	8
1.0001379	1.0000689	8
1.0000689		

Savannah seems to be playing well now. How is she doing this?

2. If she continues to play this well, what do you think her score will be if she goes to ▓▓▓▓▓ 1. ?

3. During the early part of the game, some of Savannah's guesses were much better than others. See if you can figure out some of the strategies she used. Some of the following hints may help:

   A. $(10x + 5)^2 = 100 (x^2 + x) + 25$. So, for example, $75^2 = 5600 + 25 = 5625$, and $85^2 = 7200 + 25 = 7225$.

   B. $(x + 1)^2 = x^2 + x + x + 1$. So, for example, $31^2 = 30^2 + 30 + 31 = 961$.

   C. Some people remember certain squares, such as $11^2 = 121$, $12^2 = 144$, $13^2 = 169$, and $14^2 = 196$.

CHAPTER 10

FUNCTIONS
COMPUTER
UNDERSTANDING

10

Function Rules and Function Charts

1. Copy and complete these function charts.

   a. $x \rightarrow (\times 5) \rightarrow n \rightarrow (-8) \rightarrow y$

x	y
0	−8
1	
2	

   b. $x \rightarrow (\times \frac{1}{2}) \rightarrow n \rightarrow (+3) \rightarrow y$

x	y
−2	
	3
	4

   c. $x \rightarrow (\div 2) \rightarrow n \rightarrow (+1) \rightarrow y$

x	y
−2	
	1
	2

2. In the following, the instruction "square" means to multiply the number you have by itself. Copy and complete these function charts. When 2 answers are possible, give either.

   a. $x \rightarrow (\text{square}) \rightarrow y$

x	y
1	
2	
	9

   b. $x \rightarrow (\text{square}) \rightarrow y$

x	y
−2	4
	9
−4	

   c. $x \rightarrow (\text{square}) \rightarrow n \rightarrow (-4) \rightarrow y$

x	y
	0
1	
3	

3. **a.** Do you think there is more than 1 number whose square is 9?
   b. If so, what are they?

4. **a.** Is there any number whose square is −9?
   b. If −9 were the value of y in problem 2a or 2b, could you find a value for x?

5. Copy and complete these function charts. When 2 answers are possible, give either.

   a. $x \rightarrow (+3) \rightarrow n \rightarrow (\text{square}) \rightarrow y$

x	y
	0
−2	
	4

   b. $x \rightarrow (\times 2) \rightarrow n \rightarrow (\text{square}) \rightarrow y$

x	y
2	
	4
	36

   c. $x \rightarrow (\text{square}) \rightarrow n \rightarrow (\times 4) \rightarrow y$

x	y
2	
	4
	36

Writing function rules using arrows is a good method for some purposes. Usually these rules are written in a different form, which we will call *standard notation*.

x —⊗5→ n —⊖8→ y is written $5x - 8 = y$.

Either way, the rule tells us to start with x, multiply by 5, and then subtract 8 to get y.

x —(square)→ n —⊕5→ y is written $x^2 + 5 = y$.

Either way, start with x, square it (multiply it by itself), and add 5 to get y.

x —⊕3→ n —(square)→ y is written $(x + 3)^2 = y$.

Notice that since you add 3 to x before squaring, the $x + 3$ is written inside parentheses.

Copy and complete these function charts. Use a calculator if necessary. Round decimal answers to the nearest hundredth. When 2 answers are possible, give both.

1. $\frac{1}{2}x + 3 = y$

x	y
−2	▨
▨	3
▨	4
6	▨

2. $2x - 3 = y$

x	y
0	▨
▨	−1
▨	1
6	▨

3. $x^2 = y$

x	y
3	▨
▨	4
▨	0
▨	1

4. $x^2 = y$

x	y
1.73	▨
−1.73	▨
▨	3
▨	2

5. $x^3 = y$

x	y
3	▨
−3	▨
▨	64
▨	−64

6. $x^3 = y$

x	y
1.913	▨
−1.913	▨
▨	5
▨	−5

It has been said that the great French mathematician René Descartes (1596–1650) liked to stay in bed late in the morning and think. A story about him says that one morning he noticed a fly crawling on the ceiling. He thought about how he could describe to someone else where the fly was. The ceiling was tiled, and there was a light hanging in the middle of the room. From the bed, the ceiling looked something like this:

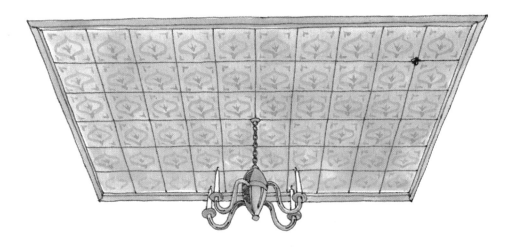

How would you describe the fly's position?

Descartes first described the fly as being "4 tiles to the right of and 2 tiles above the light."

Then he realized that saying "4 tiles to the right and 2 tiles above" took such a long time to say that the fly might move before he finished. Because of this, he decided to use just numbers to describe the fly's position.

The first number would tell how far to the right or left of the light the fly was. Positive numbers would indicate a position to the right. Negative numbers would indicate a position to the left.

The second number would tell how far above or below the light the fly was. Positive numbers would indicate a position above the light. Negative numbers would indicate a position below the light.

With this system, he would describe the fly on the ceiling as being at the point (4, 2).

The fly in problem 1 below is at (−1, 2). Tell where the flies are in problems 2−6.

1.

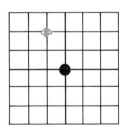

2.

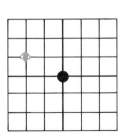

3.

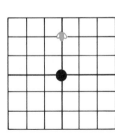

4.

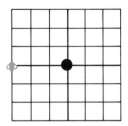

5.

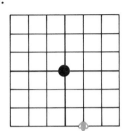

6.

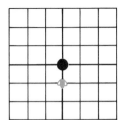

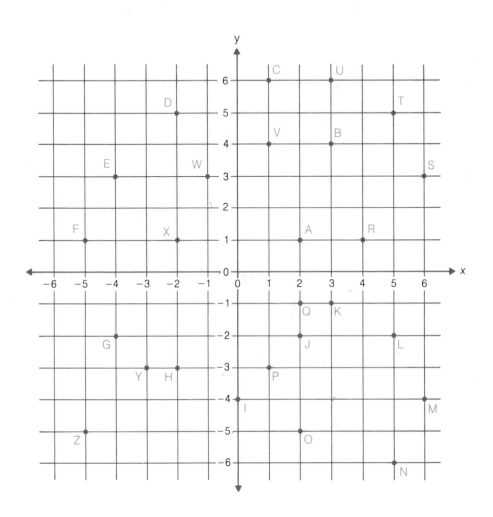

Find each point on the graph. Use the letters to decode the messages.

1. (4, 1) (−4, 3) (5, −6) (−4, 3)
   (−2, 5) (−4, 3) (6, 3) (1, 6) (2, 1) (4, 1) (5, 5) (−4, 3) (6, 3)
   (−1, 3) (2, 1) (6, 3)
   (2, 1)
   (5, −2) (2, 1) (−5, −5) (−3, −3)
   (3, 4) (3, 6) (5, 5)
   (3, 4) (4, 1) (0, −4) (−4, −2) (−2, −3) (5, 5)
   (3, 4) (2, −5) (−3, −3).

2. (1, −3) (−4, 3) (2, −5) (1, −3) (5, −2) (−4, 3)
   (−1, 3) (−2, −3) (2, −5)
   (5, 5) (−2, −3) (0, −4) (5, −6) (3, −1)
   (1, 6) (2, 1) (5, −6)
   (2, −5) (−5, 1) (5, 5) (−4, 3) (5, −6)
   (6, −4) (2, 1) (3, −1) (−4, 3)
   (−2, 5) (0, −4) (−5, 1) (−5, 1) (0, −4) (1, 6) (3, 6) (5, −2) (5, 5)
   (2, −2) (2, −5) (3, 4) (6, 3)
   (−4, 3) (2, 1) (6, 3) (0, −4) (−4, 3) (4, 1)
   (5, 5) (2, −5)
   (−2, 5) (2, −5).

3. (6, −4) (2, 1) (5, 5) (−2, −3) (−4, 3) (6, −4) (2, 1) (5, 5) (0, −4) (1, 6) (6, 3)
   (4, 1) (−4, 3) (2, −1) (3, 6) (0, −4) (4, 1) (−4, 3) (6, 3)
   (5, 5) (−2, −3) (0, −4) (5, −6) (3, −1) (0, −4) (5, −6) (−4, −2).

Make up your own messages. Use the graph to put them in code and give them to a friend to decode.

4. On a sheet of graph paper, graph the following points:
   A(1, 3) B(3, 1) C(−4, −1) D(−4, 3) E(5, −2) F(0, −3) G(4, 0)

Players: 2
Materials: Graph paper, crayons or markers (4 colors),
black pen or pencil
Object: To find the coordinates of the secret point

Rules

1. Decide what size "playing field" will be used. Each player makes a playing field by drawing coordinate axes on a sheet of graph paper.

2. The first player chooses a secret point with integer coordinates and draws 2 straight lines through the point at 45° angles to the axes. (See the sample game.) This separates the playing field into 4 parts. The first player then colors each of the 4 parts a different color.

3. Without seeing what the first player has done, the second player guesses a point by calling out its coordinates. Then the first player tells the color of that point. A point on 1 of the 2 dividing lines is described as black.

4. The second player keeps guessing points until he or she gets the secret point.

Sample Game

Lynn and Keith decided on a playing field that goes from -5 to 5 on each axis. Lynn was the first player. She chose $(3, -2)$ as the secret point, drew 2 lines, and colored the sections as shown.

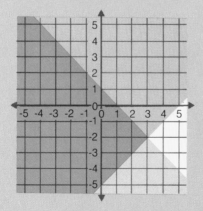

Keith made a playing field just like Lynn's but without the lines and colors. On his field, Keith kept a record of each move.

A. Keith said, "(0, 0)." Lynn said, "Red." Keith circled the point (0, 0) in red.

B. Keith said, "(1, 1)." Lynn said, "Green." Keith circled the point (1, 1) in green. He knew there was a line between (0, 0) and (1, 1). He drew this line so that he could remember where it was.

C. Keith said, "(4, −2)." Lynn said, "Yellow." Keith circled that point in yellow. Then he knew that the other line lay between (1, 1) and (4, −2).

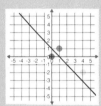

D. Keith said, "(2, 0)." Lynn said, "Green." Keith circled that point in green. Then he knew that the other line was between (2, 0) and (4, −2).

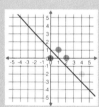

E. Keith said, "(4, −1)." Lynn said, "Black." Keith circled that point in black. Then he knew where the line was. He drew it to find the point where the 2 lines intersected.

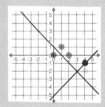

F. Keith said, "(3, −2)." Lynn said, "That's the point I chose. You got it in 6 moves."

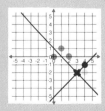

A function rule can be used to generate a set of ordered pairs of numbers. Those ordered pairs of numbers can then be graphed.

Example: Graph 10 points that satisfy the function rule
$$3x - 8 = y.$$

You can draw your function chart horizontally or vertically. This one is drawn horizontally.

x	-1	0	$\frac{1}{3}$	$\frac{2}{3}$	1	$1\frac{2}{3}$	2	$2\frac{1}{2}$	3	5
y	-11	-8	-7	-6	-5	-3	-2	$-\frac{1}{2}$	1	7

After you've chosen the points, draw your graph so that all the points will fit.

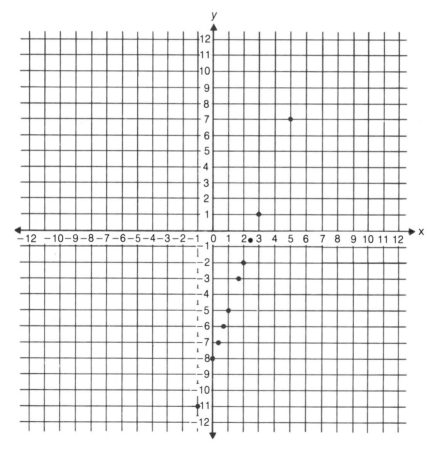

1. Do you notice anything interesting about the points we graphed on page 406? Choose another pair of numbers that satisfies the function rule $3x - 8 = y$. (Pick any number for x and calculate y.) Does the point seem to fit the same pattern as the others?

2. Hold a straightedge or ruler so that it makes a straight line along the points on the graph.

   a. Choose a point that lies along the line between $(-1, -11)$ and $(5, 7)$. Does this pair of numbers satisfy the function rule $3x - 8 = y$?

   b. Choose a point on the line that lies below $(-1, -11)$ and one that lies above $(5, 7)$. Does this pair of numbers satisfy the function rule $3x - 8 = y$?

3. Graph 10 points that satisfy the function rule $x + 2 = y$. What appears to be true about the points?

4. Graph 5 points that satisfy the function rule $2x - 5 = y$. What seems to be true about the points?

5. Graph 5 points that satisfy the function rule $\frac{1}{2}x + 3 = y$. Comment on the pattern of the points.

6. Graph 10 points that satisfy the function rule $x^2 = y$. Comment on the pattern of the points.

Remember

The horizontal line with x at the end and numbers under it is called the *x-axis*. The vertical line with y at the end is called the *y-axis*. The first number (the one that tells how far to go sideways) is called the *x-coordinate*. The second number is called the *y-coordinate* and tells how far to go up and down. The point $(0, 0)$ where the *x*-axis and *y*-axis meet is the *origin*. The plural of axis is *axes (ax′ · ēs)*.

Play Get the Point.

If you graph only a few points of a function (that is, points whose coordinates satisfy the function rule), you may not see a pattern. Usually, however, if you plot many points, a pattern becomes clear.

For example, we have plotted below 4 points of the function whose function rule is $y = 3x^2 - 4x + 6$. First we evaluated y for 4 values of x. We chose $x = -2, 0, 2,$ and 3.

x	y = 3x² − 4x + 6
−2	3(−2)² − 4(−2) + 6 = 26
0	3(0)² − 4(0) + 6 = 6
2	3(2)² − 4(2) + 6 = 10
3	3(3)² − 4(3) + 6 = 21

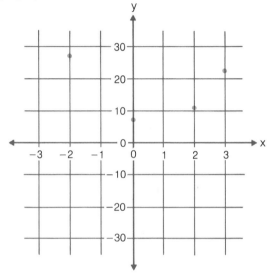

Notice that we use a different scale for the x and y directions. That is all right to do as long as the scale is clearly marked.

You may also have noticed that when we write function rules, y is sometimes on the left side of the equals sign and sometimes on the right side of the equals sign. It doesn't matter which way a function rule is written. $y = 3x$ and $3x = y$ both describe the same function.

[1] **From the graph, can you guess what the value of y is for x = 1?**

[2] **For x = −1?**

[3] **For x = −5?**

If many more points are graphed, we can imagine a smooth curve through them that allows us to make much better guesses for missing points. Look at the graph made with these values for $y = 3x^2 - 4x + 6$:

x	y
-2	26
-1.5	18.75
-1	13
-0.5	8.75
0	6
0.5	4.75
1	5
1.5	6.75
2	10
2.5	14.75
3	21
3.5	28.75

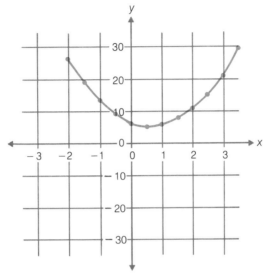

From these 12 points, we can imagine a smooth curve drawn through the points that shows where we are likely to find other points.

[4] **From the graph, guess what the value of y is for x = 1.2. Check to see how close you are.**

[5] **What kinds of function rules seem to produce points that are all on a straight line?**

[6] **What kinds of function rules seem to produce points that are not on a straight line?**

For each of the following function rules, first guess whether the points with coordinates satisfying the rule will be on a straight line. Then graph at least 8 points that satisfy the function rule. Compare your graphs with those of other students.

1. $y = \frac{1}{3}x + 5$ **3.** $y = 2x^2 - 10$ **5.** $y = -2x + 4$

2. $x + 7 = y$ **4.** $y = -2x^2 - 10$ **6.** $y = \frac{1}{x}$

Play Get the Point.

Graphs can be used to help solve various problems. Remember the formula that shows a relationship between the speed (or velocity) of a car and the distance required to stop after the driver's foot hits the brake:

$$210d = v^2$$

In this equation, v is the speed (or velocity) in kilometers per hour, and d is the approximate distance in meters required to stop.

The graph of the function defined by this formula looks like this:

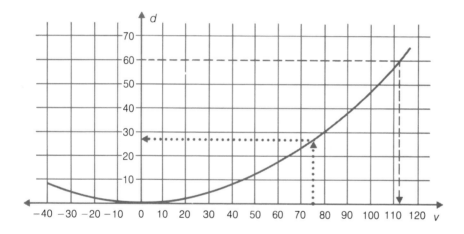

If a car is going 75 kilometers per hour, what is the distance required to stop? To read the answer on the graph, find the point of the graph corresponding to a velocity of 75 kilometers per hour and then see that it corresponds to a distance of about 27 meters. (Follow the dotted lines.)

If a car's tires left black rubber marks for a distance of 60 meters before it came to a stop, about how fast was it going? You can discover this by finding the point of the graph corresponding to 60 meters and seeing that it corresponds to about 112 kilometers per hour. (Follow the dashed lines.)

Use the graph on page 410 to do problems 1–5.

1. If a car is traveling 100 kilometers per hour, about how long a distance will be needed to stop it?

2. If a car is traveling 50 kilometers per hour, about how long a distance will be needed to stop it?

3. **a.** Is your answer to problem 2 half your answer to problem 1?
   b. What is the relationship between the answers? (If the graph were a straight line, the answer to problem 2 would be half the answer to problem 1.)

4. About how far will a car traveling 25 kilometers per hour travel after the driver steps on the brake?

5. **a.** What do you suppose it might mean for v to be -40?
   b. Do you think that for most purposes it would make sense to leave off the portion of the graph where v is negative?

6. Use a calculator to make a table of values for $y = x^2$ when x is $-2, -1.5, -1, -0.5, 0, 0.5, 1, 1.5, 2, 2.5, 3, 3.5, 4, 4.5$, and 5. Graph the points.

Use your graph and table of values from problem 6 to do problems 7 and 8.

7. **a.** What is the square root of 4?
   b. Are there 2 square roots of 4?
   c. What are they?

8. About what are the square roots of the following numbers? (Give answers to the nearest tenth.)
   a. 3
   b. 10
   c. 15

[1] Can you estimate the negative square roots using only the positive side of the graph?

[2] How would you do this?

[3] Why does this work?

Cube Roots on a Graph

1. Use a calculator to help you make a table of values for $y = x^3$ when x is -4, -3, -2, -1, 0, 0.2, 0.4, 0.6, 0.8, 1.0, 1.2, 1.4, 1.6, 1.8, 2.0, 2.2, 2.4, 2.6, 2.8, 3.0, 3.2, 3.4, 3.6, 3.8, 4.0, 4.2, 4.4, 4.6, 4.8, 5.0. Then make a graph for $y = x^3$. Compare your graph with other students'.

2. Use the graph and table of values from problem 1 to estimate (to the nearest tenth) the answers to the following.

   a. $\sqrt[3]{8}$ b. $\sqrt[3]{-8}$ c. $\sqrt[3]{20}$ d. $\sqrt[3]{-20}$ e. $\sqrt[3]{100}$

   [1] How can you use your graph and table to estimate cube roots of negative numbers?

   [2] Could you estimate those answers without using the part of the graph where x and y are negative?

   [3] How?

   [4] Look back at the graph you made for problem 6 on page 411. Can you use that graph to estimate the square root of -4?

   [5] Why or why not?

   [6] Is there a number that can be multiplied by itself to give a product -4?

   [7] Try to explain your answer.

3. Use your graph to estimate to the nearest tenth the answers to the following.

   a. $\sqrt[3]{30}$ b. $\sqrt[3]{60}$ c. $\sqrt[3]{90}$ d. $\sqrt[3]{0.5}$ e. $\sqrt[3]{0.25}$

4. Is $\sqrt[3]{60}$ about twice as big as $\sqrt[3]{30}$?

5. Is $\sqrt[3]{90}$ about 3 times $\sqrt[3]{30}$?

6. Is $\sqrt[3]{90}$ less than 3 times $\sqrt[3]{30}$?

7. Is $\sqrt[3]{0.5}$ about 2 times $\sqrt[3]{0.25}$?

8. Is $\sqrt[3]{0.5}$ more than 2 times $\sqrt[3]{0.25}$?

ROLL A 15 GAME

Players: 2
Materials: Two 0–5 cubes, two 5–10 cubes
Object: To get the sum closer to 15

Rules

1. Roll the cubes one at a time.

2. Add the numbers as you roll. The sum of all the cubes you roll should be as close to 15 as possible.

3. You may stop after 2, 3, or 4 rolls.

If you rolled: The sum would be:

7 and 1 and 4 and 7   19

8 and 5   13

4 and 4 and 8   16

9 and 3 and 3   15

5 and 10   15

4. The player with the sum closer to 15 wins the round. (The best score is 15; the next best scores are 14 and 16, and so on.)

Have you ever shot down alien spaceships as they attacked your missile bases? Or chased hungry monsters through a maze? Or played baseball, football, or basketball games on a television screen?

When you played these games, you were playing against a computer.

Have you ever wondered how the computers inside these game machines know how to play? You know that they can't think the same way that you can. The computers in these machines are programmed with a set of specific instructions. They must follow these instructions when they play. So when you play a game against a computer, you're really playing against a set of instructions.

The paper-player computer below is a "computer" that is "programmed" to play the Roll a 15 Game. Play against it to see how it works. Here's how to play:

A. On your turn, play as you would in a regular game.

B. On the computer's turn, the computer decides what to do, but it needs help from you to roll the cubes and keep score.

Try a few rounds. See how you do.

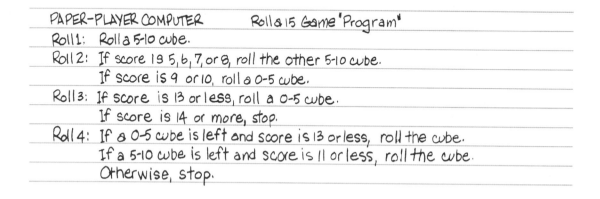

PAPER-PLAYER COMPUTER   Roll a 15 Game "Program"
Roll 1: Roll a 5-10 cube.
Roll 2: If score is 5, 6, 7, or 8, roll the other 5-10 cube.
         If score is 9 or 10, roll a 0-5 cube.
Roll 3: If score is 13 or less, roll a 0-5 cube.
         If score is 14 or more, stop.
Roll 4: If a 0-5 cube is left and score is 13 or less, roll the cube.
         If a 5-10 cube is left and score is 11 or less, roll the cube.
         Otherwise, stop.

How did you do when you played Roll a 15 against the paper-player computer?

Now try making your own paper-player computer. How do you want your computer to play? Write instructions to tell your computer what to do in each kind of situation. Remember, your computer must be able to decide which cube to roll and when to stop.

As you write your program, play against it. This will help you see where the program works well and where it has problems. People who work with computers call this way of fixing a program debugging. *Debugging* is short for "taking the bugs out."

Test your computer by seeing how it does in these situations.

	Computer roll:	Computer score:	Cubes left:	Your score:
1.	2	10	5–10, 0–5, 0–5	14
2.	3	16	0–5, 0–5	13
3.	4	13	0–5	13
4.	3	10	0–5, 0–5	15
5.	4	12	0–5	15

Make up more situations of your own to test your computer. Now have your computer play against a friend's computer. Have a computer tournament. Try to make computers that will play other games.

Be sure to include this special rule for computers: If a situation comes up and the computer doesn't know what to do, it loses that round.

CUBE 100 GAME

Players: 2
Materials: Two 0–5 cubes, two 5–10 cubes
Object: To score as close to 100 as possible without going over

Rules

1. Roll the cubes one at a time, adding the numbers as you roll.

2. After any roll, instead of adding that number you may multiply it by the sum of the previous numbers. But then your turn is over.

3. The player with the score closer to, but not over, 100 wins the round.

Sample Game

Polly rolled **6** and then **3**
6 + 3 = 9

Then she rolled **9**
9 × 9 = 81

She stopped after 3 rolls.
Polly's score was 81.

Ian rolled **5** and then **5**
5 + 5 = 10

Then he rolled **6**
10 + 6 = 16

He rolled **6** again.
16 × 6 = 96

Ian's score was 96.
Ian won the round.

Programming the Paper-Player Computer

A computer is not "smart" in the way humans are smart. A computer does exactly what it is told (or programmed) to do, and it does this very quickly. But doing stupid things quickly is usually not as good as doing smart things slowly. A computer can be made "smarter" by programming it better.

Try to program a paper-player computer to do each of the following jobs in a smart way.

1. Play Roll a 15 better than the program you wrote before.
2. Play the Cube 100 Game.
3. Find $\sqrt{5}$ to 8 places. (Assume that the calculator in your paper-player computer doesn't have a $\sqrt{}$ key. It can only add, subtract, multiply, and divide.)
4. Make up other jobs for your paper-player computer and program it to do them.

Look back in chapter 3 at pages 121–123 and Mark's experiments with seed germination. After making the chart with percentages of seed germination, Mark made a graph to show the results of his experiment.

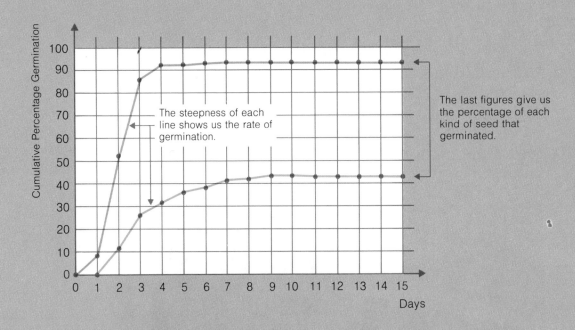

Germination of new (——) and old (——) radish seeds over a period of days. Each group was allowed to germinate under identical conditions. Mark used 132 new seeds and 321 old seeds.

Use Mark's graph to discuss and answer the following questions.

[1] **Estimate as closely as you can how many hours it took for 50% of the new seeds to germinate.**

[2] **Estimate as closely as you can how many hours it took for 25% of the old seeds to germinate.**

To show and compare only the actual rates of germination, we should consider only those seeds that actually germinated. For Mark's experiment that means considering only 123 new seeds and 138 old seeds. If we do this, then at the end of the first day the percentage germination for new seeds was $\frac{10}{123} \times 100 = 8.1\%$ and that for old seeds was $\frac{1}{138} \times 100 = 0.7\%$.

Here is the table of Mark's original data:

| | New Seeds | | Old Seeds | |
Day	Number Germinated	Cumulative Number Germinated	Number Germinated	Cumulative Number Germinated
0	0	0	0	0
1	10	10	1	1
2	59	69	38	39
3	45	114	44	83
4	7	121	20	103
5	0	121	11	114
6	1	122	9	123
7	1	123	7	130
8	0	123	4	134
9	0	123	0	134
10	0	123	3	137
11	0	123	1	138
12	0	123	0	138
13	0	123	0	138
14	0	123	0	138
15	0	123	0	138

Use this data to make a new table showing the percentage germinated each day of those seeds that actually germinated. Then graph new data, using the graph on page 418 as your model. Label your graphs so that somebody unfamiliar with Mark's experiment would understand the results.

[3] Which graph, the one on page 418 or the one you just made, shows better how fast each group of seeds germinated?

[4] Which graph shows better the percentage of seeds that actually germinated?

Chapter Review

Copy and complete these function charts. Then make a graph for each function.

1. $y = 3x - 7$

x	-1	0	1	2	3	4
y	-10					

2. $2x + 1 = y$

x	-3	-2			1	2
y			-1	1		

3. $y = x^2$

x	-3	-2	-1	0	0.5	1	1.5	2	2.5	3	3.5	4
y												

Use your graphs for problems 1–3 to help you do problems 4–6.

4. For the function rule $y = 3x - 7$, what value of x would make $y = 0$?

5. For the function rule $2x + 1 = y$, what value of x will make $y = 0$?

6. What is $\sqrt{10}$ (to the nearest tenth)?

The formula $210d = v^2$ gives the approximate distance in meters required to stop a car going v kilometers per hour. The graph of this function is shown here:

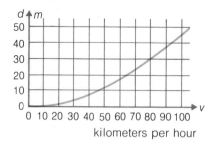

kilometers per hour

Use the graph to answer problems 7–9.

7. About how many meters will be required to stop a car going 85 kilometers per hour?

8. A car required 25 meters to stop. About how fast was it going?

9. A car required 55 meters to stop. Was it going faster than 100 kilometers per hour?

Here are 3 puzzling problems. They are difficult. When you have an answer you think is right, compare it with a friend's answer. Be prepared to defend your answers.

1. Matthew Whizzer drove up a mountain at 50 kilometers per hour. He turned around instantly at the top and drove back down very fast. When he returned to his starting place he discovered he had averaged 100 kilometers per hour for the entire trip. How fast did he come down the mountain?

2. Emmett Messer had a large glass of lemonade and a small glass of orange juice. He took a teaspoonful of the lemonade, put it in the orange juice, and mixed thoroughly. Then he took a teaspoonful of the mixture and put it in the lemonade. When he finished, was there more lemonade in the orange juice or more orange juice in the lemonade?

3. Astrid Ortiz was hunting for bears. One day she started at camp and walked 1 mile straight south. Then she walked 1 mile due east. There she shot a bear. She dragged the bear 1 mile back to camp.
   a. What color was the bear?
   b. Where was the camp located?
   c. How many other places on earth are there where you could walk 1 mile south, then 1 mile east, then 1 mile back to the starting place?
   d. Where are these places?

Copy and complete these function charts. Then make a graph for each function.

1. $y = 4x - 5$

x	−1	0	1	2	3	4
y	−9					

2. $3x + 2 = y$

x	−3	−2			1	2
y			−1	1		

3. $y = x^2$

x	−3	−2	−1	0	0.5	1	1.5	2	2.5	3	3.5	4
y												

Use your graphs for problems 1–3 to help you do problems 4–6.

4. For the function rule $y = 4x - 5$, what value of x would make $y = 0$?

5. For the function rule $3x + 2 = y$, what value of x will make $y = 0$?

6. What is $\sqrt{8}$ (to the nearest tenth)?

The formula $210d = v^2$ gives the approximate distance in meters required to stop a car going v kilometers per hour. The graph of this function is shown here:

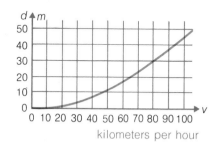

kilometers per hour

Use the graph to answer problems 7–9.

7. About how many meters will be required to stop a car going 75 kilometers per hour?

8. A car required 20 meters to stop. About how fast was it going?

9. A car required 60 meters to stop. Was it going faster than 100 kilometers per hour?

Here are some word-number puzzles. You did some on page 37 in chapter 1.

Replace each letter by 1 and only 1 digit. No 2 letters can be replaced by the same digit. First digits are not usually allowed to be zero. The goal is to make true statements.

The last puzzle on page 37 was

$$\begin{array}{r} SEND \\ + \ MORE \\ \hline MONEY \end{array}$$

There is only 1 solution if $M \neq 0$. It is $9567 + 1085 = 10{,}652$. See how many solutions you can find if $M = 0$.

Now try these word-number puzzles. Tell how many solutions there are for each and explain how you know.

1. $(HE)^2 = SHE$
2. $(ME)^2 = MAT$
3. $HE + SHE = THEY$
4. $(ALL)^2 = ULTRA$
5. $AB \cdot CD = EEE$

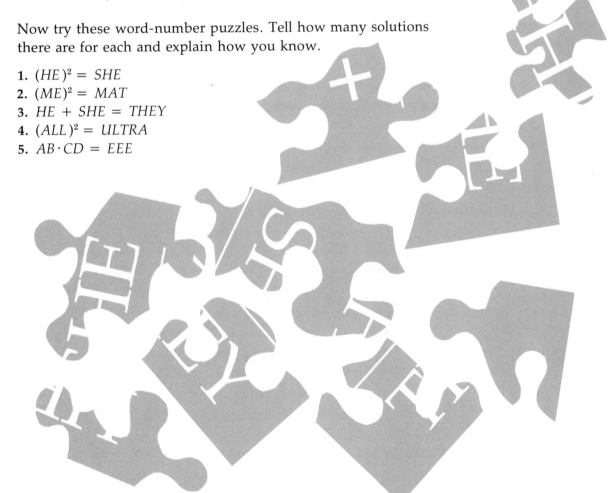

Length	Weight (mass)	Liquid Volume (capacity)
millimeter (mm) 0.001 m	**milligram** (mg) 0.001 g	**milliliter** (mL) 0.001 L
centimeter (cm) 0.01 m	centigram (cg) 0.01 g	centiliter (cL) 0.01 L
decimeter (dm) 0.1 m	decigram (dg) 0.1 g	deciliter (dL) 0.1 L
meter (m)	**gram** (g)	**liter** (L)
dekameter (dam) 10 m	dekagram (dag) 10 g	dekaliter (daL) 10 L
hectometer (hm) 100 m	hectogram (hg) 100 g	hectoliter (hL) 100 L
kilometer (km) 1000 m	**kilogram** (kg) 1000 g	kiloliter (kL) 1000 L

Units of area are derived from units of length.

square centimeter (cm²)	1 cm² = 0.0001 m²	The area of this square is 1 square centimeter.
square meter (m²)	1 m² = 10,000 cm²	A square 1 meter on a side has an area of 1 square meter.
hectare (ha)	1 ha = 10,000 m²	A square 100 meters on a side has an area of 1 hectare.
square kilometer (km²)	1 km² = 1,000,000 m²	A square 1 kilometer on a side has an area of 1 square kilometer.

Units of volume can also be derived from units of length.

cubic centimeter (cm³)		The volume of this cube is 1 cubic centimeter.
cubic meter (m³)	1 m³ = 1,000,000 cm³	A cube 1 meter on a side has a volume of 1 cubic meter.

The unit of temperature is the degree Celsius (°C).

Water freezes at 0°C and boils at 100°C.

Descriptions of some common units:

kilometer	You can walk a kilometer in about 12 minutes.
meter	Most classroom doors are about 1 meter wide.
centimeter	This line segment is 1 centimeter long.
millimeter	This line segment is 1 millimeter long.
liter	4 average-size glasses hold about 1 liter of liquid.
milliliter	This cube holds about 1 milliliter:

kilogram	A pair of size-10 men's shoes weighs about 1 kilogram.
gram	A nickel (or a marble) weighs about 5 grams.

Length

inch (in) $1 \text{ in} = \begin{cases} \frac{1}{12} \text{ ft} \\ \frac{1}{36} \text{ yd} \end{cases}$

foot (ft) $1 \text{ ft} = \begin{cases} 12 \text{ in} \\ \frac{1}{3} \text{ yd} \end{cases}$

yard (yd) $1 \text{ yd} = \begin{cases} 36 \text{ in} \\ 3 \text{ ft} \end{cases}$

mile (mi) $1 \text{ mi} = \begin{cases} 5280 \text{ ft} \\ 1760 \text{ yd} \end{cases}$

Liquid Volume (capacity)

fluid ounce (fl oz) $1 \text{ fl oz} = \frac{1}{8} \text{ cup}$

cup (c) $1 \text{ c} = \begin{cases} 8 \text{ fl oz} \\ \frac{1}{2} \text{ pt} \end{cases}$

pint (pt) $1 \text{ pt} = \begin{cases} 16 \text{ fl oz} \\ 2 \text{ c} \\ \frac{1}{2} \text{ qt} \end{cases}$

quart (qt) $1 \text{ qt} = \begin{cases} 32 \text{ fl oz} \\ 4 \text{ c} \\ \frac{1}{4} \text{ gal} \end{cases}$

gallon (gal) $1 \text{ gal} = \begin{cases} 128 \text{ fl oz} \\ 16 \text{ c} \\ 8 \text{ pt} \\ 4 \text{ qt} \end{cases}$

Area

square inch (sq in or in²)
square foot (sq ft or ft²) $1 \text{ ft}^2 = 144 \text{ in}^2$
square yard (sq yd or yd²) $1 \text{ yd}^2 = 9 \text{ ft}^2$
acre (A) $1 \text{ A} = 4840 \text{ yd}^2$
square mile (sq mi or mi²) $1 \text{ mi}^2 = 640 \text{ A}$

Volume

cubic inch (cu in or in³)
cubic foot (cu ft or ft³) $1 \text{ ft}^3 = 1728 \text{ in}^3$
cubic yard (cu yd or yd³) $1 \text{ yd}^3 = 27 \text{ ft}^3$

Dry Measure (capacity)

pint (pt)
quart (qt) $1 \text{ qt} = 2 \text{ pt}$
peck (pk) $1 \text{ pk} = 8 \text{ qt}$
bushel (bu) $1 \text{ bu} = 4 \text{ pk}$

Weight

ounce (oz) $1 \text{ oz} = \frac{1}{16} \text{ lb}$
pound (lb) $1 \text{ lb} = 16 \text{ oz}$
ton (T) $1 \text{ T} = 2000 \text{ lb}$

The unit of temperature is the degree Fahrenheit (°F).

Water freezes at 32°F and boils at 212°F.

absolute value The numerical value of a real number without consideration of its sign. It is the (positive) distance of the number from zero on a number line. $|-7| = 7, |+7| = 7$.

acute angle An angle that measures less than 90°. These are right angles: These are acute angles:

addend A number that is added to another number to make a sum. For example:

35—addend	$7 + 8 = 15$—sum
+ 48—addend		
83—sum	addend addend

algorithm A step-by-step procedure for solving a certain type of problem.

approximation An answer to a mathematical problem that is not precise but is close enough for the purpose. Sometimes an approximate answer is more appropriate than a precise answer. (See *estimate*.)

area The number of square units enclosed by a figure. The area of this rectangle is 6 square centimeters:

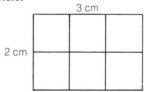

arrow operation A notation for showing an action of a function machine. In $7 \longrightarrow \times 8 \longrightarrow 56$, 7 goes in and is multiplied by 8 to give 56. The *function rule* in this case is ×8. In the operation $6 \longleftarrow -5 \longrightarrow 11$, 11 goes in and 5 is subtracted from it to give 6. The function rule in this case is −5.

associative law In both addition and multiplication, the law that states for any numbers x, y, and z, it doesn't matter whether y is first combined with x or with z. $x + (y + z) = (x + y) + z; x \times (y \times z) = (x \times y) \times z$.

average A number that can sometimes be used to describe a group of numbers. To find the average of a set of numbers, add the numbers and divide the sum by how many numbers were added. The average of 5, 6, 6, 8, and 10 is 7 ($5 + 6 + 6 + 8 + 10 = 35$ and $35 \div 5 = 7$). (Also called *mean*.)

axes (of a graph) The 2 zero lines of a graph that give the coordinates of points. The horizontal axis is the x-axis. The vertical axis is the y-axis.

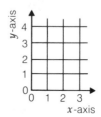

balance 1. The amount of money remaining in an account. 2. An instrument used to measure weight, as a double-pan balance.

bar graph A graph in which quantities are shown by bars. Also called *histogram*. Each bar in this bar graph shows the average number of rainy days per year in a selected U.S. city:

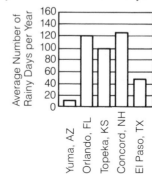

base 1. The side or face of a geometric figure used with the altitude or height to calculate area or volume. 2. The number on which a number system is built. 3. In exponential notation, the number that is used as the factor. In 6^3, 6 is the base and 3 is the exponent: $6^3 = 6 \times 6 \times 6$.

bisect To divide into 2 equal parts.

bound A number that an answer must be greater than or less than. For example, 36×21 must be less than 40×30, or 1200. So 1200 is an *upper bound*. The answer to 36×21 must be greater than 30×20, or 600. So 600 is a *lower bound*.

Celsius (C) A temperature scale, named after a Swedish astronomer, in which 0° is the temperature at which water freezes and 100° is the temperature at which water boils under standard conditions.

circle A figure (in a plane) in which all the points are the same distance from a point called the center. In this figure, for example, points A, B, and C are the same distance from point O, the center of the circle:

commutative law In both addition and multiplication, the law stating that for any numbers x and y, the sum or product will be the same regardless of the order in which they are added or multiplied: $x + y = y + x$; $x \cdot y = y \cdot x$.

composite function A function with 2 or more operations. For example:

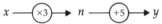

composite number A whole number with factors other than 1 and itself.

congruent Figures that are the same size and same shape; that is, they fit perfectly when placed on top of each other.

These triangles are congruent: These are not:

coordinates Numbers that give the position of a point on a graph. In the figure shown, for example, the coordinates of point A are (2, 3). 2 is the x-coordinate. 3 is the y coordinate.

cube A solid figure with 6 equal square faces. For example:

decimal point A dot used to separate the ones digit from the tenths digit.

degree 1. A unit of measure of temperature. See *Fahrenheit* and *Celsius*. 2. A unit of measure of angles. There are 360° in a circle. There are 90° in a right angle.

denominator The part of a fraction written below the line. The part written above the line is called the *numerator*. The denominator tells how many equal parts something is divided into; the numerator tells how many of those parts are being referred to. In the fraction $\frac{3}{4}$ the denominator (4) indicates that something is divided into 4 equal parts. The numerator (3) says to consider 3 of those parts.

deposit To add money to an account. (Also, the amount of money added.)

diagonal Any line connecting 2 vertices of a polygon that is not a side of a polygon. AC is a diagonal of $ABCD$:

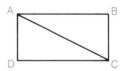

diameter A line segment, going through the center of a circle, that starts at one point on the circle and ends at the opposite point on the circle. (Also, the length of that line segment.) AB is a diameter of this circle:

difference The amount by which one number is greater or less than another. For example:

$$43\text{—minuend}$$
$$-\ 16\text{—subtrahend}$$
$$27\text{—difference}$$

$$10 - 7 = 3\text{—difference}$$
subtrahend
minuend

digit Any of the numbers 0, 1, 2, 3, 4, 5, 6, 7, 8, and 9. The two digits in 15 are 1 and 5.

distributive law For both multiplication and division, the law stating that for any numbers x, y, and z, the product or quotient will be the same whether the operation is carried out on the whole or on its parts: $x(y + z) = xy + xz$; $x(y - z) = xy - xz$; $x \div (y + z) = (x \div y) + (x \div z)$; $x \div (y - z) = (x \div y) - (x \div z)$.

dividend A number that is divided by the divisor. For example:

$$6 \div 3 = 2\text{—quotient}$$
divisor
dividend

$$43\text{—quotient}$$
$$\text{divisor—}8\overline{)347}\text{—dividend}$$
$$\underline{32}$$
$$27$$
$$\underline{24}$$
$$3$$

divisor A number that the dividend is divided by. (See *dividend*.)

equation A mathematical statement with an equal sign stating that 2 quantities are equal. For example, $4 + 2 = 6$ and $6 + n = 10$ are equations.

equilateral triangle A triangle with all 3 sides the same length. For example:

equivalent fractions Fractions that have the same value. $\frac{2}{6}$, $\frac{4}{12}$, and $\frac{1}{3}$ are equivalent fractions.

estimate A judgment about the size or quantity of something. (Also, to make such a judgment.) Sometimes it is more appropriate to make an estimate than to measure or count precisely. (See *approximation*.)

even number Any multiple of 2. 0, 2, 4, 6, 8, and so on are even numbers.

exponent In exponential notation, the superscript number that tells how many times the base is used as a factor. In 6^3, 3 is the exponent and 6 is the base: $6^3 = 6 \times 6 \times 6$.

Fahrenheit (F) A temperature scale, named for a German physicist, in which 32° is the temperature at which water freezes and 212° is the temperature at which water boils under standard conditions.

fraction $\frac{1}{2}$, $\frac{3}{4}$, and $\frac{7}{8}$ are examples of fractions. The fraction $\frac{3}{4}$ means that something is divided into 4 equal parts and that we are considering 3 of those parts. (See *denominator* and *numerator*.)

function machine A device (sometimes imaginary) that does the same thing to every number that is put into it. (See *arrow operation*.)

function rule See *arrow operation*.

hexagon A polygon with 6 sides.

histogram See *bar graph*.

hundredth One part of 100 equal parts of a whole. If a whole is divided into 100 equal parts, each part is one-hundredth of the whole.

improper fraction A fraction in which the numerator is greater than the denominator.

inequality A statement that tells which of 2 numbers is greater. For example: $4 > 3$ is read "4 is greater than 3." $3 + 6 < 10$ is read "3 plus 6 is less than 10."

intersecting lines Lines that meet. In this figure lines *AB* and *CD* intersect at point *E*.

inverse operation An operation that "undoes" the results of another operation. Multiplication and division are inverse operations; addition and subtraction are inverse operations.

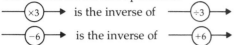

is the inverse of

isosceles triangle A triangle with two equal sides. These are isosceles triangles:

line graph A graph made up of lines. This line graph shows John's height at different times in his life. The marked points show his height at the times when he was measured.

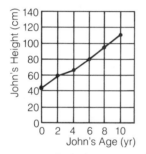

line segment A part of a line with 2 endpoints. For example, *AB* is a line segment; points *A* and *B* are its endpoints.

mean See *average.*

median The middle value in a group of numbers arranged in increasing order. The median of 5, 6, 6, 8, and 10 is 6.

minuend A number from which another number is subtracted. (See *difference.*)

mixed number A number made up of a whole number and a fraction. $1\frac{1}{2}$, $2\frac{3}{4}$, and $7\frac{7}{8}$ are mixed numbers.

mode The most common value in a group of numbers. The mode of 5, 6, 6, 8, and 10 is 6.

multiple A number that is some whole number of times another number. 12 is a multiple of 3 because $3 \times 4 = 12$.

multiplicand A number that is multiplied by another number, the multiplier. For example:

The multiplier and multiplicand are also called the factors of the product.

multiplier See *multiplicand.*

negative number A number less than zero. For example, −2 is 2 less than zero.

numerator The part of a fraction written above the line. (See *denominator.*)

obtuse angle An angle that measures between 90° and 180°.

These angles are obtuse: These are not:

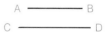

octagon A polygon with 8 sides.

odd number A whole number that is not a multiple of 2. All whole numbers that are not even are odd. 1, 3, 5, 7, 9, 11, and so on are odd numbers.

odds The ratio of the number of favorable cases to the number of unfavorable cases.

ordered pair Two numbers written so that one is considered before the other. Coordinates of points are written as ordered pairs, with the *x*-coordinate written first. For example: (3, 4). (See *coordinates.*)

parallel lines Lines in a plane that do not intersect. Lines *AB* and *CD* are parallel:

Lines *EF* and *GH* are not parallel:

parentheses A symbol ( ) used in mathematics to show in which order operations should be done. For example: $(3 \times 5) + 7$ says to multiply 5 by 3 and then add 7; $3 \times (5 + 7)$ says to add 5 and 7 and then multiply by 3.

partial product The product that comes from multiplying the multiplicand by one of the digits of the multiplier. For example:

$$
\begin{array}{r}
36 \\
\times\ 12 \\
\hline
72 \\
36 \\
\hline
432
\end{array}
$$

⎡ This partial product comes
⎣ from multiplying 36 by 2 ones.

⎡ This partial product comes
⎣ from multiplying 36 by 1 ten.

⎡ The product comes from adding
⎣ the partial products.

pentagon A polygon with 5 sides.

perimeter The distance around a figure. The perimeter of this rectangle is 6 centimeters:

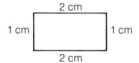

2 cm
1 cm   1 cm
2 cm

percent Parts per hundred, shown by the symbol %. For example, 95 out of 100 is 95%.

perpendicular bisector A line that bisects another line and is perpendicular to it.

AB is a perpendicular bisector of *CD*.

A
C ———————— D
B

perpendicular lines Lines that intersect at right angles.

These lines are perpendicular:

So are these: But these are not:

place value The value of a digit in a number. The value of 7 in 27 is 7 ones; in 74 its value is 70, or 7 tens; in 726 its value is 700, or 7 hundreds.

polygon One of a certain type of figure. These figures are polygons:

These are not:

Here are the names of some common polygons and the number of sides:

Number of Sides	Name
3	triangle
4	quadrilateral
5	pentagon—a regular pentagon has 5 equal sides:

6	hexagon—a regular hexagon has 6 equal sides:

8	octagon—a regular octagon has 8 equal sides:

polyhedron A 3-dimensional figure with faces formed by planes. The tetrahedron, cube, octahedron, dodecahedron, and icosahedron are the 5 regular polyhedra.

positive number A number that is greater than zero. For example, +2 is 2 more than zero.

prime number A whole number divisible only by 1 and itself.

probability How likely something is to happen. The probability that some particular thing will happen is a fraction in which the denominator is the total number of possible things that can happen and the numerator is the number of ways this particular thing can happen. The probability that an ordinary coin will show heads when flipped is about $\frac{1}{2}$.

product The result of multiplying 2 numbers together. (See *multiplicand*.)

profit In a business, the money that is left after all expenses have been paid.

proper fraction A fraction in which the denominator is greater than the numerator.

quadrilateral A polygon with 4 sides.

quotient The result (other than the remainder) of dividing one number by another. (See *dividend*.)

radius A line segment that goes from the center of a circle to a point on the circle. (Also, the length of such a segment.) *OA* is a radius of the circle shown here. The radius of the circle is 1 centimeter.

range The 2 numbers that show the highest and the lowest values of a group of numbers. The range of 5, 6, 6, 8, and 10 is 5 to 10.

rational number A number that can be expressed as the ratio of 2 integers.

rectangle A quadrilateral in which all 4 angles are right angles.

regroup To rename a number to make adding and subtracting easier.

Example of regrouping in subtraction:

$$\begin{array}{r} {\scriptstyle 1\ 15} \\ \not{2}\not{5} \\ -17 \\ \hline 8 \end{array}$$

(To subtract in the ones column, 2 tens and 5 is regrouped to 1 ten and 15.)

Example of regrouping in addition:

$$\begin{array}{r} {\scriptstyle 1} \\ 296 \\ +442 \\ \hline 738 \end{array}$$

(After adding the tens column, 13 tens is regrouped to 1 hundred and 3 tens.)

relation signs The 3 basic relation signs are > (greater than), < (less than), and = (equal to). (See *inequality*.)

remainder A number less than the divisor that remains after the dividend has been divided by the divisor as many times as possible. For example, when you divide 25 by 4, the quotient is 6 with a remainder of 1:

$$\begin{array}{r} 6\ \text{R1} \\ 4\overline{)25} \\ \underline{24} \\ 1 \end{array}$$

right angle An angle that forms a square corner.

These are right angles: These are not:

rounding Changing a number to another number that is easier to work with and that is close enough for the purpose. (See *approximation*.)

similar Figures that are the same shape but not the same size.

These triangles are similar: These are not:

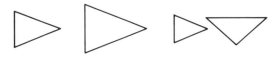

square A quadrilateral with 4 equal sides and 4 equal angles.

straight angle An angle that forms a straight line.

This is a straight angle: These are not:

subtrahend A number that is subtracted from another number. (See *difference*.)

sum The result of adding 2 or more numbers. (See *addend*.)

tenth One of 10 equal parts of a whole. If a whole is divided into 10 equal parts, each part is one-tenth of the whole.

transversal A line that intersects 2 or more lines. *AB* is a transversal.

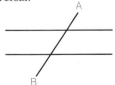

triangle A polygon that has 3 sides.

unit 1. An amount used as a standard for measuring. For example, meters, liters, seconds, and kilograms are units in the metric system of measure, and feet, quarts, and pounds are units in the traditional system of measure. Sometimes nonstandard units are used for measuring. See pages 424–425 for tables of metric and traditional measure.   2. One of anything.

unit cost The cost of 1 item or 1 specified amount of an item. If 20 pencils cost 40¢, then the unit cost is 2¢ for each pencil. If dog food cost $9 for 3 kilograms, then the unit cost is $3 per kilogram.

vertex The point where the 2 sides of an angle meet. *B* is the vertex of < *ABC*.

vertical angles The equal angles formed by 2 intersecting lines.

< 1 and < 2 are vertical angles.

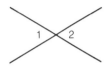

whole number The numbers that we use to show how many (0, 1, 2, 3, and so on). 3 is a whole number, but $3\frac{1}{2}$ and 4.5 are not whole numbers.

zero The number that tells how many things there are when there aren't any. Zero times any number is zero; zero plus any number is that number: $0 \times 3 = 0$ and $0 + 3 = 3$.

INDEX

Absolute value, 262
Acute angles, 135–136
Addition with decimals, 99–101
Addition with fractions, 198–200, 202–205
Addition with mixed numbers, 250–251, 253–255, 258
Addition with signed numbers, 263–265, 267, 269, 271
Addition of whole numbers
  approximating answers for, 70, 88
  associative law for, 44–45, 58
  in base five, 8–11, 33
  checking, 71
  commutative law for, 16, 44–45, 58
  facts of,· 16–17, 65
  multidigit, 12, 15, 63
Angles
  acute, 135–136
  alternate interior, 139, 141
  base of, 142
  bisecting, 150–151, 163
  congruent, 137
  constructing, 151
  corresponding, 138
  labeling, 138
  measuring, 133–137
  obtuse, 135–136
  right, 131–136
  straight, 131
  supplementary, 137
  vertical, 137, 141, 143
Approximation
  applications of, 110–111
  of circumference, 383
  of differences, 70, 88
  of pi (π), 382–383
  of powers, 88
  of products, 70, 88, 106
  of quotients, 70, 88, 106
  of sums, 68, 70, 88
Area
  of circles, 384–385
  of irregular figures, 312–313, 322–323
  of parallelograms, 316–317
  of rectangles, 46–47, 314–315
  of rhombuses, 317
  of squares, 298, 372–373
  of trapezoids, 324–325
  of triangles, 315, 318

units of, 237–238, 242
Associative law
  for addition, 44–45, 58
  for multiplication, 44–45, 58
Averages, 278, 281–284
  applications of, 282–283
Axes, 407

Babylonian numbers, 39
Bar graphs, 279
Base
  with exponents, 86
  five, 4–11, 32–35
  ten, 2–3, 6–7
Bisecting
  angles, 150–151, 163
  line segments, 140, 142
Bounds
  lower, 378–381
  upper, 378–381

Calculators
  basic operations on, 81–83, 85
  and computers, 78–80
  constant feature on, 84, 90
  cube roots on, 367
  errors with, 361
  exponents on, 84
  history of, 78–80
  square roots on, 362–365
Capacity, 243–244
Casting out nines, 66–67, 71
Circles
  area of, 384–385
  circumference of, 298, 380–381, 383
  diameter of, 298, 380–381
  measurement of, 380–381
  and pi (π), 382–387
  radius of, 384–385
Circumference, 298, 380–381
  approximation of, 383
Colburn, Zerah, 78, 178–179
Commutative law
  for addition, 16, 44–45, 58
  for multiplication, 20, 44–45, 58, 191
Computers
  calculators and, 78–80
  programs and, 414–415, 417
Congruent angles, 137

Congruent figures, 152–154
Constructions
  of angles, 151
  of congruent figures, 152–154
  of figures, 155
  of parallel lines, 155
  of triangles, 158
Coordinate graphing, 400–412
Corresponding angles, 138
Counting
  in base five, 4–7
  in base ten, 2–3
Cube numbers, 338
Cube roots, 338–339, 366–367
  applications of, 370
  graph of, 412
Cubes, 340, 343
Cylinders
  surface area of, 386–387
  volume of, 386–387

Decimals
  addition with, 99–101
  applications of, 110–111
  approximating answers in, 106, 110
  division with, 103–104, 212
  fractional equivalents of, 113, 120, 216–218
  multiplication with, 102, 104, 212
  order of, 96–97
  percents and, 113, 120
  place value of, 96–97
  subtraction with, 99–101
Degrees, angle measurement in, 133–137
Descartes, René, 400–401
Deviation, average, 281
Diameter, 298, 380–381
Direction, 130–132
Discount, 114, 117
Distributive law, 46–47, 58, 61, 377
Divisibility rules, 180
Division with decimals, 103–104, 212
Division with fractions, 206–208
Division with mixed numbers, 256–258
Division with signed numbers, 267, 269, 271

Division of whole numbers
  approximating answers for,
    70, 88
  in base five, 34–35
  facts of, 20, 65
  multidigit, 28–30, 63
Dodecahedra, 344–345

Enrichment
  Babylonian Numbers, 39
  Develop a Metric System, 271
  A Different Kind of
    Addition, 308
  Doing Puzzles for Fun, 161
  Driving a Car, 227
  Measuring Time, 271, 273
  Möbius Strip, 169
  Paper Folding, 173–175
  Percent Error, 125, 127
  Polyhedra and Probability,
    356
  Problems to Solve, 309
  Puzzling Problems, 421
  Taking Multiple-Choice
    Tests, 73
  A Variation of Calculator
    Square Root Game, 395
  Word-Number Puzzles, 37,
    423
Equilateral triangles, 143
Equivalent fractions, 182–183
Error analysis
  and bounds, 378–381
  in measurement, 376–377
  and percent error, 125
Estimating
  area, 321–323
  time, 23
Exponents, 86–87, 144
  on a calculator, 84
  rules for, 87

Factors, 179–181
Fractions
  addition with, 198–200,
    202–205
  applications of, 192–193,
    210–211
  commutative law for, 191
  decimal equivalents of, 113,
    120, 216–218
  division with, 206–208
  equivalent, 182–183
  improper, 190–191

as mixed numbers, 190–191
multiplication with, 186–188,
  191–193, 203–205
percents and, 113, 120
probability and, 194–197
reducing, 184–185
simplifying, 184
subtraction with, 200,
  202–205
Function charts, 92–94, 371,
  398–399
Function machines, 91
Function rules, 91–95, 206,
  398–399
  graphing, 406–412
  standard notation for, 399
Functions
  composite, 94–95
  graphing, 408–411
  inverse, 206–207
  standard notation for, 399

Games
  All in a Row (Addition and
    Subtraction Facts), 19
  Approximation, 89
  Area, 336–337
  Calculator Square Root,
    394–395
  Constant Comparison, 225
  Cube Averaging, 280
  Cube 100, 416
  Cubomat, 21
  Exponent, 213
  Get the Point, 404–405
  Key Keys, 85
  Make $\frac{1}{2}$, 201
  Make a Problem, 105
  Make 25, 109
  Make 25,000, 27
  Match the Measure, 249
  Mental Multiplication, 51
  Nimble 100, 75
  Roll a 15, 413
  Roll a Fraction, 209
  Roll and Regroup a Decimal, 98
  Roll a Problem (Base-Five
    Addition), 11
  Roll a Problem Fraction, 259
  Signed Mathness, 268
  Square Scores, 64
  Stop at 1000, 14

3 Questions, 148
Tips, 119
Triangle, 159
Triangle Tangle, 357
Up to 1, 219
Gauss, Karl Friedrich, 42–43
Geometry
  acute angles, 135–136
  alternate interior angles, 139,
    141
  angle measurement, 133–137
  angles, 131–132
  area of circles, 384–385
  area of irregular figures,
    312–313, 322–323
  area of parallelograms,
    316–317
  area of rectangles, 46–47,
    314–315
  area of rhombuses, 317
  area of squares, 298, 372–373
  area of trapezoids, 324–325
  area of triangles, 315, 318
  bisecting angles, 150–151, 163
  bisecting line segments, 140,
    142
  circumference of circles, 298,
    380–381, 383
  congruent angles, 137
  congruent figures, 152–154
  congruent triangles, 145
  constructing angles, 151
  constructing figures, 155
  constructing parallel lines, 155
  constructing triangles, 158
  corresponding angles, 138
  cubes, 340, 343
  diameter of circles, 298,
    380–381
  dodecahedra, 344–345
  equilateral triangles, 143
  hexagons, 343
  hexahedra, 344
  hypotenuse, 374
  icosahedra, 344–345
  isosceles triangles, 142–143
  obtuse angles, 135–136
  octahedra, 344–345
  paper folding, 162–165,
    173–175
  parallel lines, 137–138, 145
  parallelograms, 146–147
  pentagons, 343

perimeter, 298, 321
perpendicular bisector, 142
perpendicular lines, 142, 145
pi (π), 382–387
polyhedra, 342–345
prisms, 332
quadrilaterals, 143, 146–147
radius of a circle, 384–385
ratios, 298
rectangles, 147
rhombuses, 147
right angles, 131–136
right prisms, 332, 334
right triangles, 372–373
similar triangles, 145, 156–157
squares, 147
straight angles, 131
supplementary angles, 137
surface area, 328–329
surface area of cylinders,
    386–387
symbols, 145
tetrahedra, 165, 340–341, 344
transversals, 138–139, 141
trapezoids, 146
vertex (vertices), 131, 342
vertical angles, 137, 141, 143
volume of cylinders, 386–387
volume of prisms, 332–335
volume of rectangular boxes,
    328–329
German bell, 173–175
Graphs
    bar, 279
    coordinate, 400–412
    of functions, 406–412
    histogram, 279
    line, 350
Graunt, John, 276–277

Halley, Edmund, 290–292
Hexagons, 343
Hexahedra, 344
Histograms, 279
Hypotenuse, 374

Icosahedra, 344–345
Improper fractions, 190–191
    applications of, 255
    mixed numbers and, 250,
        253–254
Interest, 115, 222–223
Inverse, multiplicative, 207
Inverse functions, 206–207

Isosceles triangles, 142–143

Kepler, Johannes, 360

Length, 234–235, 242
Lines
    parallel, 137–138, 145
    perpendicular, 142, 145
    perpendicular bisector, 142
    transversal, 138–139, 141

Mean, 278, 281–286
Measurement
    angle, 133–137
    area, 237–238, 242
    capacity, 243–244
    of circular objects, 380–381
    errors in, 376–377
    length, 234–235, 242
    surface area, 328–329,
        386–387
    temperature, 244
    time, 230–233
    volume, 236–237, 243
    weight, 236–237, 244
Median, 279, 284–286
Metric system, 230
    converting within, 238–241
    prefixes in, 238–239
    units of area in, 236–237
    units of length in, 234–235
    units of volume in, 236–237
    units of weight in, 236–237
    See also Tables of Measure
Mixed numbers, 190–191
    addition with, 250–251,
        253–255, 258
    applications of, 255
    division with, 256–258
    improper fractions and, 250,
        253–254
    multiplication with, 256–258
    subtraction with, 252–255,
        258
Möbius, August Ferdinand, 169
Möbius strip, 169
Mode, 279, 284–286
Multiplication with decimals,
    102, 104, 212
Multiplication with fractions,
    186–188, 191–193, 203–205
Multiplication with mixed
    numbers, 256–258
Multiplication with signed

numbers, 266–267, 269, 271
Multiplication of whole
    numbers
    algorithms for, 55–57
    approximating answers for,
        70, 88
    associative law for, 44–45, 58
    in base five, 34–35
    checking, 66–67, 71
    commutative law for, 20,
        44–45, 58
    facts of, 20, 65
    mental, 22, 50
    multidigit, 24–26, 55–57, 63
Multiplicative inverse, 207

Negative numbers
    See Signed numbers
Newton, Sir Isaac, 360
Numeration, 2–7, 96–97

Obtuse angles, 135–136
Octahedra, 344–345
Odds, 293–294
Order of operations, 48–49
Origin, 407

Paper folding
    German bell, 173–175
    tetrahedron, 165
    triangles, 162–164
Parallel lines, 137–138, 145
Parallelograms, 146–147
    area of, 316–317
Pentagons, 343
Percents
    applications of, 114–115,
        117–118
    decimals and, 113, 120
    and discounts, 114, 117
    fractions and, 113, 120
    and interest, 115
    of a number, 116, 149, 160
    and sales tax, 112, 115, 117
Perimeter, 298, 321
Perpendicular bisectors, 142
Perpendicular lines, 142, 145
Pi (π), 382–387
Place value
    in base five, 6–7
    decimal, 96–97
Polyhedra, 342–345, 356
Powers of numbers, 59

Powers of ten, 22
  multiplying by, 22, 144
Prisms, 332
  right, 332, 334
  volume of, 332–335
Probability, 293–295, 356
  and expected results, 194–197
  and odds, 293–294
Protractor, 134–136
Puzzles
  Doing Puzzles for Fun, 161
  Presidential Puzzlers, 18
  Word-Number, 37, 423
Pythagoras, 374
Pythagorean Theorem, 374

Quadrilaterals, 143, 146–147
  parallelograms, 146–147
  rectangles, 147
  rhombuses, 147
  squares, 147
  sum of the angles of, 146
  trapezoids, 146

Radius, 384–385
Range, 279
Rates, 220–221
  interest, 222–223
  and ratios, 221
Rational numbers, 23, 308
Ratios, 220–221, 296–301
  gear, 297
  in geometry, 298
  in maps and blueprints, 299
  and pi (π), 382
  and rates, 221
  and statistics, 300–301
Recorde, Robert, 52–54
Rectangles, 147
  area of, 46–47, 314–315
Rhombuses, 147
  area of, 317
Right angles, 131–136
Right prisms, 332, 334
Right triangles, 372–373
Rounding, 68–70

Sales tax, 112, 115, 117
Seminars
  Body Temperatures of Living
    Things, 346–351
  Conserving Electricity,
    214–215
  Constructing Figures, 155

Estimating Time in School,
  23
Graphing Results of Seed
  Germination Experiment,
  418–419
The Great Ice-Melting
  Contest, 330–331
Robert Recorde's Method for
  Subtraction, 52–54
Saltwater Fish, 303
Saving on Home Heating,
  388–389
Seed Germination, 121–123
The Traditional System 120
  Years Ago, 247
Signed numbers, 260–261, 302
  absolute value and, 262
  addition and subtraction
    with, 263–265, 269, 271
  division with, 267, 269, 271
  multiplication with, 266–267,
    269, 271
Similar triangles, 145, 156–157
Square numbers, 59–62, 64,
  338, 398–399
Square roots, 338–339,
  362–365, 368–370
  applications of, 368, 370
Squares, 147
  area of, 298, 372–373
Statistics
  applications of, 286–287
  bar graphs, 279
  histograms, 279
  mean, 278, 281–286
  median, 279, 284–286
  mode, 279, 284–286
  range, 279
  ratios and, 300–301
Straight angles, 131
Subtraction with decimals,
  99–101
Subtraction with fractions, 200,
  202–205
Subtraction with mixed
  numbers, 252–255, 258
Subtraction with signed
  numbers, 263–265, 267,
  269, 271
Subtraction of whole numbers
  algorithm for, 52–54
  approximating answers for,
  70, 88

in base five, 32–33
  checking, 71
  facts of, 16–17, 65
  multidigit, 13, 15, 52–55, 63
Supplementary angles, 137
Surface area, 328–329
  of cylinders, 386–387
Symbols, for geometry, 145

Tables of Measure
  metric system, 424
  traditional system, 425
Temperature
  Celsius, 236
  Fahrenheit, 244
Tetrahedra, 165, 340–341, 344
Time, 230–233
Traditional system
  converting within, 248
  units of area in, 242
  units of capacity in, 243–244
  units of length in, 242
  units of temperature in, 244
  units of volume in, 243
  units of weight in, 244
  See also Tables of Measure
Transversals, 138–139, 141
Trapezoids, 146
  area of, 324–325
Triangles
  area of, 315, 318
  congruent, 145
  constructing, 158
  equilateral, 143
  isosceles, 142–143
  paper folding, 162–164
  similar, 145, 156–157
  sum of the measures of angles
    of, 141

Vertex (vertices), 131, 342
Vertical angles, 137, 141, 143
Volume
  of cylinders, 386–387
  of prisms, 332–335
  of rectangular boxes, 328–329
  units of, 236–237, 243

Weight, 236–237, 244

x-axis, 407
x-coordinate, 407
y-axis, 407
y-coordinate, 407